INTERNATIONAL SERIES IN PHYSICS
F. K. RICHTMYER, Consulting Editor

THE STRUCTURE OF LINE SPECTRA

INTERNATIONAL SERIES IN PHYSICS

F. K. RICHTMYER, CONSULTING EDITOR

Condon and Morse—

QUANTUM MECHANICS

Ruark and Urey—

ATOMS, MOLECULES AND QUANTA

Pauling and Goudsmit—

THE STRUCTURE OF LINE SPECTRA

THE STRUCTURE OF LINE SPECTRA

BY

LINUS PAULING, PH.D.

Associate Professor of Theoretical Chemistry, California Institute of Technology

AND

SAMUEL GOUDSMIT, PH.D.

Associate Professor of Theoretical Physics, University of Michigan

FIRST EDITION

McGRAW-HILL BOOK COMPANY, INC.
NEW YORK: 370 SEVENTH AVENUE
LONDON: 6 & 8 BOUVERIE ST., E. C. 4
1930

PRINTED IN THE UNITED STATES OF AMERICA

THE MAPLE PRESS COMPANY, YORK, PA.

PREFACE

The years 1922 to 1926 saw great progress in the analysis of spectra. The introduction of the vector model and the formulation of semi-empirical rules governing the interactions of the various vectors led to the systematization and clarification of a great body of spectral data. Since 1926 the quantum mechanics has been shown to provide a justification for the previously developed rules; in fact, it is possible now to discuss spectra by means of the quantum mechanics without the use of the vector model at all. It seems probable, however, on account of its simplicity and ease of visualization, that the vector model will continue to be used as the basis for the treatment of spectra for many years to come.

We have attempted to present in this book a description of the vector model of the atom and an account of the interpretation of line spectra in terms of it. We have aimed to write lucidly and intelligibly rather than encyclopedically, having in mind readers entirely unacquainted with the subject as well as those familiar with the empirical side of spectra but not with their interpretation. The book is designed primarily as a textbook for those working in the field of spectroscopy. The recent developments in theoretical physics have, however, caused spectroscopic facts and laws to become of importance for other fields in physics and chemistry, so that we are convinced that many chapters will be of use to workers in these fields also.

The book gives the theoretical background of the principles governing the structure of line spectra, but not an account of all observed spectra, experimental data being introduced only as illustrative examples (as in Appendix III). A detailed account of the structure of spectra of different types with mention of all those known in 1927 is given in the excellent book by F. Hund, "Linienspektren und periodisches System der Elemente," J. Springer, Berlin, 1927. Reference may also be made to W. Grotrian, "Graphische Darstellung der Spektren von Atomen und Ionen mit ein, zwei und drei Valenzelektronen," I and II, J. Springer, Berlin, 1928, and for questions relating to the Zeeman effect especially to E. Back and A. Landé, "Zeemaneffekt und Multiplettstruktur," J. Springer, Berlin, 1925. Our treatment has not been based on the quantum mechanics, but reference to the periodical literature and to treatises on quantum mechanics, in particular to that of Condon and Morse, is often made in footnotes.

The second chapter, dealing with the structure of the hydrogen atom, need not be studied in detail. Those who have not followed developments in atomic structure would do well, however, to read this chapter, giving particular heed to the significance of the various quantum numbers and to the discussion of the properties of stationary states and their interpretation in terms of a model (Sec. 7).

During the preparation of this book there has been proposed a revised notation for line spectra.[1] The most important suggested change is the use of capital letters L, S, J, etc., for the resultant moments of several electrons, small letters being used only for the moments of the individual electrons. Similarly, F would be written for the fine structure quantum number and I for the nuclear moment, the use of the latter expressing the hope that it may soon be possible to resolve the resultant moment of the nucleus into the moments of its constituent particles. We recommend the use of this new notation for the sake of uniformity, although we were not able to make the changes in this book. On the other hand, we are convinced that no confusion is introduced by our notation. Wherever resultant moments and the moments of individual electrons are mentioned together, the latter are designated by means of subscripts, such as j_i or j_1, j_2, with resultant j.

We are indebted to Profs. P. Zeeman and E. Back for the photometer curves of Figs. 58 and 60.

LINUS PAULING.
SAMUEL GOUDSMIT.
GATES CHEMICAL LABORATORY, CALIFORNIA INSTITUTE OF TECHNOLOGY;
DEPARTMENT OF PHYSICS, UNIVERSITY OF MICHIGAN,
February, 1930.

[1] H. N. RUSSELL, A. G. SHENSTONE, and L. A. TURNER, *Phys. Rev.*, **33**: 900, 1929.

CONTENTS

CHAPTER IV

THE SPINNING ELECTRON AND THE FINE STRUCTURE OF ALKALI-LIKE SPECTRA

CHAPTER V

THE VECTOR MODEL FOR ALKALI-LIKE ATOMS

CHAPTER VI

THE VECTOR MODEL FOR ATOMS WITH TWO VALENCE ELECTRONS

CHAPTER VII

THE VECTOR MODEL FOR MANY-ELECTRON ATOMS

THE STRUCTURE OF LINE SPECTRA

CHAPTER I

ATOMIC THEORIES AND ATOMIC MODELS

1. SPECTRA AND THEIR INTERPRETATION

On resolving the radiation emitted from a light source into a spectrum it is found that the distribution of intensity with wave-length depends on the nature of the source. The intensity of light from a glowing solid body varies gradually from place to place in the spectrum, and is a function principally of the temperature of the body. A hot gas, or a gas excited to the emission of light by an electrical discharge or the absorption of radiation or in some other way, may also emit a faint continuous spectrum; but its spectrum will consist mainly of sharp lines. Sometimes many lines occur close together and separated by approximately equal intervals; they are then said to compose a band.[1] Sharp lines are also observed to be absorbed when continuous radiation is passed through a gas. Such a spectrum of dark lines on a light background is called an "absorption spectrum."

The suggestion of Helmholtz that band spectra are shown in emission or absorption by molecules containing two or more atoms and line spectra by single atoms has been substantiated by all further investigations. The characteristic structure of bands is related to the oscillations of the nuclei of the atoms within the molecule, and to the rotation of the molecule as a whole.[2]

[1] The word "band" came into use because with apparatus of low dispersion the individual lines are not resolved, the groups of lines then giving the appearance of broad bands.

[2] An extensive account of band spectrum theory is given in *Bulletin* of the National Research Council, "Report on Molecular Spectra in Gases," **1927.** There has been considerable progress since this report was published, arising especially from the applications of the new quantum mechanics.

1a. Spectral Lines and Spectral Series.—The intensities and wave-lengths of spectral lines are characteristic of the emitting or absorbing atoms or molecules. The measurement of intensities and wave-lengths of lines, the identification of the emitting or absorbing molecule or atom, and the determination of the conditions necessary for the emission or absorption of spectra are the problems set for the experimental spectroscopist; the theoretical spectroscopist must then explain these facts.

The position of a line in the spectrum is indicated by giving either its wave-length λ, measured in Ångström units (1 Å = 10^{-8} cm.), its frequency[1] $\tilde{\nu} = \frac{c}{\lambda}$, with c the velocity of light, or its

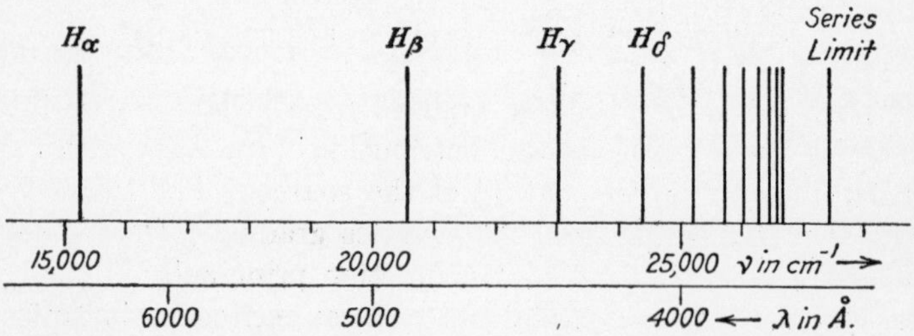

FIG. 1.—The positions of lines in the Balmer series of hydrogen.

wave-number or reciprocal wave-length $\nu = \frac{1}{\lambda}$, measured in cm.$^{-1}$. The visible region extends from about $\lambda = 7700$ Å (red) to about $\lambda = 3800$ Å (violet). Optical spectra (spectra produced by the outer electrons of atoms) have been studied in the ultraviolet as far as about 200 Å, and X-ray spectra (which are produced in the interior of atoms) from this wave-length down to 0.1 Å. It is customary to write for a line at, say, $\lambda = 2536$ Å the symbol λ2536.

A characteristic feature of simple line spectra is that the lines can be grouped in *series*. The separation between succeeding lines in a series decreases gradually toward the violet, the wave-lengths being such that a series limit can be found by extrapolation. It was shown in 1885 by Balmer[2] that the four lines of the hydrogen spectrum lying in the visible region (Fig. 1) can be represented by a simple formula containing only one arbitrary constant.

[1] The symbol ν is usually adopted for both frequency and wave-number, its significance being evident from the context.

[2] J. J. BALMER, *Wied. Ann.*, **25**: 80, 1885.

Balmer's formula rewritten in a form in accordance with modern practice is

$$\nu = R_{\mathrm{H}}\left(\frac{1}{2^2} - \frac{1}{n^2}\right) \tag{1}$$

in which n can assume the integral values 3, 4, 5, . . . , and R_{H}, called the Rydberg constant for hydrogen, has the value 109,677.76 cm.$^{-1}$. This formula gives with an accuracy of one part in 100,000 the frequencies not only of the four lines discussed by Balmer

H_α	λ = 6562.8 Å	ν = 15,233.0 cm.$^{-1}$
H_β	4861.3	20,564.6
H_γ	4340.5	23,032.3
H_δ	4101.7	24,372.8

but also of all of the other observed lines in the Balmer series, twenty of which have been measured in emission in the laboratory. (Thirty-three have been measured in stellar spectra.) There have since been discovered other hydrogen series, whose existence was suspected by Balmer and Ritz; namely, the Lyman series with

$$\nu = R_{\mathrm{H}}\left(\frac{1}{1^2} - \frac{1}{n^2}\right) \qquad n = 2, 3, 4, \cdots,$$

the Paschen series with

$$\nu = R_{\mathrm{H}}\left(\frac{1}{3^2} - \frac{1}{n^2}\right) \qquad n = 4, 5, 6, \cdots$$

the Brackett series with

$$\nu = R_{\mathrm{H}}\left(\frac{1}{4^2} - \frac{1}{n^2}\right) \qquad n = 5, 6, \cdots.$$

The existence of various series for hydrogen corresponding to the formula

$$\nu = R_{\mathrm{H}}\left(\frac{1}{m^2} - \frac{1}{n^2}\right) \tag{2}$$

suggests that, in general, a system of *terms* (in this case R/n^2) can be found for each spectrum such that the wave-number of each line of the spectrum is the difference of two terms. This is effectively a statement of the combination principle of Ritz, which has been of great importance in the interpretation of spectra.

It has been found that the terms of other spectra can be represented similarly by formulas containing further parameters.

Thus Rydberg[1] gave for the alkali spectra a term formula $\frac{R}{(n-\Delta)^2}$, in which R, the Rydberg constant, has nearly the same value for all elements (about 109,737.4 cm.$^{-1}$) and Δ is a constant characteristic of the series.[2] Such formulas will be discussed in detail later in connection with their theoretical explanation.

1b. Stationary States. The Bohr Frequency Principle.—The concept of the atom as a system of one nucleus and one or more electrons was developed to explain the experiments of Lenard and of Rutherford on the passage of cathode rays (rapidly moving electrons) and of α-particles (helium nuclei) through matter. Both the negatively charged electrons and the positively charged nuclei are thought to have a spatial extension small in comparison with atomic dimensions. The charge of the electron is found experimentally to be $-e = -4.770 \times 10^{-10}$ e.s.u., and its mass $m_0 = 0.904 \times 10^{-27}$ grams or $\frac{1}{1838}$ that of the hydrogen nucleus. The magnitude of the charge of a nucleus is always an integral multiple of that of the electron, and is expressed as Ze; an electrically neutral atom accordingly contains Z electrons. Rutherford's experiments and the work of Barkla and others on the scattering power of atoms for X-rays indicated that Z for a given element was equal to about half the atomic weight, in atomic weight units. The suggestion of Van den Broek[3] that Z might be equal to the number of the element in the series obtained by ordering according to atomic weight, as in Mendelejeff's periodic table, was brilliantly confirmed by Moseley's measurements[4] of the wave-lengths of the characteristic X-ray spectral lines of many elements. Z is called the "atomic number."

The facts indicating that nuclei are themselves composed of electrons and protons (hydrogen nuclei) in such numbers as to give each nucleus its charge and mass do not need to be discussed here.

According to the laws of classical mechanics the system of electrons and nucleus composing an atom would reach final

[1] J. R. Rydberg, *K. Svenska Akad. Handl.*, **23,** 1889.

[2] About sixty members of the principal series of sodium have been measured in the laboratory.

[3] A. van den Broek, *Phys. Z.*, **14**: 32, 1913.

[4] H. G. J. Moseley, *Phil. Mag.*, **26**: 1024, 1913; **27**: 703, 1914.

equilibrium only when the electrons had fallen into the nucleus. Before this final equilibrium is obtained the electrons would describe orbits about the nucleus, and the accompanying acceleration of the charged particles would give rise to the emission of energy as radiation. The frequencies involved in the motion of the electrons would then gradually change during the emission of light, a fact incompatible on the classical theory with the sharply defined frequencies of spectral lines. Furthermore, the spectral lines do not show the overtones, with frequencies double, triple, etc., that of the fundamental frequency, which would be expected classically. The existence of non-radiating normal states of atoms in which the electrons have certainly not fallen into the nucleus is a further point of disagreement with the classical theory, indicating the necessity for the development of a new atomic mechanics, differing from the classical mechanics of macroscopic systems.

Two postulates which are fundamental to the interpretation of spectra are the *existence of stationary states* and the *Bohr frequency rule.* They were enunciated by Bohr in 1913 in the famous paper[1] which has led in sixteen years to the complete elucidation of spectral phenomena. Planck[2] had previously announced (in 1900) that the distribution of energy with frequency of radiation in thermodynamic equilibrium with matter (black-body radiation) could be represented by the equation

$$dE = \frac{8\pi\tilde{\nu}^2}{c^3}\frac{h\tilde{\nu}}{e^{h\tilde{\nu}/kT} - 1}d\tilde{\nu}, \tag{3}$$

in which $\tilde{\nu}$ is the frequency of the light, k is Boltzmann's constant, T the absolute temperature, and h a constant of nature called "Planck's constant." This equation is not that which is obtained from classical statistical mechanics; Planck showed that it could be derived if the following assumption were made: radiant energy is not emitted continuously by resonators in equilibrium with radiation, but only in discrete portions of magnitude $h\tilde{\nu}$. Einstein[3] suggested that one of these energy quantities was not emitted uniformly in all directions by the radiation, but instead unidirectionally, like a particle. These portions of radiant energy are called "light quanta."

[1] N. Bohr, *Phil. Mag.*, **26**: 1, 1913; also *Ibid.*, **26**: 476, 857, 1913, etc.

[2] M. Planck, *Ann. d. Phys.*, [4] **4**: 553, 1901.

[3] A. Einstein, *Ann. d. Phys.*, [4] **22**: 180, 1907.

The next phenomenon explained in terms of quanta was the photoelectric effect, interpreted by Einstein. When light falls on a metal plate electrons are emitted from the surface of the plate, but not with velocities related to the intensity of the light, as would be expected from the classical theory. Instead, the maximum velocity of the ejected electrons (the photoelectrons) depends on the frequency of the light; the brilliant experiments of Millikan[1] verified that this maximum velocity corresponds to the conversion into kinetic energy of just the energy $h\tilde{\nu}$ of one light quantum. Einstein also enunciated at the same time his law of photochemical equivalence, according to which the absorption of one light quantum of energy $h\tilde{\nu}$ will activate one molecule to chemical reaction. In all of these cases the system emitting or absorbing radiation in quanta changes discontinuously from a state with a given energy to one with energy $h\tilde{\nu}$ greater or less.

This was the inspiration for Bohr's two postulates, which may be expressed in the following way:

I. An atomic system can exist in certain stationary states, each one corresponding to a definite value of the energy W of the system; and transition from one state to another is accompanied by the emission or absorption as radiation, or the transfer to or from another system, of an amount of energy equal to the energy difference of the two states.

II. The frequency of the radiation emitted by a system and associated with the transition from an initial state with energy W_1 to a final state with energy W_2 is

$$\tilde{\nu} = \frac{W_1 - W_2}{h} \tag{4}$$

(Negative values of $\tilde{\nu}$ correspond to absorption.)

These postulates, while still of extreme importance and usefulness in the interpretation of spectra, are not always in strict accordance with the new quantum mechanics. They cannot be used in the discussion of some phenomena connected with the interaction of radiation and matter, such as those involving the width of spectral lines, which require a more detailed treatment with the new mechanics; but they suffice for the interpretation of experiments involving the measurement of the wave-lengths and intensities of spectral lines. The discussion given in the following chapters will be based entirely upon them.

[1] R. A. Millikan, *Phys. Rev.*, **7**: 362, 1916.

1c. Terms and Energy Levels.—The first step in the interpretation of spectra consists in finding a set of energy levels which gives the observed spectral lines as combinations by means of Equation 4. This equation gives the frequency, in sec.^{-1}. To obtain the wave-number used customarily in spectroscopy it is necessary to divide by c, the velocity of light. For the convenient consideration of the empirical material the name "terms" or "term values" T[1] has been given to the energy values of the various quantum states divided by $-hc$; that is,

$$T = -\frac{W}{hc}; \quad T_2 - T_1 = \nu \text{ (in cm.}^{-1}\text{)}. \tag{5}$$

The change in sign is especially to be noted. As a result of it the lowest and most stable energy level has the largest term value. This convention has been adhered to only for those spectra for which the term values are known with certainty; in many spectra the term value of the *lowest* level has been placed equal to zero, and those of the higher levels are taken *positive*, and equal to the energy difference for these levels and the lowest level divided by $+hc$. Especial care is necessary in referring to the literature to avoid confusion.

2. THE OLD QUANTUM THEORY

Bohr also extended the quantum theory in such a way as to permit the calculation of the energy levels of hydrogen from the atomic model. His fundamental assumption was that the motion of the electron about the proton is that to be predicted classically, neglecting the radiation of energy by the accelerated electron, but that of the continuous series of classical orbits only those fulfilling certain quantum conditions involving integral "quantum numbers" are allowed, and these compose the stationary states of the atom. (The theory will be presented in the following chapter.) The theory was rapidly extended and perfected, and an extraordinarily large number of experimental phenomena inexplicable by the classical theory were found to be in agreement with it. Its success in accounting for the fine structure, Stark effect, and Zeeman effect of hydrogen and ionized helium in particular was so striking as to cause the belief to become widely prevalent that a satisfactory atomic mechanics was to be obtained by the superposition of classical mechanics and the quantum

[1] Terms are often represented by the symbol ν instead of T.

rules. With the aid of the correspondence principle (to be discussed in Chap. VIII) it was further possible to derive selection rules and polarization rules and to account qualitatively for the intensities of spectral lines.[1]

But the old quantum theory possessed no mechanism for calculating quantitatively the probability of a transition from one stationary state to another, and the intensity of the corresponding spectral line; and also did not account for the related phenomena of dispersion. It was further found necessary in many cases, in particular in band spectra, to introduce for the quantum numbers determining the allowed states of the system the "half-integral" values $\frac{1}{2}$, $\frac{3}{2}$, $\frac{5}{2}$ . . . instead of integral values in order to obtain agreement with experimental observations. And finally many predictions made with the old quantum theory were found to be in definite contradiction with observation. The main success of the old quantum theory was in calculating energy levels, and yet it led to definitely incorrect levels when applied to helium, the simplest atom next to hydrogen. Such failures made it increasingly evident that the old quantum theory would have to be abandoned in favor of a more powerful and accurate theory.

3. THE DEVELOPMENT OF THE NEW QUANTUM MECHANICS[2]

3a. Matrix Mechanics.—Actuated by these considerations, Heisenberg in 1925 boldly cast aside the fundamental equations of classical mechanics and formulated a mechanics to be applicable to atomic systems.[3] In his equations there occur only symbols representing quantities of observational significance, as the frequencies and intensities of spectral lines; the non-observable quantities of the old quantum theory, such as the mechanical frequencies of the electron in its orbit about the nucleus, play no part in the new theory. The quantum mechanical frequencies involved in the representation of any mechanical quantity satisfy the combination principle for spectral lines.

[1] A complete account of the old quantum theory as applied to spectra just before the introduction of the new quantum mechanics is given by J. H. Van Vleck, "Quantum Principles and Line Spectra," *Bull.*, National Research Council No. 54, 1926. The quantum theory is discussed in detail in Sommerfeld's "Atombau und Spektrallinien," 4th ed., 1924.

[2] See also E. U. Condon and P. M. Morse, "Quantum Mechanics," McGraw-Hill Book Co. Inc., 1929.

[3] W. Heisenberg, *Z. f. Phys.*, **33**: 879, 1925.

They cannot, accordingly, be used in a Fourier development, as in classical mechanics, but instead can be introduced as the elements of matrix schemes representing mechanical quantities (such as coordinates and momenta). By postulating simple rules for calculating with these matrices and for obtaining the fundamental equations of the quantum mechanics from the classical equations for a given mechanical system, Heisenberg was able to evaluate numerically the various matrix elements, which could then be interpreted in terms of stationary states and quantum transitions. The matrices obey most of the rules of ordinary algebra, but not the commutative rule of multiplication; matrices $\boldsymbol{p}$ and $\boldsymbol{q}$ representing conjugate variables in the classical Hamiltonian equations fulfill the exchange rule

$$\boldsymbol{pq} - \boldsymbol{qp} = hi/2\pi \cdot \mathbf{1}$$

in which **1** is a unit matrix. This equation provides a far more satisfactory introduction of Planck's constant h into the quantum mechanics than the artificial quantum rules of the old quantum theory.

Heisenberg's matrix mechanics was rapidly developed, especially by Born and Jordan and by Dirac. From its very inception it was eminently satisfactory in permitting the calculation not only of the frequencies but also of the intensities of spectral lines; in every case in agreement with the results of observation.

3b. Wave Mechanics.—Independently of Heisenberg and only a few months later, Schrödinger[1] suggested an atomic mechanics completely different in form from the matrix mechanics. Influenced by the ideas of L. de Broglie regarding the association of a wave phenomenon with matter and by the desire to reduce atomic mechanics to a classical form involving no discontinuities, he set up a "wave equation," a characteristic value differential equation representing a mechanical system. Such a differential equation possesses satisfactory solutions only for specific values of the parameter or parameters in it (see the discussion of the hydrogen atom in the following chapter), and these values determine the energy values of the system in its stationary states. The intensities of spectral lines can also be calculated with the wave equation in terms of the functions ψ which occur as solutions of the equation. In every application made the calculated quantities were in agreement

[1] E. Schrödinger, *Ann. d. Phys.*, **79**: 361, 489; **80**: 437; **81**: 109, 1926.

with experiment and with the matrix mechanics; and it was soon shown that, despite the pronounced differences in their form, derivation, and terminology, and in the interpretations given them by Heisenberg and Schrödinger, the matrix mechanics and the wave mechanics are mathematically identical.[1]

3c. The Dirac Transformation Theory.—A general quantum mechanics including within it the matrix mechanics and the wave mechanics and providing a satisfactory correlation between the symbols involved in calculation and the results of experimental observation has been developed by Dirac.[2]

In the Dirac transformation theory a mechanical quantity which has been given a fixed numerical value is represented by a diagonal matrix (one whose elements are all zero except the diagonal elements). Corresponding to this diagonal matrix there are other matrices representing other mechanical quantities. The diagonal elements of these matrices give the *average* values which would be obtained by measurement of the corresponding quantities.[3] The transformation theory provides equations which permit the transformation from a matrix scheme in which one quantity is a diagonal matrix to a scheme in which another quantity is a diagonal matrix. The most important of these equations is that involving the transformation from a diagonal matrix representing the energy to those representing the coordinates of the system; this equation is the Schrödinger wave equation. Schrödinger's energy values are just the values which the energy of the system can assume under conditions in which the energy is completely fixed by measurement. Corresponding to each value of the energy parameter there is a transformation function ψ, the solution of the transformation equation or wave equation, and the product of ψ and its complex conjugate $\bar{\psi}$ gives the probability that the coordinates will be found to have given numerical values on measurement.

3d. The Uncertainty Principle.—It is seen from Heisenberg's exchange rule that two canonically conjugate quantities cannot

[1] E. Schrödinger, *Ann. d. Physik*, **79**: 734, 1926; C. Eckart, *Phys. Rev.*, **28**: 711, 1926.

[2] P. A. M. Dirac, *Proc.*, Roy. Soc., A **113**: 621; **114**: 243, 1927.

[3] The deviation of individual observed values from the average can be found by the consideration of the corresponding average values of the square, the cube, and higher powers of the quantity. Corresponding diagonal terms in a power of a matrix are equal to that power of the diagonal terms of the matrix itself only if the matrix is a diagonal matrix.

simultaneously be represented by diagonal matrices (which multiply commutatively). Hence the prediction of the simultaneous values which will be found for two such quantities as a result of measurement cannot be made; instead only the average values can be predicted, and repetition of the measurement would lead to values scattered about the average for at least one of the two quantities. As an illustration we may consider the measurement of the position of an electron. The position of the electron can, in thought at least, be determined as accurately as desired by the use of a beam of light of sufficiently short wave-length defined by fine slits and observed through a suitable instrument (a "γ-ray microscope"). But there will always be some uncertainty in the measurement of the position of the electron, of the order of magnitude of the aperture of the microscope; that is, in the most favorable case, of one wavelength. There will also be some uncertainty in the direction of the beam of light scattered into the microscope, on account of the divergence of the light included within the field of vision, and this will involve a corresponding uncertainty in the amount of momentum transmitted to the electron by the light quantum as a result of the Compton effect. The product of the uncertainties to be anticipated in the measurement of two canonically conjugate quantities cannot be smaller than h:

$$\Delta p \Delta q \geq h.$$

This is the content of *Heisenberg's uncertainty principle.*[1]

4. ATOMIC MODELS

The discussion of spectra in the remainder of this book will be based upon a visualizable atomic model, the *vector model.* Throughout we shall use the language of classical mechanics, and we shall refer often to interpretations of spectral phenomena suggested by the old quantum theory.

A satisfactory model must, in agreement with the correspondence principle, coincide with the system as it is represented classically in the region of large quantum numbers. It should furthermore be chosen in such a way as to obviate as far as possible the necessity of corrections in the formulas obtained by its use. In general such quantum mechanics corrections

[1] W. Heisenberg, *Z. f. Phys.* **43:** 172, 1927. A detailed discussion is given by Condon and Morse, Secs. 6 and 62.

will have to be made; they serve to show that the model is only an approximation, and to emphasize the fundamental importance of the quantum mechanics itself. The model which we use is, however, so constructed that it leads directly to formulas depending essentially on geometrical angles (the interval rules, the Landé g-factor, etc.) without the necessity of corrections, thus eliminating the difficulty introduced in the interpretation of spectra with the aid of a model if it is assumed that the quantum mechanics abrogates the laws of geometry. In describing the model in terms of the motion of electrons in orbits about the nucleus we shall offer, for the sake of concreteness and to assist those who think geometrically rather than analytically, an interpretation of the quantum mechanics which is not accepted as correct, but which is justified by the same arguments which support the introduction of the vector model.

The justification of the model is its usefulness in aiding the memory, in assisting in the interpretation of deductive results and their application to experiment, in suggesting new experiments and the theoretical explanation of new facts, and in permitting the easy derivation of equations which can be rigorously deduced only with difficulty. The historical development of the theory of line spectra is intimately connected with the origination and perfection of the vector model; and the advent of the quantum mechanics with its more fundamental interpretations of spectral phenomena has served only to increase the usefulness of the model by delineating clearly its sphere of application.

In the following chapter there will be presented discussions of the hydrogen atom according to the old quantum theory and according to the quantum mechanics, followed by a comparison of the two theories designed to show the possibility of the interpretation of stationary states of the hydrogen atom in terms of a model.

CHAPTER II

STATIONARY STATES OF THE HYDROGEN ATOM

The feature of line spectra which must be treated first relates to the values of terms; that is, the energy values of atoms in various stationary states. An accurate theoretical discussion of term values can be given only for the simplest case, that of the hydrogen atom and hydrogen-like ions, consisting of a positive nucleus and a single electron. In the following paragraphs there is given a detailed discussion of the stationary states of the hydrogen atom according to both the old quantum theory and the quantum mechanics. This is followed by a consideration of the properties of stationary states and their interpretation in terms of a visualizable atomic model. In the succeeding chapter it is shown that this model permits generalization in such a way as to give rise to a satisfactory qualitative discussion of the energy levels of many-electron atoms.

The following detailed mathematical treatment of the hydrogen atom presupposes some knowledge of both the old quantum theory and the quantum mechanics on the part of the reader. It is, however, not essential for the understanding of the rest of the book that these sections be studied; instead it suffices to read the description of electron orbits on pages 19 and 24, and then to begin at the section dealing with stationary states and their interpretation in terms of a model (Sec. 7).

5. THE OLD QUANTUM THEORY OF THE HYDROGEN ATOM

5a. The Two-dimensional Hydrogen Atom.—It is convenient to discuss at first a simplified model of a hydrogen-like atom, in which the nucleus is considered to be fixed in space (as though its mass were very large compared with that of the electron) and the motion of the electron is restricted to a plane. The state of the system can then be expressed by polar coordinates r and ψ of the electron E relative to the nucleus O (Fig. 2). Representing the mass of the electron by m_0 and its charge by $-e$, and the charge of the nucleus by $+Ze$, the potential energy of the system is given by

$$V = -\frac{Ze^2}{r}. \tag{1a}$$

Its kinetic energy is

$$T = \frac{m_0}{2}(\dot{r}^2 + r^2\dot{\psi}^2), \tag{1b}$$

in which

$$\dot{r} = \frac{dr}{dt} \text{ and } \dot{\psi} = \frac{d\psi}{dt}.$$

Using non-relativistic mechanics, the Lagrangian function is

$$L = T - V = \frac{m_0}{2}(\dot{r}^2 + r^2\dot{\psi}^2) + \frac{Ze^2}{r}. \tag{2}$$

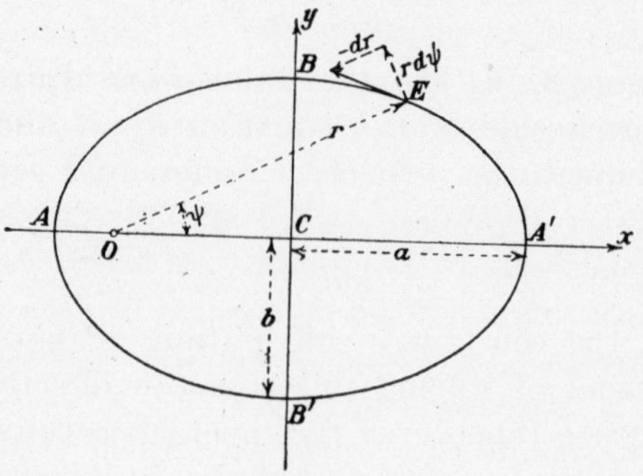

FIG. 2.

The momenta p_ψ and p_r canonically conjugate to ψ and r are then given by the expressions

$$\left.\begin{aligned} p_\psi &= \frac{\partial L}{\partial \dot{\psi}} = m_0 r^2 \dot{\psi}, \\ p_r &= \frac{\partial L}{\partial \dot{r}} = m_0 \dot{r}. \end{aligned}\right\} \tag{3}$$

With these the Hamiltonian function can be formed:

$$H(p_i, q_i) = \sum_i p_i\dot{q}_i - L = \frac{1}{2m_0}\left(p_r{}^2 + \frac{p_\psi{}^2}{r^2}\right) - \frac{Ze^2}{r}. \tag{4}$$

The classically allowed states of motion of the system can now be found by the use of the Hamiltonian equations

$$\frac{\partial H}{\partial p_i} = \dot{q}_i \tag{5a}$$

$$\frac{\partial H}{\partial q_i} = -\dot{p}_i \tag{5b}$$

Equation 5*a* leads to nothing new. Equation 5*b* for ψ gives

$$\dot{p}_\psi = -\frac{\partial H}{\partial \psi} = 0,$$

and hence

$$p_\psi = p, \text{ a constant.} \tag{6}$$

The angular momentum p_ψ of the system is accordingly a constant, not varying with the time. From this value of $p_\psi = m_0 r^2 \dot{\psi}$ it is seen that this leads to Kepler's "area law" for planetary motion: the radius vector r describes equal areas in equal times.

Equation 5*b* for r is

$$\dot{p}_r = -\frac{\partial H}{\partial r} = \frac{p^2}{m_0 r^3} - \frac{Ze^2}{r^2}.$$

From Equation 3, $\dot{p}_r$ has the value $m_0\ddot{r}$. Introducing this, multiplying each side of the equation by $\dot{r}$, and integrating, there is obtained the first-order differential equation for r

$$\frac{m_0}{2}\dot{r}^2 = -\frac{p^2}{2m_0 r^2} + \frac{Ze^2}{r} + W, \tag{7}$$

in which W, the constant of integration, is the energy of the system. Instead of solving this equation directly to find the radius vector as a function of the time, let us convert it into an equation connecting r and ψ; for we are interested primarily in the shape and size of the electron orbit. From Equation 6, $\dot{r}$ is seen to be given by

$$\dot{r} = \frac{dr}{dt} = \frac{dr}{d\psi}\dot{\psi} = \frac{p}{m_0 r^2}\frac{dr}{d\psi},$$

so that Equation 7 may be written

$$\frac{p^2}{2m_0 r^4}\left(\frac{dr}{d\psi}\right)^2 = -\frac{p^2}{2m_0 r^2} + \frac{Ze^2}{r} + W,$$

or, multiplying through by $2m_0 r^2/p^2$,

$$\left(\frac{1}{r}\frac{dr}{d\psi}\right)^2 = \frac{2m_0 Ze^2 r}{p^2} + \frac{2m_0 W r^2}{p^2} - 1. \tag{8}$$

In discussing this differential equation it is convenient to consider the ellipse $ABA'B'$ shown in Figure 2, which is defined by the equation in cartesian coordinates

$$\frac{x^2}{a^2} + \frac{y^2}{b^2} = 1, \tag{9}$$

$2a$ and $2b$ being its major and minor axes. The numerical eccentricity ϵ of the ellipse may be defined by the equation

$$b = a\sqrt{1 - \epsilon^2}. \tag{10}$$

Let O be a point on the line of the apsides AA' such that $OC = \epsilon a$; choosing this as the origin for polar coordinates r and ψ, the equation of the ellipse becomes

$$\frac{1}{r} = \frac{1}{a}\frac{1 - \epsilon \cos \psi}{1 - \epsilon^2}. \tag{11a}$$

Logarithmic differentiation of r with respect to ψ converts this into the equation

$$\frac{1}{r}\frac{dr}{d\psi} = \frac{-\epsilon \sin \psi}{1 - \epsilon \cos \psi}. \tag{11b}$$

Squaring each side of this equation, and eliminating ψ from the right side by the use of Equation 11a, there is obtained the differential equation of an ellipse in polar coordinates:

$$\left(\frac{1}{r}\frac{dr}{d\psi}\right)^2 = \frac{2r}{a(1 - \epsilon^2)} - \frac{r^2}{a^2(1 - \epsilon^2)} - 1. \tag{12}$$

Comparison of Equations 12 and 8 shows that they are identical in form, and differ only in the representation of the constant coefficients of r and r^2. They become completely identical on placing

$$a(1 - \epsilon^2) = \frac{p^2}{m_0 Z e^2} \tag{13a}$$

and

$$\frac{2m_0 W}{p^2} = -\frac{1}{a^2(1 - \epsilon^2)} \tag{13b}$$

It is thus found that ellipses with the nucleus at one focus are classically possible orbits. An orbit is determined by two constants: its major axis and eccentricity, say, or the energy constant and the angular momentum constant p. The energy is determined by the major axis alone, according to the relation

$$W = -\frac{Ze^2}{2a} \tag{14}$$

resulting from Equations 13a and 13b; and is independent of the eccentricity.

Of these orbits only certain ones correspond to stationary states of the atom in the old quantum theory; namely, those fulfilling the Wilson-Sommerfeld quantum conditions. These conditions are that the phase-integral corresponding to each coordinate should be an integral multiple of Planck's constant; that is,

$$\oint p_i dq_i = n_i h. \tag{15}$$

In our case the quantum conditions are

$$\int_0^{2\pi} p_\psi d\psi = kh \text{ and } \oint p_r dr = n'h,$$

in which k is the *azimuthal quantum number* and n' the *radial quantum number*. Since $p_\psi = p$ is constant, the first of these equations becomes

$$p = \frac{kh}{2\pi}. \tag{16}$$

The angular momentum of the system is thus found to be equal to an integral multiple of $h/2\pi$ for all allowed orbits. The second equation can be transformed by replacing dr by $\frac{dr}{d\psi}d\psi$ and p_r by its value $m_0\dot{r} = m_0\frac{dr}{d\psi}\dot{\psi} = \frac{p}{r^2}\frac{dr}{d\psi}$, and becomes, with the use of Equation 11*b*,

$$\epsilon^2 p \int_0^{2\pi} \frac{\sin^2\psi}{(1 - \epsilon\cos\psi)^2} d\psi = n'h. \tag{17}$$

The value of the definite integral[1] is $\frac{2\pi}{\epsilon^2}\left(\frac{1}{\sqrt{1 - \epsilon^2}} - 1\right)$, so that this equation becomes, introducing for p its value $kh/2\pi$,

$$\frac{1}{\sqrt{1 - \epsilon^2}} - 1 = \frac{n'}{k},$$

or

$$1 - \epsilon^2 = \frac{k^2}{(n' + k)^2} = \frac{k^2}{n^2}. \tag{18}$$

In this equation a third quantum number $n = n' + k$ has been introduced. This quantum number, called the "principal" or "total quantum number," is not independent; only two of the three n, n', and k need be specified.

The system is now completely quantized; for it is determined completely by the integral values assigned to two quantum numbers, as n' and k or n and k. The angular momentum and energy of the orbit and its major and minor axes may be expressed in terms of the principal quantum number n and the azimuthal

[1] A. Sommerfeld, "Atombau," 4th ed., p. 774.

quantum number k; the numerical eccentricity is so expressed in Equation 18, and the total angular momentum in Equation 16. From Equations 13a and 13b we obtain

$$W = -\frac{m_0 Z^2 e^4 (1 - \epsilon^2)}{2p^2},$$

which gives, on substitution of the values of $1 - \epsilon^2$ and p^2 in terms of k and n,

$$W = -\frac{2\pi^2 m_0 Z^2 e^4}{n^2 h^2} = -\frac{RhcZ^2}{n^2}, \tag{18a}$$

in which

$$R = \frac{2\pi^2 m_0 e^4}{ch^3} = 109{,}737.42 \text{ cm.}^{-1} \tag{19}$$

is the Rydberg constant.[1] Equations 14 and 10 give for the major and minor semiaxes

$$\left.\begin{aligned} a &= \frac{n^2 h^2}{4\pi^2 m_0 Z e^2} = \frac{n^2 a_0}{Z} \\ b &= \frac{nkh^2}{4\pi^2 m_0 Z e^2} = \frac{nka_0}{Z}, \\ &\text{in which} \\ a_0 &= \frac{h^2}{4\pi^2 m_0 e^2} = 0.529 \times 10^{-8} \text{ cm.} \end{aligned}\right\} \tag{20}$$

The energy of an orbit is thus seen to depend only on the principal quantum number n, and not on k; that is, it is a function only of the major axis of the ellipse, and not of its eccentricity. The term values found are just those deduced empirically by Balmer (Sec. 1), when n is given the integral values 1, 2, 3, . . . To each energy level there belong several orbits of varying eccentricity, with values for k of 1, 2, 3, . . . n.

In his original treatment of the hydrogen spectrum in 1913, Bohr considered only circular orbits, with $k = n$; this is sufficient to account for all the principal energy levels. It was then shown by Sommerfeld, in 1916, that the consideration of the relativistic change of mass of the electron leads to slightly different energies for orbits of equal major axis but different eccentricity, so that each energy level will show an n-fold fine structure. The equations derived in this way by Sommerfeld for the fine structure

[1] The value of the Rydberg constant obtained by substituting their experimental values for the constants involved is 109,744 ± 170 cm.$^{-1}$ (R. T. Birge, *Phys. Rev. Sup.*, **1**; 1, 1929), which agrees within the limits of error with the spectroscopic value of Equation 19.

of hydrogen-like atoms were in quantitative agreement with experimental measurements for hydrogen and ionized helium, and for the X-ray levels of heavy atoms. The interpretation of Sommerfeld's equations in terms of the spinning electron and the quantum mechanics is discussed in Chap. IV.

The orbit corresponding to the normal state of the hydrogen atom is that with $n = 1$, $k = 1$. It is a circular orbit of radius

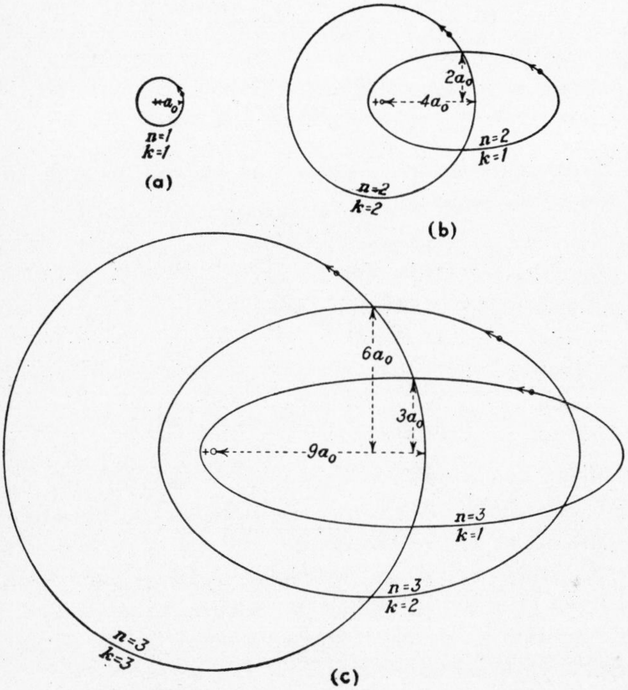

FIG. 3.—Bohr orbits for hydrogen in the normal state, the first excited state, and the second excited state, drawn to the same scale.

a_0 (for $Z = 1$), as is shown in Figure 3*a*. In ionized helium, He^+, the radius of this orbit is $a_0/2$. The electron is thought of as describing this orbit with constant velocity, and with a correspondingly definite frequency of revolution.

The orbit with $k = 0$ would correspond to an ellipse with minor axis equal to zero. As a result of this the electron would collide with the nucleus during every revolution; and for this reason such orbits were not included among those allowed by the old quantum theory.

For the first excited state of the hydrogen atom the principal quantum number n is equal to 2, and the azimuthal quantum number k equal to 1 or 2. With $k = 2$ the orbit is circular, of radius $a = 4a_0 = 2.116$ Å. With $k = 1$ the orbit is an ellipse with the same major semiaxis $4a_0$, and minor semiaxis $2a_0$, giving an eccentricity $\epsilon = \frac{\sqrt{3}}{2}$ (Fig. 3*b*).

Similarly there are three orbits with $n = 3$, with the common major semiaxis $9a_0$, and with minor semiaxes $9a_0(k = 3)$, $6a_0$ $(k = 2)$, and $3a_0(k = 1)$. These orbits are shown in Figure 3*c*, drawn to the same scale as Figures 3*a* and 3*b*.

It is further found that the time τ required for the electron to complete one revolution in its orbit is given by the equation

$$\tau = \frac{n^3h^3}{4\pi^2 m_0 Z^2 e^4}. \tag{21}$$

This expression is useful for the calculation of properties of penetrating orbits (Sec. 15*a*).

5b. Motion of the Nucleus. Spatial Quantization.—Next to be discussed are the changes produced by taking into consideration the finite mass of the nucleus and by no longer restricting the motion of the electron to a plane. Let the mass of the nucleus be M, and its Cartesian coordinates relative to a stationary set of axes be X, Y, Z; and let x, y, z be the coordinates of the electron. The Lagrangian function for the system is then

$$L = \frac{m_0}{2}(\dot{x}^2 + \dot{y}^2 + \dot{z}^2) + \frac{M}{2}(\dot{X}^2 + \dot{Y}^2 + \dot{Z}^2) - V. \tag{22}$$

Now let us introduce new coordinates

$$\left.\begin{aligned} \xi &= \frac{m_0 x + MX}{m_0 + M} \\ \eta &= \frac{m_0 y + MY}{m_0 + M} \\ \zeta &= \frac{m_0 z + MZ}{m_0 + M} \\ r\cos\theta &= z - Z \\ r\sin\theta\cos\varphi &= x - X \\ r\sin\theta\sin\varphi &= y - Y \end{aligned}\right\} \tag{23}$$

ξ, η, ζ are now the Cartesian coordinates of the center of mass of the system, and r, θ, φ the polar coordinates of the electron with reference to the nucleus (Fig. 4). On substitution in Equation 22 the Lagrangian function becomes

$$L = \frac{m_0 + M}{2}(\dot{\xi}^2 + \dot{\eta}^2 + \dot{\zeta}^2) + \frac{\mu}{2}(\dot{r}^2 + r^2\dot{\theta}^2 + r^2 \sin^2\theta\dot{\varphi}^2) - V \quad (24)$$

with

$$\frac{1}{\mu} = \frac{1}{m_0} + \frac{1}{M}. \quad (25)$$

This transformation is independent of the form of the potential energy V, and so holds in general for two particles acted on only by forces between them. The first term in L shows that the center of mass moves with uniform velocity, as a single particle of mass $m_0 + M$. The remainder shows that the motion of one particle relative to the other is the same as the motion of a particle of mass μ (the "reduced mass" of the two particles) attracted to a fixed center by the forces acting between the two particles. As a result of this, the Rydberg constant R entering in the equation for the energy of the system (Equation 19) will have the value $2\pi^2\mu e^4/ch^3$. For hydrogen, with $M = 1.0078/N$ grams (N, Avogadro's number, $= 0.6064 \times 10^{24}$), R will be smaller than for helium, with $M = 4/N$ grams, while this in turn will be smaller than that for $M = \infty$. The observed values for hydrogen and helium,

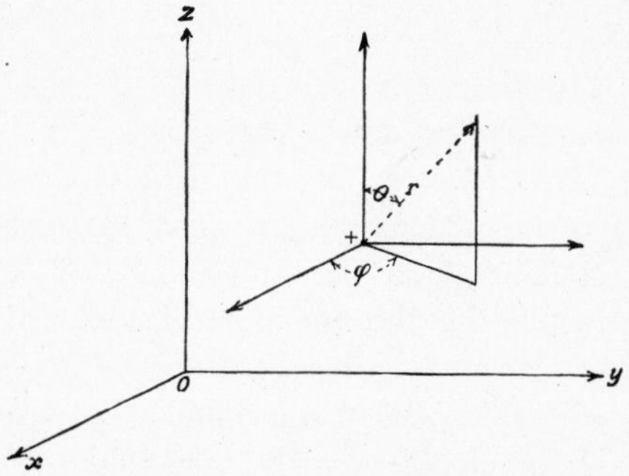

FIG. 4.

$$R_{\text{H}} = 109{,}677.76 \text{ cm.}^{-1}$$
$$R_{\text{He}} = 109{,}722.40 \text{ cm.}^{-1},$$

are in satisfactory agreement with those calculated from the known values of the constants in Equation 19, and indeed can be used for the evaluation of the ratio of the masses of the electron and the hydrogen nucleus.

Neglecting the translational motion of the system, three coordinates are involved in the determination of the orbit, instead of the two discussed previously. The corresponding momenta are

$$\left.\begin{aligned} p_r &= \frac{\partial L}{\partial \dot{r}} = \mu \dot{r} \\ p_\theta &= \frac{\partial L}{\partial \dot{\theta}} = \mu r^2 \dot{\theta} \\ p_\varphi &= \frac{\partial L}{\partial \dot{\varphi}} = \mu r^2 \sin^2\theta \dot{\varphi}, \end{aligned}\right\} \tag{26}$$

and the Hamiltonian function (neglecting the term in ξ, η, ζ) becomes

$$H = \frac{1}{2\mu}\left(p_r^2 + \frac{1}{r^2} p_\theta^2 + \frac{1}{r^2 \sin^2\theta} p_\varphi^2\right) - \frac{Ze^2}{r}. \tag{27}$$

The motion of the system can now be determined as before with the use of the canonical equations of motion. The equation in φ is

$$\dot{p}_\varphi = -\frac{\partial H}{\partial \varphi} = 0, \quad \text{or } p_\varphi = p_1, \text{ a constant.} \tag{28}$$

Hence the component of angular momentum in the direction of the z-axis remains constant during the motion.[1] The equation for θ is

$$\dot{p}_\theta = \mu r^2 \ddot{\theta} = -\frac{\partial H}{\partial \theta} = +\frac{p_1^2}{\mu r^2}\frac{\cos\theta}{\sin^3\theta}.$$

Multiplying by $\dot{\theta}$ and integrating, this becomes

$$\frac{1}{2}\mu r^2 \dot{\theta}^2 + \frac{p_1^2}{2\mu r^2 \sin^2\theta} = \text{a constant, say } \frac{2p^2}{\mu}. \tag{29}$$

Now let us introduce the angle ψ lying in a plane cutting the xy plane at the angle α, as shown in Figure 5. $\dot{\psi}$ is related to $\dot{\theta}$ and $\dot{\varphi}$ by the equation

$$\dot{\psi}^2 = \dot{\theta}^2 + \sin^2\theta \dot{\varphi}^2. \tag{30}$$

The corresponding momentum is

$$p_\psi = \mu r^2 \dot{\psi}, \tag{31}$$

[1] Angular momenta are conventionally represented by vectors in the following way: the angular momentum vector of a particle of mass m, radius vector $\mathbf{r}$, and velocity vector $\mathbf{v}$ is equal to m times the vector product of $\mathbf{r}$ and $\mathbf{v}$; that is, to $m\mathbf{r} \times \mathbf{v}$. The angular momentum vector for an electron revolving about a nucleus in an elliptical orbit is perpendicular to the plane of the orbit, of length proportional to the magnitude of the angular momentum, and of positive sense in the direction of longitudinal motion of a right-hand screw rotating with the electron.

so that Equation 29 can be written, after a slight rearrangement, as

$$\frac{1}{2}\mu r^2\dot{\psi}^2 = \frac{2p^2}{\mu}$$

or

$$p_\psi = p, \text{ a constant.} \tag{32}$$

The equation in r is found on introducing this value of p_ψ to be the same as that obtained previously (Equation 7), and its solution can be carried out as before.

The classically allowed orbits of the electron about the nucleus are, then, ellipses of undetermined size and eccentricity lying in planes making an undetermined angle α with the xy plane. These parameters are restricted as before to definite values by the quantum conditions, which may be written

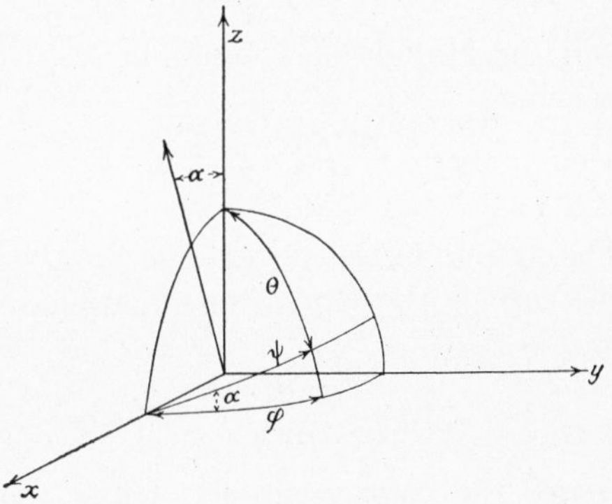

FIG. 5.

$$\int_0^{2\pi} p_\varphi d\varphi = mh, \oint p_\theta d\theta = k'h, \oint p_r dr = n'h. \qquad 33)$$

The first integral is easily evaluated, leading to the result

$$p_1 = \frac{mh}{2\pi}. \tag{34}$$

The component of angular momentum in the direction of the z-axis is thus restricted to values which are integral multiples of $h/2\pi$. m is called the "equatorial" or "magnetic quantum number."

The second integral can be transformed in the following way, with the aid of Equation 30:

$$\begin{aligned}\oint p_\theta d\theta &= \oint \mu r^2\dot{\theta}d\theta = \int_0^\tau \mu r^2\dot{\theta}^2 dt\\ &\int_0^\tau \mu r^2\dot{\psi}^2 dt - \int_0^\tau \mu r^2 \sin^2\theta\dot{\varphi}^2 dt\\ &= \int_0^{2\pi} p d\psi - \int^{2\pi} p_1 d\varphi\\ &= 2\pi(p - p_1)\end{aligned}$$

or, introducing the value of p_1, the quantum condition becomes

$$p = \frac{(k' + m)h}{2\pi} = \frac{kh}{2\pi}, \tag{35}$$

in which $k = k' + m$ is the *azimuthal quantum number.* The third integral can now be treated as before.

In size and eccentricity the quantised orbits are, then, identical with those previously discussed. The plane in which the motion takes place, however, is now distinguished by the result that

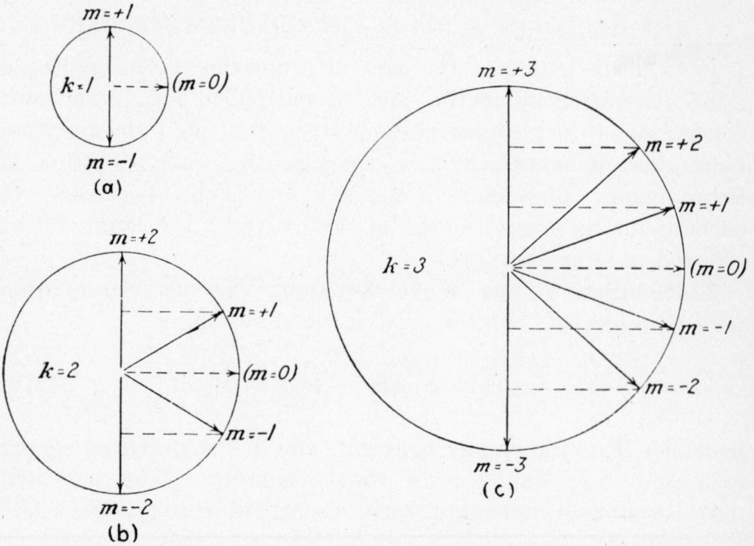

FIG. 6.—Spatial quantization of Bohr orbits with k = 1, 2, and 3.

the angle α between the total angular momentum vector and the z-axis must satisfy the equation

$$\cos \alpha = \frac{p_1}{p} = \frac{m}{k}. \tag{36}$$

The quantum number m can assume the values $\pm 1, \pm 2, \pm 3 \cdots \pm k$. (The orbits with $m = 0$ were discarded on the grounds that the application of an electric field would then cause the electron to collide with the nucleus.) For $k = 1$, as in the normal state of hydrogen, two orientations are possible: one with $\cos \alpha = 1$, and one with $\cos \alpha = -1$ (Fig. 6*a*). Similarly there are four orbits with $k = 2$, six with $k = 3$, and so on (Figs. 6*b* and *c*).

It must be mentioned that spatial quantization has meaning only in case the z-direction in space is physically specified, by an externally applied magnetic field, for example. The treatment we have just given the hydrogen atom with the old quantum theory would, then, be supposed to apply in case there were an external magnetic field strong enough to exert a significant perturbing influence on the motion of the electron about the nucleus.

6. THE HYDROGEN ATOM IN THE QUANTUM MECHANICS

For the discussion of the general properties of the hydrogen atom in stationary states, and in particular to obtain some conception of the "orbital motion" of the electron in the quantum mechanics, it is sufficient to consider the wave equation of Schrödinger. The more extended treatment necessary to account for the fine structure of the hydrogen spectrum will be referred to later (Sec. 14).

6a. Solution of the Wave Equation.—The wave equation for a conservative Newtonian dynamical system is

$$\nabla^2\psi + \frac{8\pi^2}{h^2}(W - V)\psi = 0 \tag{37a}$$

in which W is the energy constant, and V the potential energy expressed as a function of the coordinates. The indicated differential operations are with respect to coordinates whose line element is given by

$$ds^2 = 2T(q_i, \dot{q}_i)dt^2,$$

in which T is the kinetic energy expressed as a function of the velocities.

ψ is restricted by the conditions that it be everywhere continuous, single valued, and bounded. Only certain functions, called "characteristic functions" or "eigenfunctions," satisfy these requirements for a given system; correspondingly, there are certain characteristic values of the energy constant W.

For a hydrogen-like atom defined by Cartesian coordinates x, y, z, X, Y, Z the wave equation is

$$\frac{1}{m_0}\left\{\frac{\partial^2\psi}{\partial x^2} + \frac{\partial^2\psi}{\partial y^2} + \frac{\partial^2\psi}{\partial z^2}\right\} + \frac{1}{M}\left\{\frac{\partial^2\psi}{\partial X^2} + \frac{\partial^2\psi}{\partial Y^2} + \frac{\partial^2\psi}{\partial Z^2}\right\} + \frac{8\pi^2}{h^2}(W' - V)\psi = 0. \tag{37b}$$

This can be transformed by the introduction of the coordinates ξ, η, ζ, r, θ, φ defined before (Equation 23), becoming

$$\frac{1}{m_0 + M}\left\{\frac{\partial^2\psi}{\partial\xi^2} + \frac{\partial^2\psi}{\partial\eta^2} + \frac{\partial^2\psi}{\partial\zeta^2}\right\} + \frac{1}{\mu}\left\{\frac{1}{r^2}\frac{\partial}{\partial r}\left(r^2\frac{\partial\psi}{\partial r}\right) + \frac{1}{r^2\sin^2\theta}\frac{\partial^2\psi}{\partial\varphi^2} + \frac{1}{r^2\sin\theta}\frac{\partial}{\partial\theta}\left(\sin\theta\frac{\partial\psi}{\partial\theta}\right)\right\} + \frac{8\pi^2}{h^2}(W' - V)\psi = 0. \quad (38)$$

If we now place ψ equal to the product of a function of ξ, η, ζ and a function of r, θ, φ:

$$\psi = F(\xi, \eta, \zeta)\Psi(r, \theta, \varphi),$$

the equation can be separated into two equations:

$$\frac{\partial^2 F}{\partial\xi^2} + \frac{\partial^2 F}{\partial\eta^2} + \frac{\partial^2 F}{\partial\zeta^2} + \frac{8\pi^2(m_0 + M)}{h^2}W_t F = 0 \quad (39)$$

and

$$\frac{1}{r^2}\frac{\partial}{\partial r}\left(r^2\frac{\partial\Psi}{\partial r}\right) + \frac{1}{r^2\sin^2\theta}\frac{\partial^2\Psi}{\partial\varphi^2} + \frac{1}{r^2\sin\theta}\frac{\partial}{\partial\theta}\left(\sin\theta\frac{\partial\Psi}{\partial\theta}\right) + \frac{8\pi^2\mu}{h^2}(W - V)\Psi = 0, \quad (40)$$

in which W_t represents the translational energy of the system and W the residual energy. Equation 39 is just the wave equation representing free translational motion of a particle of mass $m_0 + M$, while Equation 40 is the wave equation for a particle of mass μ (the reduced mass of the system) attracted to a fixed center in accordance with the potential V. Accordingly the results previously derived regarding the effect of the mass of the nucleus on the energy levels hold also in the quantum mechanics.

Introducing for V its value $-\frac{Ze^2}{r}$, and replacing Ψ by the product of a function of r alone, one of θ alone, and one of φ alone,

$$\Psi = R(r)\Theta(\theta)\Phi(\varphi), \quad (41)$$

Equation 40 becomes separable into three total differential equations:

$$\frac{1}{\Phi}\frac{d^2\Phi}{d\varphi^2} = -\alpha, \quad (42a)$$

$$\frac{1}{\Theta\sin\theta}\frac{d}{d\theta}\left(\sin\theta\frac{d\Theta}{d\theta}\right) - \frac{\alpha}{\sin^2\theta} = -\beta, \quad (42b)$$

and

$$\frac{1}{r^2}\frac{d}{dr}\left(r^2\frac{dR}{dr}\right) - \frac{\beta}{r^2}R + \frac{8\pi^2\mu}{h^2}\left(W + \frac{Ze^2}{r}\right)R = 0. \quad (42c)$$

Eigenfunctions satisfying Equation 42*a* exist only when α is equal to m^2, with m having any positive or negative integral value. With any given value of m, solutions of Equation 42*b* exist only when β is equal to $l(l + 1)$, in which l has any positive integral value equal to or greater than the absolute value of m. Equation 42*c* then possesses solutions only when the energy constant W is given by

$$W = -\frac{2\pi^2\mu Z^2e^4}{n^2h^2}, \tag{43}$$

in which n can assume the integral values $l + 1$, $l + 2$, $l + 3$, $\cdots \infty$.[1] n is evidently equival nt to the principal quantum number of the old quantum theory; l, with possible values 0, 1, 2, $\cdots n - 1$, is to be identified with $k - 1$, and is thus the analogue of the azimuthal quantum number; while m, with the values 0, ± 1, ± 2, $\cdots \pm l$, is the magnetic quantum number.

Equation 43 is identical with the energy expression given by the old quantum theory, and gives correctly the energy levels of hydrogen and ionized helium. The straightforward way in which the quantum numbers come into consideration, as characteristic values of the parameters (α, β, W) of the differential equations, is in distinct contrast to the artificiality of the quantum rules of the old quantum theory, by whose aid certain classical orbits were selected as satisfactory, and all others rejected.

6b. Hydrogen-like Eigenfunctions.—The eigenfunction corresponding to given values of n, l, and m is[1]

$$\Psi_{nlm} = R_{nl}(r)\Theta_{lm}(\theta)\Phi_m(\varphi),$$

in which

$$\left.\begin{aligned} R_{nl}(r) &= \left\{\left(\frac{2Z}{na_0}\right)^3 \frac{(n-l-1)!}{2n[(n+l)!]^3}\right\}^{\frac{1}{2}} e^{-\frac{\xi}{2}}\xi^l L_{n+l}^{(2l+1)}(\xi) \\ \text{with} \qquad \xi &= \frac{2Z}{na_0}r \\ \Theta_{lm}(\theta) &= \left\{\left(l + \frac{1}{2}\right)\frac{(l-m)!}{(l+m)!}\right\}^{\frac{1}{2}} P_l^m(\cos\theta) \\ \Phi_m(\varphi) &= \frac{1}{\sqrt{2\pi}}e^{im\varphi} \end{aligned}\right\} \tag{44}$$

[1] E. SCHRÖDINGER, *Ann. d. Phys.*, **79**: 361, 1926; I. WALLER, *Z. f. Phys.*, **38**: 635, 1926.

$L_{n+l}^{(2l+1)}(\xi)$ represents the $(2l + 1)$th derivative of the $(n + l)$th Laguerre polynomial; and $P_l^m(\cos\theta)$ is Ferrers' associated Legendre function of the first kind, of degree l and order m. $\Theta_{lm}\Phi_m$ thus constitutes a tesseral harmonic. The Ψ's are in

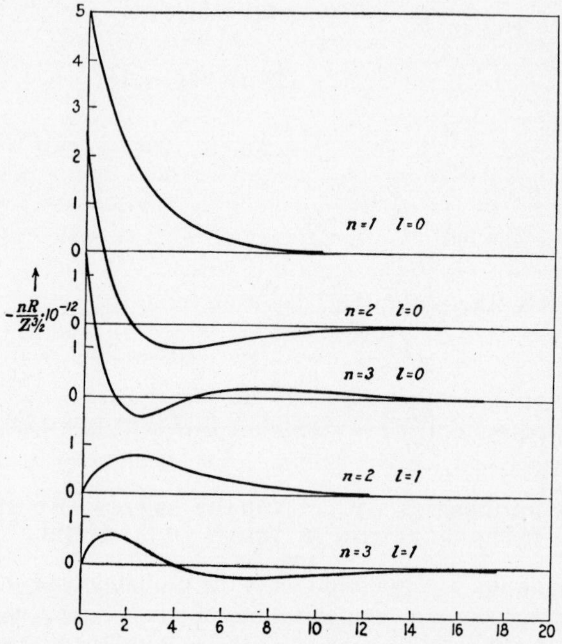

FIG. 7.—Eigenfunctions for hydrogen-like states; as ordinates are shown values of $-nR_{nl}(r)Z^{-3/2} \cdot 10^{-12}$, with values of ξ as abscissae.

this form orthogonal and normalized with respect to unity, so that they fulfill the conditions

$$\int \Psi_{nlm}\overline{\Psi}_{n'l'm'}dV = \begin{cases} 1 \text{ for } n = n', l = l', m = m', \\ 0 \text{ otherwise,} \end{cases}$$

in which dV is an element of volume in the r, θ, φ configuration space, and the integral is to be taken throughout this space. $\overline{\Psi}$ is the complex conjugate of Ψ.

For $l = 0$, $\Theta_{00}(\theta)\Phi_0(\varphi)$ is constant; these eigenfunctions are spherically symmetrical. The dependence on r of several eigenfunctions is shown by the following equations, and by Figure 7, in which $-nR_{nl}(r)Z^{-3/2}10^{-12}$ is plotted as a function of ξ.

$$R_{10}(r) = -2\left(\frac{Z}{a_0}\right)^{3/2} \cdot e^{-\frac{\xi}{2}},$$

$$R_{20}(r) = \frac{2}{2^{5/2}}\left(\frac{Z}{a_0}\right)^{3/2} \cdot e^{-\frac{\xi}{2}}(\xi - 2),$$

$$R_{30}(r) = -\frac{2}{3^{5/2}2!}\left(\frac{Z}{a_0}\right)^{3/2} \cdot e^{-\frac{\xi}{2}}(\xi^2 - 6\xi + 6),$$

$$R_{40}(r) = \frac{2}{4^{5/2}3!}\left(\frac{Z}{a_0}\right)^{3/2} \cdot e^{-\frac{\xi}{2}}(\xi^3 - 12\xi^2 + 36\xi - 24),$$

$$R_{50}(r) = -\frac{2}{5^{5/2}4!}\left(\frac{Z}{a_0}\right)^{3/2} \cdot e^{-\frac{\xi}{2}}(\xi^4 - 20\xi^3 + 120\xi^2 - 240\xi + 120).$$

$$R_{21}(r) = -\frac{2}{2^2\sqrt{3!}}\left(\frac{Z}{a_0}\right)^{3/2} e^{-\frac{\xi}{2}} \cdot \xi,$$

$$R_{31}(r) = \frac{2}{3^2\sqrt{4!}}\left(\frac{Z}{a_0}\right)^{3/2} e^{-\frac{\xi}{2}} \cdot \xi(\xi - 4),$$

$$R_{41}(r) = -\frac{2}{4^2\sqrt{5! \cdot 2!}}\left(\frac{Z}{a_0}\right)^{3/2} e^{-\frac{\xi}{2}} \cdot \xi(\xi^2 - 10\xi + 20),$$

$$R_{51}(r) = \frac{2}{5^2\sqrt{6! \cdot 3!}}\left(\frac{Z}{a_0}\right)^{3/2} e^{-\frac{\xi}{2}} \cdot \xi(\xi^3 - 18\xi^2 + 90\xi - 120).$$

7. THE PROPERTIES OF STATIONARY STATES AND THEIR INTERPRETATION IN TERMS OF A MODEL

The quantity $\rho = \Psi\overline{\Psi}$ represents the probability of the corresponding microscopic configuration of the system; neglecting the motion of the nucleus, it gives the probability that the electron will be found in the region characterized by specified values or r, θ, and φ. In Figure 8 there are plotted values of Ψ_{100} and of ρ_{100} as functions of r. The quantity $\rho r^2 \sin \theta dr d\theta d\varphi$ represents the probability that the electron in a hydrogen atom in the normal state will be found as a result of experimental investigation, say with a γ-ray microscope, to occupy the elementary volume $r^2 \sin \theta dr d\theta d\varphi$. Since Ψ_{100} is independent of θ and φ, there is just as much chance of the electron being in any particular region on the surface of a sphere about the nucleus as in any other region on this surface; the atom is spherically symmetrical. This was not true of the hydrogen atom of the old quantum theory, for the electron in the lowest orbit was restricted to a single plane.

It is to be seen from the figure that the probability that the electron will lie within an element of volume of given size is large in the immediate neighborhood of the nucleus, and falls off rapidly as r increases, approaching the value zero asymptotically.

The electron distribution function $D = 4\pi r^2 \rho$ is also shown in Figure 8. The quantity Ddr gives the probability that the electron will be found in the element of volume lying between spheres of radii r and $r + dr$ described about the nucleus. D has a maximum at $r = a_0 = 0.529$ Å. The electron has a greater probability of being at this distance from the nucleus than at any other distance. Here there is seen a connection between the hydrogen atom of the quantum mechanics and that of the old quantum theory, for the radius of the smallest Bohr orbit was just a_0. The electron is, however, no longer restricted to just this value of r.

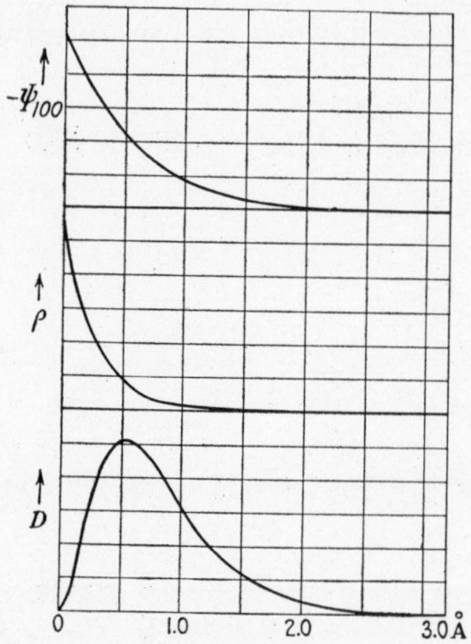

FIG. 8.—The eigenfunction Ψ_{100}, the electron density $\rho = \Psi_{100}{}^2$, and the electron distribution function $D = 4\pi r^2 \rho$ for the normal state of the hydrogen atom, as functions of r.

The electron distribution function D for a number of quantum states is shown in Figure 9. In the case of the states with l not equal to zero the eigenfunction Ψ is not independent of θ and φ, so that the atom is in these states not spherically symmetrical. It has been shown by Unsöld,[1] however, that the sum of the functions $\Psi\bar{\Psi}$ for the states comprising a subgroup (n and l constant, $m = -l, -l + 1, \cdots 0 \cdots +l$) is not dependent on θ and φ.

It will be observed that the function D differs appreciably from zero only within a radius of the order of magnitude of the major axis of the corresponding ellipse of the old quantum theory; namely, $r = 2a_0n^2/Z$, or $\xi = 4n$. So although in every quantum state the atom must be considered as extending to an unlimited

[1] A. UNSÖLD, *Ann. d. Phys.*, **82**: 355, 1927. It has recently been shown by D. R. HARTREE (*Proc.*, Cambridge Phil. Soc., **25**; 225, 1929), using Dirac's relativistic theory of the electron, that this is true for a Stoner subgroup also (consisting of the $2j + 1$ electrons with given l and j).

distance, still the electron remains most of the time within a region in the neighborhood of the nucleus. For further comparison there are indicated by heavy lines along the ξ-axis in Figure 9 the electron-nucleus distances corresponding to the orbits of the old quantum theory; however, instead of giving the azimuthal quantum number k the values 1, 2, . . . it has been replaced by the quantity $\sqrt{l\,(l + 1)}$, in which l has the integral

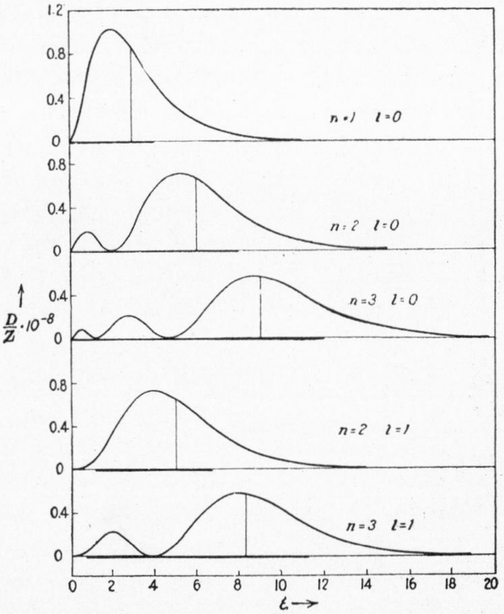

FIG. 9.—The electron distribution function D for various states of hydrogen-like atoms; the ordinates are values of $DZ^{-1} \cdot 10^{-8}$, with values of ξ as abscissae. The vertical lines correspond to $\bar{r}$, the average of r.

values of the quantum mechanics. The approximation of these orbits to the distribution given by the quantum mechanics is considerably better than that of the orbits with k integral. This is also evident from the consideration of the average value of r. The quantum mechanics expression for this average is

$$\bar{r} = \int r\Psi\bar{\Psi}dV.$$

The method of evaluating this integral has been given by Waller,[1] whose equations lead to the result

$$\bar{r} = \frac{a_0 n^2}{Z}\left[1 + \frac{1}{2}\left\{1 - \frac{l(l+1)}{n^2}\right\}\right].$$

[1] I. WALLER, *Z. f. Phys.*, **38**: 635, 1926.

The old quantum theory gave for the time-average value of r

$$\bar{r} = \frac{1}{\tau}\int_0^\tau r dt = \frac{a_0 n^2}{Z}\left[1 + \frac{1}{2}\left\{1 - \frac{k^2}{n^2}\right\}\right],$$

which differs from the quantum mechanics value if k is integral, but is identical with it if k is replaced by $\sqrt{l(l+1)}$. Values of ξ corresponding to $\bar{r}$ are indicated in Figure 9 by vertical lines.

Average values are of significance in the theory of perturbations; the first-order perturbation energy for a non-degenerate state of a system is in both the quantum mechanics and the old quantum theory equal to the average value of the perturbation function. The following averages are useful in spectral theory:

Quantum Mechanics	Old Quantum Theory
$\bar{r} = \frac{a_0 n^2}{Z}\left[1 + \frac{1}{2}\left\{1 - \frac{l(l+1)}{n^2}\right\}\right]$	$\bar{r} = \frac{a_0 n^2}{Z}\left[1 + \frac{1}{2}\left\{1 - \frac{k^2}{n^2}\right\}\right]$
$\overline{r^2} = \frac{a_0^2 n^4}{Z^2}\left[1 + \frac{3}{2}\left\{1 - \frac{l(l+1) - \frac{1}{3}}{n^2}\right\}\right]$	$\overline{r^2} = \frac{a_0^2 n^4}{Z^2}\left[1 + \frac{3}{2}\left\{1 - \frac{k^2}{n^2}\right\}\right]$
$\overline{\left(\frac{1}{r}\right)} = \frac{Z}{a_0 n^2}$	$\overline{\left(\frac{1}{r}\right)} = \frac{Z}{a_0 n^2}$
$\overline{\left(\frac{1}{r^3}\right)} = \frac{Z^3}{a_0^3 n^3 l(l+\frac{1}{2})(l+1)}$	$\overline{\left(\frac{1}{r^3}\right)} = \frac{Z^3}{a_0^3 n^3 k^3}$
$\overline{\left(\frac{1}{r^4}\right)} = \frac{\frac{3}{2}Z^4\left[1 - \frac{l(l+1)}{3n^2}\right]}{a_0^4 n^3 (l+\frac{3}{2})(l+1)(l+\frac{1}{2})l(l-\frac{1}{2})}$	$\overline{\left(\frac{1}{r^4}\right)} = \frac{\frac{3}{2}Z^4\left(1 - \frac{k^2}{3n^2}\right)}{a_0^4 n^3 k^5}$

The values given by the old quantum theory deviate considerably from those of the quantum mechanics. The approximation they afford is consistently better if k is replaced by $\sqrt{l(l+1)}$. This suggests that the quantum mechanics can be interpreted by means of a model based upon the orbits of the old quantum theory with k equal to $\sqrt{l(l+1)}$. These orbits are to be thought of as rather indefinite—the electron may be considered to revolve about the nucleus in a way approximating its classical motion, but such that its distribution function and other properties are those given by the quantum mechanics. Equations derived with the old quantum theory, even with $k = \sqrt{l(l+1)}$, will sometimes not be identical with those of the quantum mechanics; for example, in the formula for $\overline{\left(\frac{1}{r^3}\right)}$, k^3 must be replaced by $l(l + \frac{1}{2})(l + 1)$. The necessity for such changes in the equations of the old quantum theory had been observed before the development of the quantum mechanics. The application of these "quantum mechanics corrections" is sometimes called "refining" the formulas.

The component of angular momentum in the direction of the z-axis (specified by an external magnetic field, for example) is $mh/2\pi$. The total angular momentum in the model under discussion is $\sqrt{l(l+1)}\frac{h}{2\pi}$. Angular momenta are the features of an atomic model which are most significant for spectral theory; they compose the structural units of the vector model to be discussed in Chaps. V, VI, and VII. The angular momentum of an orbit will be represented by the vector **l** (in units of $h/2\pi$), and other angular momenta will be denoted by the symbols **s** and **j**. The components of these vectors in the field direction will be called $\mathbf{m}_l$, $\mathbf{m}_s$, and **m**. There are two conventions either of which can be adopted in regard to the magnitudes of these vectors. In both conventions the magnitudes of the vector components $\mathbf{m}_l$, $\mathbf{m}_s$, and **m** are taken to be the quantum numbers m_l, m_s, and m (with integral or half-integral values). With the first convention, which corresponds to the atomic model discussed in the preceding paragraph, the magnitudes of the angular momentum vectors **l**, **s**, and **j** are taken to be $\sqrt{l(l+1)}$, $\sqrt{s(s+1)}$, and $\sqrt{j(j+1)}$. Calculations of quantities depending essentially upon angles (Landé g-factor, interval rules) made with this model do not need to be corrected.[1]

In the treatment which has been used principally in the course of development of the vector model the second convention was adopted: the angular momenta **l**, **s** and **j** were considered to have the magnitudes l, s, and j. All equations derived in this way required then to be corrected by the introduction of $l(l + 1)$ in place of l^2 etc., so that the same results are obtained as with the other model.

[1] The quantum mechanical proof that the values of the square of an angular momentum vector and its component along a given axis are $l(l + 1)$ and m_l, say, with l and m_l integral or half-integral, is given by H. Weyl, "Gruppentheorie und Quantenmechanik," Secs. 12 and 35; and by Condon and Morse, Sec. 64.

On account of the inconvenience involved in printing $\sqrt{l(l+1)}$, etc., and because of its historical significance, the second convention will usually be followed in this book in the derivation of equations. However, the model corresponding to the alternative convention, which is preferable for many purposes, will be utilized frequently in the discussion.

CHAPTER III

TERM VALUES FOR ALKALI-LIKE ATOMS

8. PENETRATING ORBITS AND NON-PENETRATING ORBITS

The alkali atoms, lithium, sodium, potassium, rubidium, and cesium, have but one valence electron, and except under unusual conditions of excitation changes in state of one of these atoms involve only changes in the quantum numbers of this electron. If the valence electron is removed from an alkali atom, the ion (Li^+, Na^+, etc.) is formed. These ions have the same structure as the noble gases (Chap. IX); thus potassium has two electrons with $n = 1$ (called the K shell), eight with $n = 2$ (the L shell), eight with $n = 3$, and one (the valence electron) with $n = 4$, as shown in Table I. The electrons in each shell except the valence-electron shell compose completed subgroups. As was mentioned in Section 7, it has been shown by Unsöld that the electron probability function $\Sigma\Psi\bar{\Psi}$ for completed subgroups is a function of r only. Hence the alkali ions can be considered as spherically symmetrical in the discussion of their interaction with the valence electron.

TABLE I.—THE ELECTRONIC STRUCTURES OF THE ALKALI ATOMS

Shell	K	L	M	N	O	P
$n =$	1	2	3	4	5	6
Li	2	1				
Na	2	8	1			
K	2	8	8	1		
Rb	2	8	18	8	1	
Cs	2	8	18	18	8	1

The approximate calculation of the electron-distribution function $D = \Sigma 4\pi r^2 \Psi\bar{\Psi}$ (summed over all the electrons in the ion) has been carried out[1] with the aid of the quantum mechanics. The results of the calculation for Li^+ and Na^+ are shown in

[1] LINUS PAULING, *Proc.*, Roy. Soc., A **114**: 181, 1927.

Figure 10. In Li^+ the two K electrons remain in the region about the nucleus, the average nucleus-electron distance being $0.53a_0$ or 0.28 Å. The two K electrons in Na^+ are on the average only 0.07 Å from the nucleus, while the L electrons are $0.77a_0$

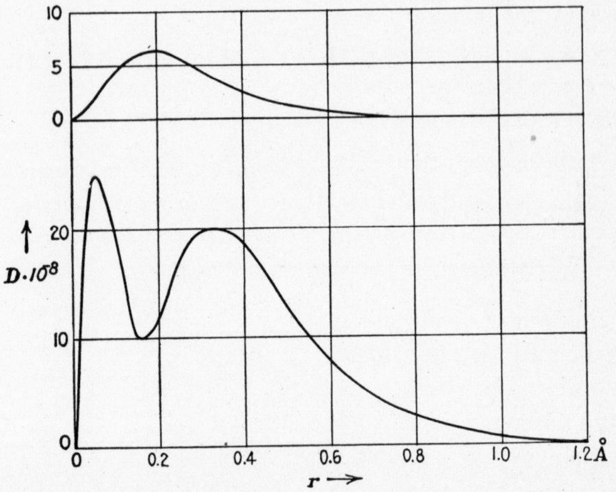

FIG. 10.—The electron distribution as a function of the distance from the nucleus for the lithium ion (above) and the sodium ion.

or 0.41 Å away. Values of $\bar{r}$ calculated in this way for the outer shell of electrons in the alkali ions are given in Table II.

TABLE II.—AVERAGE ELECTRON-NUCLEUS DISTANCE FOR OUTER ELECTRON SHELLS OF THE ALKALI IONS

Ion	Li^+	Na^+	K^+	Rb^+	Cs^+
$\bar{r}$	0.28 Å	0.41 Å	0.82 Å	1.20 Å	1.48 Å
$\zeta = \bar{r}/a_0$	0.53	0.77	1.54	2.26	2.80

Similar electron distributions have been obtained by Hartree[1] by a more accurate method of treatment. The calculated values of D have been directly verified experimentally (particularly for Na^+, K^+, and Cl^-) by the use of observed intensities of reflection of X-rays by crystals.[2]

[1] D. R. HARTREE, *Proc.*, Cambridge Phil. Soc., **24**: 89, 111, 1928.

[2] R. W. JAMES, I. WALLER, and D. R. HARTREE, *Proc.*, Roy. Soc. A **118**: 334, 1928; R. W. JAMES and G. W. BRINDLEY, *Ibid.*, A **121**: 155, 1928; R. W. JAMES, G. W. BRINDLEY, and R. G. WOOD, *Ibid.*, A **125**: 401, 1929.

In order to simplify the treatment of the interaction of the valence electron and the inner shells, Schrödinger[1] suggested an idealized model in which each electron shell is replaced by an equivalent charge of electricity distributed uniformly over the surface of a sphere of suitable radius. If we represent the valence of the ion by z ($z = 1$ for alkali ions, 2 for the alkaline earths, etc.), then the potential outside of the outermost shell is simply ze/r, while that inside the shell is $\frac{Z_ie}{r} - \frac{(Z_i - z)e}{\zeta a_0}$, in which $Z_i - z$ is the number of electrons in the shell, and ζa_0 the radius of the sphere on which the charge is distributed. Z_ie is then the effective nuclear charge inside the shell.

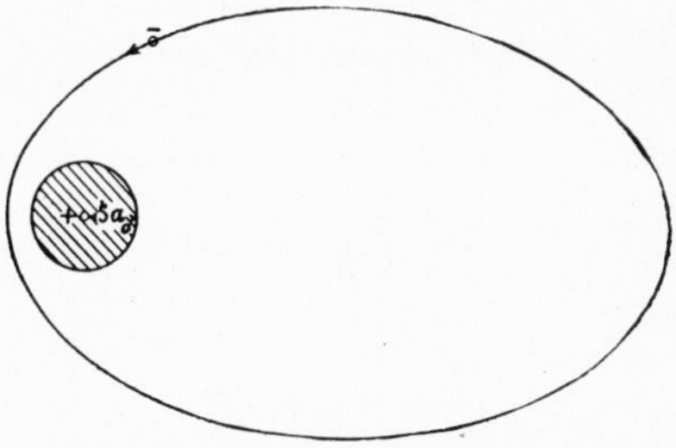

FIG. 11.—A non-penetrating orbit in an alkali-like atom.

The orbit of the valence electron in such an atom may be one of two kinds, represented in Figures 11 and 12. If the orbit is sufficiently large, it will be completed in the outer region, and will resemble more or less closely a hydrogen-like orbit in an atom with nuclear charge ze. The interaction of such non-penetrating orbits with the atom core (the inner electron shells) is small, and the term values corresponding to such orbits differ only slightly from those for hydrogen-like atoms. These orbits will be discussed in Section 11.

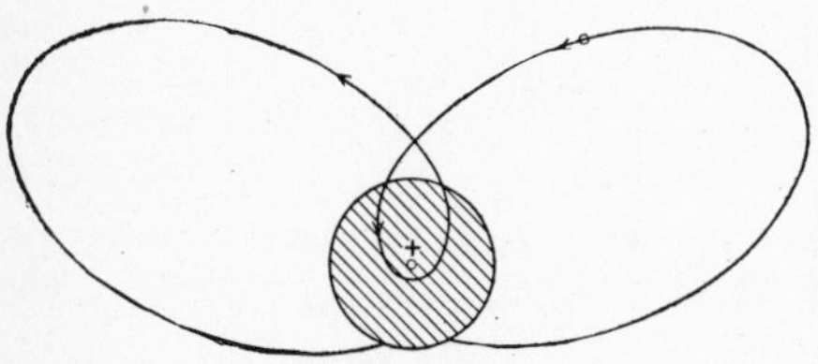

FIG. 12.—A penetrating orbit in an alkali-like atom.

Often the orbit penetrates the shell of electricity. It then consists of a segment of one Kepler ellipse in the outer region, and a segment of another Kepler ellipse in the inner region. As a result of the penetration the outer elliptical segment undergoes an effective precession about an axis normal to its plane; with every successive revolution the electron penetrates the shell at a different place, always the same distance from that of the previous revolution. The term value of a pene-

[1] E. SCHRÖDINGER, *Z. f. Phys.*, **4**: 347, 1921.

trating orbit is larger than that of a hydrogen-like orbit with the same principal quantum number and with the effective nuclear charge ze, since the electron is part of the time in a region with much larger effective nuclear charge. A quantitative treatment of penetrating orbits is given in Section 10.

Some information regarding the classification of orbits as penetrating or non-penetrating can be obtained in the following way. The distance of closest approach of electron and nucleus for an elliptical orbit in the region of effective nuclear charge ze is (Fig. 2)

$$OA = (1 - \epsilon)a = \left\{1 - \sqrt{1 - \frac{k^2}{n^2}}\right\}\frac{n^2 a_0}{z}.$$

For n large, this reduces on expansion of the radical to

$$OA = \frac{n^2 a_0}{z}\left\{1 - 1 + \frac{1}{2}\frac{k^2}{n^2} - \cdots\right\} \cong \frac{k^2 a_0}{2z},$$

or, on making the quantum mechanics replacement of k^2 by $l(l + 1)$,

$$OA \cong \frac{l(l + 1)a_0}{2z}. \tag{1}$$

The values of OA for $z = 1$ are, then,

$$\begin{array}{cccccc} l = 0 & 1 & 2 & 3 & 4. \\ OA = 0 & a_0 & 3a_0 & 6a_0 & 10a_0. \end{array}$$

If this distance is smaller than the radius of the electron shell, the orbit will penetrate. For the alkali ions the most reasonable value for the radius of the outer shell is $\bar{r}$, given in Table II. Hence we may say with certainty that for the alkali atoms all orbits with the values of l shown unbracketed in Table III will be penetrating orbits. Furthermore, the electron shells in actual ions extend a considerable distance beyond the average distance $\bar{r}$, so that some other orbits will be expected to penetrate to some extent. Values of l for these partly penetrating orbits are bracketed in Table III.

TABLE III.—PENETRATING ORBITS IN THE ALKALI ATOMS

Li	$l = 0$		
Na	0	[1]	
K	0	1	[2]
Rb	0	1	[2]
Cs	0	1	[2]

The description of orbits as penetrating or non-penetrating retains its significance in the quantum mechanics. If the valence-electron eigenfunction is large in a region where the eigenfunctions of the core electrons are large, the interaction will be great; otherwise it will be small. Since a hydrogen-like eigenfunction is large only for the values of r traversed by an electron in a Kepler ellipse with $k^2 = l(l+1)$ (Fig. 9, Chap. II), this consideration also leads to the results given above.

9. TERM SERIES AND TERM VALUES. THE FORMULAS OF RYDBERG AND RITZ

We have just seen that the classification of an orbit of the valence electron of an alkali-like atom as penetrating or non-penetrating depends mainly on its azimuthal quantum number l, and not on n. This grouping of states according to the value of l is further suggested by the observed term values. Let us take sodium as an example. The term values found experimentally for small values of n and l are given in Table IV. The ground state or normal state of the atom (highest term value) is that with $n = 3$, $l = 0$. The term value of the normal state multiplied by hc is just the energy needed to remove the electron to infinity; that is, to ionize the atom.

TABLE IV.—TERM VALUES FOR SODIUM IN CM.$^{-1}$*

$n =$	3	4	5	6
s $l = 0$	41,449.0	15,709.5	8,248.3	5,077.3
p† $l = 1$	24,475.7	11,176.1	6,406.3	4,151.3
d $l = 2$	12,276.2	6,900.4	4,412.5	3,061.9
f $l = 3$	....	6,860.4	4,390.4	3,043.

* F. PASCHEN, *Ann. d. Phys.*, **71:** 142, 1923.
† The lower term values of the doublet terms are given.

Extending from this normal state is a series of states, all with $l = 0$, which can be expressed as a first approximation by the common formula

$$T = \frac{Rz^2}{(n - \Delta_0)^2}, \quad n = 3, 4, \cdots \qquad (2)$$

This approximate formula is called the "Rydberg formula." A more exact formula is that of Ritz, which has the form

$$T = \frac{Rz^2}{\left(n - \Delta_0 + \frac{\delta_0}{n^2}\right)^2} \qquad (3)$$

This series of energy levels, all with $l = 0$, is called the "*s* series." In the same way energy levels with $l = 1$ form a series, called the "*p* series." The terms of this series can be represented by equations of the form of 2 or 3, but with different values of Δ and δ, indicated as Δ_1 and δ_1 (in general we write Δ_l and δ_l). The successive series have been assigned the following names:

$l = 0$	*s* series
1	*p*
2	*d*
3	*f*
4	*g*
5	*h* etc.

It is seen from Table IV that for a given value of n the lowest energy level is an *s* level, the next a *p* level, and so on.

Term values are often written

$$T = \frac{Rz^2}{n^{*2}} \tag{4}$$

in which n^* is called the effective quantum number. The quantity $n - n^*$ is called the "quantum defect" of the term, and may be represented by the symbol Δ (without subscripts).

The individual terms of a series are indicated by writing the value of n before the term symbol; as 1*s*, 2*s*, . . .

10. TERM VALUES FOR PENETRATING ORBITS

A simple treatment of penetrating orbits has been given by Van Urk.[1] Consider an atom with effective nuclear charge Z_ie within a sphere of radius ζa_0, and ze beyond this radius (the charge $(Z_i - z)e$ being distributed uniformly over the surface of the sphere). The potential energy of the valence electron of this atom will be

$$\left.\begin{aligned} V(r) &= -\frac{ze^2}{r} \text{ for } r > \zeta a_0, \\ &= -\frac{Z_ie^2}{r} + \frac{(Z_i - z)e^2}{\zeta a_0} \text{ for } r < \zeta a_0. \end{aligned}\right\} \tag{5}$$

The Hamiltonian function is

$$H = \frac{1}{2m_0}\left(p_r^2 + \frac{p_\psi^2}{r^2}\right) + V(r) = W, \text{ the energy constant.} \tag{6}$$

[1] A. Th. van Urk, *Z. f. Phys.*, **13**: 268, 1923; see also M. Born, "Atommechanik," pp. 195–198.

Since ψ does not occur in this equation, the angular momentum p_ψ is constant, and its quantization gives

$$p_\psi = \frac{kh}{2\pi}. \tag{7}$$

Comparison of Equation 6 with Equation 4 of Chap. II shows that the motion of the electron in the outer region is just that of an electron in the coulomb field of the charge ze, and in the inner region that of an electron in the coulomb field of the charge Z_ie. The portion of the orbit in each region is a segment of an ellipse, determined by the azimuthal quantum number k and the *segmentary radial quantum numbers*

$$\left.\begin{aligned} n'_{\text{outer}}h &= \oint\sqrt{2m_0\left\{W + \frac{ze^2}{r}\right\} - \frac{k^2h^2}{4\pi^2r^2}}\,dr \\ n'_{\text{inner}}h &= \oint\sqrt{2m_0\left\{W + \frac{Z_ie^2}{r} - \frac{(Z_i - z)e^2}{\zeta a_0}\right\} - \frac{k^2h^2}{4\pi^2r^2}}\,dr \end{aligned}\right\} \tag{8}$$

The *true radial quantum number* n' is given by the quantum condition

$$n'h = \int_{\text{Outer region}}\sqrt{2m_0\left\{W + \frac{ze^2}{r}\right\} - \frac{k^2h^2}{4\pi^2r^2}}\,dr + \int_{\text{Inner region}}\sqrt{2m_0\left\{W + \frac{Z_ie^2}{r} - \frac{(Z_i - z)e^2}{\zeta a_0}\right\} - \frac{k^2h^2}{4\pi^2r^2}}\,dr \tag{9}$$

The *segmentary principal quantum numbers* for the outer and inner regions are

$$\left.\begin{aligned} n^* &= n'_{\text{outer}} + k \\ n_i &= n'_{\text{inner}} + k. \end{aligned}\right\} \tag{10}$$

The energy of the electron in the two segments must be the same, and be equal to the energy of the orbit; hence, from Equations 14 and 20 of Chap. II, we obtain the equation

$$-\frac{z^2e^2}{2a_0n^{*2}} = -\frac{Z_i^2e^2}{2a_0n_i^2} + \frac{(Z_i - z)e^2}{\zeta a_0} = W, \tag{11}$$

connecting n^* and n_i.

Let us assume z/n^* small compared with Z_i/n_i, so that the left term of this equation is small. Then we have

$$\frac{Z_i^2}{2a_0n_i^2} \cong \frac{Z_i - z}{\zeta a_0}, \quad \text{or} \quad \frac{2n_i^2a_0}{Z_i} \cong \zeta a_0.$$

But $2n_i^2a_0/Z_i$ is the major axis of the inner ellipse and ζa_0 the radius of the inner region. Accordingly the inner elliptical segment must be nearly a complete ellipse. Furthermore, if n is large the outer segment will be nearly complete. The orbit will have the form shown in Figure 13. The integrals of Equation 9 will approach those of Equation 8, and there will result

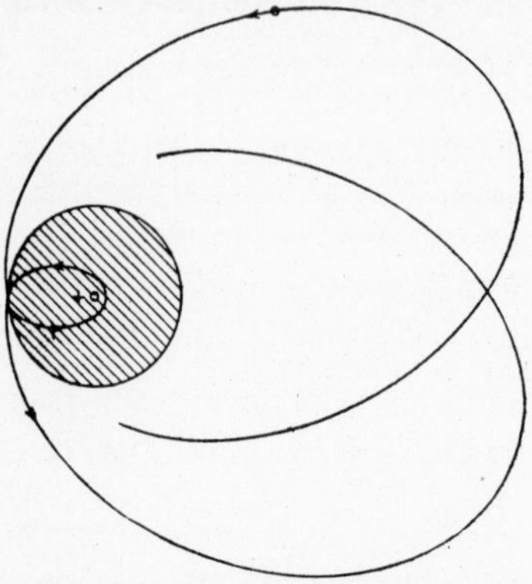

FIG. 13.—A penetrating orbit in which both the inner and the outer segments are nearly complete.

$$n' = n'_{\text{inner}} + n'_{\text{outer}}$$

or

$$n = n^* + n_i - k. \quad (12)$$

A minimum value for n_i can be obtained in the following way. The aphelion distance for the inner ellipse must be at least equal to the shell radius ζa_0, for otherwise the electron would remain in the inner region. Equating them, we have

$$a(1 + \epsilon) = \zeta a_0$$

with

$$a = \frac{n_i^2 a_0}{Z_i} \text{ and } \epsilon = \sqrt{1 - \frac{k^2}{n_i^2}}. \quad (13)$$

Solving for n_i, there results

$$n_i = \frac{\zeta Z_i}{\sqrt{2\zeta Z_i - k^2}}. \quad (14)$$

Equation 12 thus gives for the Rydberg correction or quantum defect

$$\Delta = n - n^* = n_i - k.$$

Substituting Equation 14 in this, and making the quantum mechanics replacement of k^2 by $l(l + 1)$ and k by $l + \frac{1}{2}$, we obtain

$$\Delta_l = \frac{\zeta Z_i}{\sqrt{2\zeta Z_i - l(l+1)}} - \left(l + \frac{1}{2}\right). \quad (15)$$

This equation gives a satisfactory qualitative and roughly quantitative explanation of the observed features of alkali-like spectra. The most striking result, that the quantum defect Δ is independent of n and is for a given atom a function of l only, is approximately verified by experiment (see Table V). This result has indeed been derived by Bohr in a very general manner, independent of a particular atomic model, the only assumption being that the dimensions of the ion are small compared with those of the orbit of the emitting electron.[1]

TABLE V.—VALUES OF THE EFFECTIVE QUANTUM NUMBER n^* FOR TERM SERIES OF SODIUM

	$n = 3$	4	5	6	7	8
s	1.63	2.64	3.65	4.65	5.65	6.65
p	2.12	3.14	4.14	5.14	6.14	7.15
d	2.99	3.99	4.99	5.99	6.99	7.99
f	....	4.00	5.00	6.00		

In Table V are given values of n^* for sodium, calculated from the data of Table IV, from which the small effect of n in changing the quantum defect can be seen. Values of Δ_l for all the alkali metals are given in Table VI. It is evident from the magnitudes of Δ_l that for lithium only the s orbits penetrate the core, for sodium only the s and p, and for the others the s, p, and d. This is exactly the result obtained from the model, as given in Table III.

TABLE VI.—THE RYDBERG CORRECTION Δ_l FOR THE ALKALI METALS

	s	*p*	*d*	*f*	*g*
Li	0.40	0.04	0.00	0.00	0.00
Na	1.35	0.85	0.01	0.00	0.00
K	2.19	1.71	0.25	0.00	0.00
Rb	3.13	2.66	1.34	0.01	0.00
Cs	4.06	3.59	2.46	0.02	0.00

As a further test of this interpretation of the alkali terms let us calculate Δ_l by Equation 15, using for ζ the theoretical values of Table II and putting $Z_i = 3$ for lithium and 9 for the others. The resultant values, given in Table VII, are in rough general agreement with the observed ones.

[1] Published by M. BORN, "Atommechanik," p. 198.

TABLE VII.—THEORETICAL VALUES OF THE RYDBERG CORRECTION

	s	p	d
Li	0.39		
Na	1.36	0.51	
K	2.14	1.23	0.47
Rb	2.70	1.78	0.96
Cs	3.05	2.13	1.28

It is especially significant that the agreement is excellent in the case of s orbits of lithium, sodium, and potassium, for Equation 15 should give accurate results here. These s orbits, with high eccentricity, penetrate deep into the atom core (as was assumed in the derivation of the equation), so that for them the idealization of the electron shell as a surface charge of electricity is more suitable than for less eccentric orbits. The high experimental values of Δ_l for rubidium and cesium are due no doubt to the further penetration of inner electron shells.

For small values of n the distance OA in Figure 2 of Section 15 will be somewhat larger than given by Equation 1. It therefore can happen that the first orbits of a series do not penetrate but those with higher values of n do. This will cause irregularities in the quantum defect Δ of that series and has been used to give a possible explanation of anomalies occurring in some series of a few spectra (Al, Hg).[1]

Attempts have also been made to derive an atomic potential function $V(r)$, spherically symmetrical and free from discontinuities, from observed term values. The results obtained in this way have been very satisfactory.[2] Furthermore, purely theoretical expressions for $V(r)$ have been obtained which are in excellent agreement with the empirically deduced functions.[3]

[1] E. FUES, *Z. f. Phys.*, **11**: 376, 1923; G. WENTZEL, *ibid.*, **19**: 53, 1923.

[2] E. FUES, *Z. f. Phys.*, **11**: 364; **12**: 314; **13**: 211, 1923; D. R. HARTREE, *Proc.* Cambridge Phil. Soc., **21**: 625, 1923; *Proc.* Roy. Soc., A **106**: 552; 1924, Y. SUGIURA and H. C. UREY, *Kgl. Danske Vid. Selsk.*, **7**: 13, 1926; K. B. LINDSAY, *Jour. Opt. Soc.*, **11**: 17, 1925.

[3] L. H. THOMAS, *Proc.* Cambridge Phil. Soc., **23**: 542, 1927; D. R. HARTREE, *ibid.*, **24**: 89, 111, 1928; J. A. GAUNT, *ibid.*, **24**: 328, 1928; E. FERMI, *Z. f. Phys.*, **48**: 73, 1928.

11. TERM VALUES FOR NON-PENETRATING ORBITS. POLARIZATION OF THE ATOM CORE

The term values of non-penetrating orbits differ slightly but appreciably from those for the corresponding hydrogen-like orbits, the quantum defects being usually of the order of 0.01 or less. It was suggested by Born and Heisenberg[1] that this difference arises from the polarization of the atom core in the field of the valence electron; and now that the quantum mechanics has provided the correct equations expressing this effect and that accurate values of the polarizability of many atom cores are known, it can be shown that the quantum defects for non-penetrating orbits can indeed be calculated in this way with some accuracy.

In an electric field F an atom or ion becomes polarized, the center of charge of the electrons being shifted with respect to the nucleus. The electric moment of the induced dipole is αF, in which α is called the "polarizability" of the atom or ion. The polarization energy is $-\frac{1}{2}\alpha F^2$.

In an alkali atom, such as sodium, with the valence electron in a non-penetrating orbit, the atom core (Na^+) is polarized in the field $-\frac{e}{r^2}$ of the valence electron, the polarization energy being $-\frac{\alpha e^2}{2r^4}$. The perturbation theory of the quantum mechanics states that the change in the energy of the atom from that for a hydrogen-like atom will be just the average value of the polarization energy, the average being taken over the unperturbed system. In this case, then, we have

$$W = -\frac{z^2e^2}{2a_0(n-\Delta)^2} = -\frac{z^2e^2}{2a_0n^2} - \frac{\alpha e^2}{2}\overline{\left(\frac{1}{r^4}\right)}$$

Expanding in powers Δ/n, there is obtained for Δ the expression

$$\Delta = \frac{n^3\alpha a_0}{2z^2}\overline{\left(\frac{1}{r^4}\right)},$$

which becomes, on introducing the quantum mechanics value of $\overline{\left(\frac{1}{r^4}\right)}$ given in Section 8,[2]

$$\Delta = \frac{3\alpha z^2\left\{1 - \frac{l(l+1)}{3n^2}\right\}}{4a_0{}^3(l-\frac{1}{2})l(l+\frac{1}{2})(l+1)(l+\frac{3}{2})}. \tag{16}$$

[1] M. Born and W. Heisenberg, *Z. f. Phys.*, **4**: 347, 1921.

[2] This equation was given first by I. Waller, *Z. f. Phys.*, **38**: 635, 1926.

This value of Δ, containing a term in $1/n^2$, leads to the Ritz term series formula of Equation 3.

Values of α for some ions of interest, obtained by the introduction of suitable screening constants in the quantum mechanical expression for the polarizability of hydrogen-like orbits, are given in Table VIII. In Table IX are values of Δ calculated for the d series of sodium by introducing in Equation 16 the polarizability given for Na^+, and the observed values of Δ obtained from the term values of Table IV. The agreement supports the belief that polarization of the atom core is the main factor determining the quantum defect for non-penetrating orbits. The slightly low theoretical values suggest that some other less important interaction of the valence electron and the atom core is also operative.

TABLE VIII.—THE POLARIZABILITY OF CERTAIN IONS[1]

	α		α
Na^+	0.180×10^{-24}	Li^+	0.0292×10^{-24}
K^+	0.835	Be^{+2}	0.0079
Rb^+	1.41	B^{+3}	0.0030
Cs^+	2.42	C^{+4}	0.00134

[1] LINUS PAULING, *Proc.*, Roy. Soc., A **114**: 181, 1927.

TABLE IX.—QUANTUM DEFECTS FOR THE d SERIES OF SODIUM

$n =$	3	4	5	6	7	8	∞
Δ observed	0.0100	0.0112	0.0126	0.0124	0.0125	0.0110	
Δ calculated	0.0090	0.0102	0.0107	0.0110	0.0111	0.0112	0.0116

A similar treatment can be given other alkali-like atoms. In Table X are given term values for the lithium-like atoms neutral lithium, singly ionized beryllium, doubly ionized boron, and triply ionized carbon, or, denoting the degree of ionization by Roman subscripts equal to z, Li_{I}, Be_{II}, B_{III}, and C_{IV}.

These term values lead to the quantum defects for p and d terms given in Table XI. The trend of the calculated values of Δ for p terms in Table XI follows strikingly that of the observed values; particularly noteworthy is the maximum at Be_{II} for a given term. In the case of the d terms the entire quantum defect arises from polarization, but for the p terms some other interaction seems to be responsible for a small fraction of Δ.

TABLE X.—TERM VALUES OF LITHIUM-LIKE ATOMS*

	n =	2	3	4	5
	R_{Li}/n^2 =	27,433.00	12,192.44	6,858.25	4,389.28
s	Li_I	43,486.3	16,280.5	8,475.2	5,187.8
	$Be_{II}/4$	36,720.1	14,662.3	7,856.2	4,886.6
	$B_{III}/9$	33,993.1	13,970.7		
	$C_{IV}/16$	32,502.1	13,581.4		
p†	Li_I	28,582.5	12,560.4	7,018.2	4,473.6
	$Be_{II}/4$	28,736.3	12,596.2	7,030.1	4,477.6
	$B_{III}/9$	28,616.1			
	$C_{IV}/16$	28,465.3	12,504.3		
d	Li_I	....	12,203.1	6,863.5	4,389.6
	$Be_{II}/4$	....	12,206.9	6,865.1	4,393.7
	$B_{III}/9$	....	12,207.8		
	$C_{IV}/16$	....	12,208.3		

* I. S. BOWEN and R. A. MILLIKAN, *Phys. Rev.*, **28**: 256, 1926. Term values for Be_{II}, etc. are divided by z^2 for ease in comparison with hydrogen-like terms.

† The smaller term values of the p doublets are given.

TABLE XI.—QUANTUM DEFECTS FOR LITHIUM-LIKE ATOMS

		n =	2	3	4	5	∞
p	Li_I	Observed	0.0419	0.0451	0.0464	0.0479	
		Calculated	0.0327	0.0363	0.0376	0.0382	0.0392
	Be_{II}	Observed	0.0475	0.0496	0.0499	0.0502	
		Calculated	0.0356	0.0395	0.0410	0.0416	0.0427
	B_{III}	Observed	0.0431				
		Calculated	0.0305	0.0339	0.0351	0.0356	0.0366
	C_{IV}	Observed	0.0376	0.0382			
		Calculated	0.0242	0.0268	0.0278	0.0282	0.0290
d	Li_I	Observed	......	0.0013	0.0015		
		Calculated	......	0.00144	0.00163	......	0.00186

Similar approximate agreement is found between observed and calculated quantum defects for other alkali-like atoms, as well as for atoms with several outer electrons, only one of which is excited into a large non-penetrating orbit.[1]

By the use of the first-order perturbation theory of the quantum mechanics it can be shown that even for these states there is some penetration of the core, leading to a small contribution to the quantum defect, of the magnitude of the differences in Tables IX and XI. It is accordingly no longer possible to make a sharp distinction between penetrating and non-penetrating orbits. In some cases the effect of penetration is extremely small, for example, for the *d* states of lithium; and for *s* states it is large. The states bracketed in Table III occupy an intermediate position

12. ABSORPTION SPECTRA. SERIES OF SPECTRAL LINES

The difficulties in the interpretation of observed spectra are lessened considerably by the fact that absorption spectra have a very simple structure. During absorption by a "cold" vapor (one at a temperature such that the vapor emits no spectral lines) all the absorbing atoms have the same initial state, which is the normal state of the atom (for the alkalies the lowest *s* state). In this *s* state all frequencies of light are absorbed which are connected with transitions to levels in the *p* series. One obtains in this way a *series of absorption lines* which can be written symbolically, for sodium, for example, as

$$\nu = 3s - np \qquad n = 3, 4, \cdots$$

Such a succession of spectral lines was formerly called a "spectral" series; we prefer now to call it a "series of spectral lines" to prevent confusion with the series of energy levels. In emission spectra there occur still more such series of spectral lines. Thus, for example, all transitions from *s* levels to the lowest *p* level for sodium form a series with the wave-numbers

$$\nu = 3p - ns, \qquad n = 4, 5, \cdots$$

Formerly some of these line series were given names, which one still sees in the literature. For sodium these are the following (for potassium 3 is replaced by 4, for rubidium by 5, etc.):

$3s - np$, principal series;
$3p - ns$, second or sharp subordinate series;
$3p - nd$, first or diffuse subordinate series;
$3d - nf$, Bergmann or fundamental series.

[1] E. Schrödinger, *Ann. d. Phys.*, **77**: 43, 1925; D. R. Hartree, *Proc.*, Cambridge Phil. Soc., **23**: 304, 1926; B. Swirles, *Ibid.*, **23**: 403, 1926; A. Unsöld, *Z. f. Phys.*, **36**: 92, 1926.

It is as the initials of the words sharp, principal, diffuse, and fundamental that the series symbols *s*, *p*, *d*, *f* came into use.

Under ordinary conditions the transitions between the lowest levels give the strongest lines. The very strongest are transitions to the normal state.

12a. Selection Rules.—Not all spectral lines which would be expected from the preceding considerations actually occur; that is, not every difference between two term values gives an observed frequency. On the other hand, the frequency of every observed spectral line is given by the difference between the term values of two energy levels of the atom.

Under normal conditions, when the alkali atom is not perturbed by an external electric field, there occur only certain definite transitions. *Only those combinations occur for which the quantum number l changes by +1 or −1.* The theoretical discussion of this *selection rule for the quantum number l* will be given in Chap. VIII. There is no selection rule for *n*.

This signifies that in alkali-like spectra there occur transitions from the *s* term series to the *p* series only, from the *p* series to the *s* and *d* series only, from the *d* series to the *p* and *f* series only, and so on. In a perturbing electric field the selection rule is rendered invalid and "forbidden" lines are observed.

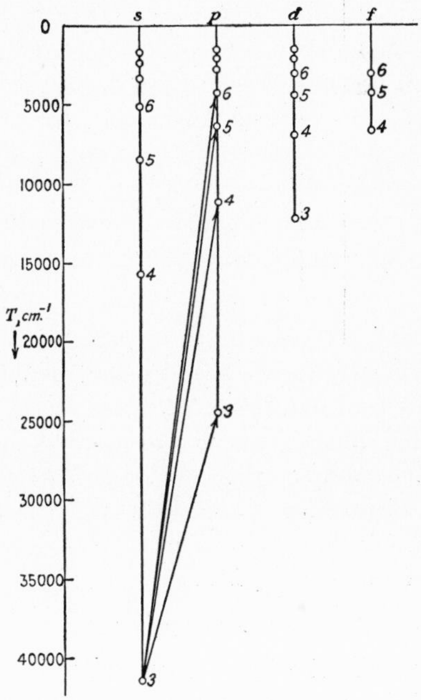

Fig. 14.—Term scheme for sodium.

12b. Term Diagrams.—In order to get a definite idea of the structure of a given spectrum the following graphical representation is used. The different energy levels are represented by dashes or dots with ordinates proportional to the energy values or term values. Usually the lowest energy level, the normal state, is farthest down in the diagram. Levels with given values of *l* are placed on parallel vertical lines. Figure 14 gives as an example the terms of the sodium atom. A scale of term values, increasing toward the bottom, is shown on the y-axis. The first vertical line to the right of the axis contains the s terms, the second the p terms, etc. All series of levels in the spectrum converge for increasing n to the value 0. The series of absorption lines of sodium is also shown in the diagram, as lines connecting the lowest s level with the different p levels. Emission lines can be similarly represented.

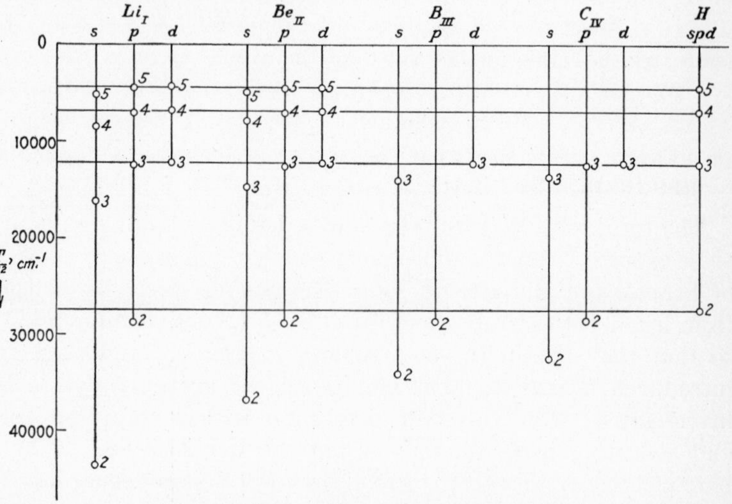

FIG. 15.—Term scheme for lithium-like atoms. Values of T/z^2 are plotted to facilitate comparison with the terms of hydrogen.

Term values of lithium-like atoms (Table X) are shown in Figure 15.

12c. Resonance Lines.—Such a graphical representation suggests directly all the peculiarities of the spectrum. For example, if sodium vapor is illuminated with monochromatic light

$$\nu = 3s - 3p, \qquad \lambda = 5890 \text{ Å},^1$$

this light will be absorbed and atoms will jump to the $3p$ state. From here they may spontaneously fall to lower states. The only possibility in this case is the transition back to the normal state $3s$, with the accompanying emission of the same line that was previously absorbed. A spectral line with this property

[1] This line is really a doublet (the yellow sodium doublet) with wavelengths λ5890 and λ5896. The doublet structure will be discussed in the next chapter.

is called a "resonance line." From the term-value diagram it can be seen that the line $3s - 3p$ is the only resonance line of sodium. In the case of the other absorption lines part of the absorbed radiation is re-emitted with unchanged frequency; but lines of other frequencies are also emitted at the same time. For example, if the absorbed light takes the atom from $3s$ to $4p$, then it can fall directly back to the normal state, or to $3d$, then to $3p$, and then to $3s$, or to $4s$, then to $3p$, and then to $3s$; so that the absorption of the line

$$\nu = 3s - 4p, \qquad \lambda = 3303 \text{ Å},$$

leads to the emission of the lines $\nu = 3s - 4p$, $\nu = 3d - 4p$, $\nu = 3p - 3d$, $\nu = 3s - 3p$, $\nu = 3p - 4s$, and $\nu = 4s - 4p$.

13. VERIFICATION OF TERM VALUES BY ELECTRON COLLISIONS. RESONANCE POTENTIALS AND IONIZATION POTENTIALS

The term level diagram also shows definitely what results are to be expected from the well-known electron collision experiments of Franck and Hertz.[1] In these experiments electrons emitted from a hot cathode are accelerated by a potential difference V, so that they obtain the translational energy eV, and then are introduced into a chamber filled with the gas or vapor to be investigated. One can now determine with a retarding field and collecting plate whether or not the electrons lose all or a part of their energy to the gas. If slowly moving electrons are sent into non-luminous sodium vapor they experience no energy loss so long as their kinetic energy is smaller than the energy difference $3s - 3p$. Only when the accelerating potential becomes so large that the electron has just enough energy to remove the atom from the normal state to the next higher state can it transfer energy to the sodium atom on collision. The necessary voltage is given by

$$eV = h\tilde{\nu} = h\nu c = hc(3s - 3p)$$

($\tilde{\nu}$ in sec^{-1}, ν in cm^{-1}, $3s$ and $3p$ term values).

On falling back to the normal state the atom emits the resonance line λ5890.

If the electron is given still more energy, it continues to lose the amount $hc(3s - 3p)$ until the next following energy difference $hc(3s - 3d)$ is reached. Then this jump, too, will be excited,

[1] See the monograph covering this field, J. Franck and P. Jordan, "Anregung von Quantensprüngen durch Stösse," Springer, Berlin, 1926.

atoms will be raised from the normal state to the state $3d$, and on falling back will emit the lines

$$\nu = 3p - 3d \text{ and } \nu = 3s - 3p.$$

It is to be borne in mind that for such transitions caused by electron collisions the selection rules do not hold, or at any rate not strictly. Experiment seems to show, however, that the probability that a transition allowed by the selection rule will take place through electron impact is greater than that for a forbidden one.

If the colliding electron has traversed the potential difference given by

$$eV_i = hc \cdot 3s,$$

it has sufficient energy to remove the valence electron from the normal state to infinity; the atom will be ionized. This potential difference V_i is accordingly called the "ionization potential," and the energy eV_i is called the "energy of ionization."

For use with these experiments of Franck and Hertz, energies and energy differences in the energy-level diagram are often expressed in "volts," or better, volt-electrons, signifying the energy quantities eV. The number of volt-electrons is given by

$$eV = h\tilde{\nu} \text{ or } eV = h\nu c, \ (\tilde{\nu} \text{ in sec}^{-1}, \nu \text{ in cm}^{-1}.)$$

Conversion factors from frequencies or wave-numbers to volts are given in Appendix II.

Resonance and ionization potentials for the alkali atoms, calculated from term values, are given in Table XII.

TABLE XII.—RESONANCE AND IONIZATION POTENTIALS FOR ALKALI ATOMS

Atom	Resonance potential	Ionization potential
Li	$2s - 2p = 1.840$ volts	$2s = 5.368$ volts
Na	$3s - 3p = 2.095$	$3s = 5.116$
K	$4s - 4p = 1.610$	$4s = 4.321$
Rb	$5s - 5p = 1.582$	$5s = 4.158$
Cs	$6s - 6p = 1.448$	$6s = 3.877$

An extensive table of ionization potentials is given in Chap. IX.

CHAPTER IV

THE SPINNING ELECTRON AND THE FINE STRUCTURE OF ALKALI-LIKE SPECTRA

So far we have seen that our atomic model gives a qualitatively and often quantitatively very good representation of the structure of simple spectra. A more careful inspection of spectra shows, however, that there are still some unexplained points. Thus we find that the yellow sodium line, the resonance line $3s - 3p$ used in the preceding discussion as an example, is not a simple line, but is a doublet, consisting of two components of wave-lengths 5890.12 Å and 5896.16 Å. The doublet separation in wave-number units is $\Delta\nu = 17.2$ cm.$^{-1}$. Similarly the line $3s - 4p$, λ3303, is a doublet, with $\Delta\nu = 5.5$ cm.$^{-1}$, and $3s - 5p$ also, with $\Delta\nu = 2.5$ cm.$^{-1}$, etc. Hence the levels $3p$, $4p$, $5p$, etc., must be double, with the above doublet separations.

The further analysis of the lines of alkali-like spectra shows that the levels of the s series are single and that all those of the p, d, f, etc. series are doublets.

14. DOUBLET STRUCTURE AND THE SPINNING ELECTRON

In order to explain this complexity of the energy levels and other spectral properties of the atom, to be mentioned later, an addition must be made to the atomic model which we have previously used. This addition consists in attributing a rotatory motion to the individual electrons.[1]

It seems to be sufficient to give all electrons the same rotation, so that they have the angular momentum $s\frac{h}{2\pi}$, with s, the spin quantum number, always ½.[2] The electron obtains a magnetic moment together with this rotation. How large this is cannot be predicted, since our information concerning the structure and

[1] G. E. Uhlenbeck and S. Goudsmit, *Naturwissenschaften*, **13:** 953, 1925; *Nature*, **107**: 264, 1926.

[2] Care must be taken not to confuse the spin quantum number s with the symbol used in writing s orbit or s level.

properties of the electron must come from experiment. The empirical spectral material and the magnetic properties of atoms indicate that the magnetic moment of all electrons is the same; namely, $2\mathbf{s}\frac{h}{2\pi} \cdot \frac{e}{2m_0c}$. An electron is thus no longer a point particle, but has, besides charge and mass, empirically determined mechanical and magnetic moments. If we interpret the quantum mechanics formulas as signifying that the magnitude of the vector $\mathbf{s}$ is $\sqrt{s(s+1)}$, in accordance with the discussion in Chap. I, then the properties of an electron may be expressed in terms of the following numerical values:

Charge............ $-e = -4.770 \cdot 10^{-10}$ e.s.u.
Mass.............. $m_0 = 0.904 \cdot 10^{-27}$ grams.

Mechanical moment... $\sqrt{\frac{1}{2} \cdot \frac{3}{2}} \cdot \frac{h}{2\pi} = 0.902 \times 10^{-27}$ erg-seconds.

Magnetic moment..... $\sqrt{\frac{1}{2} \cdot \frac{3}{2}} \cdot \frac{h}{2\pi} \cdot \frac{e}{m_0c} = 1.589 \times 10^{-20}$ erg-gauss^{-1}.

The question immediately suggests itself as to whether the electron can be given a structure such that it will possess all of these properties. Attempts in this direction have been made, but have always run into difficulties. Formal methods of introducing the spin of the electron into the quantum mechanics equation have, so far, been only partially satisfactory.[1] Dirac has, however, concluded recently that the quantum mechanics in combination with the theory of relativity necessitates the introduction of equations which may be interpreted in terms of the electron spin.[2] Without doubt this method of introducing the quantum number s is to be preferred to the more intuitive treatments used previously; we shall, however, find it convenient in discussing the vector model to retain the visualizable conception of the electron as a spinning top.

14a. The Total Angular Momentum of the Atom.—We shall now see what properties of the atom can be explained with the aid of the spinning electron. We might first consider how the orbit would be influenced according to the old quantum theory. It is found that as a result of the spin the orbit of the electron would no longer remain plane, but that the orbital plane itself would undergo

[1] In addition to the references given later in this chapter, mention must be made of the work of W. Pauli, *Z. f. Phys.*, **43**: 601, 1927 and of C. G. Darwin, *Proc.*, Roy. Soc., A **115**: 1, 1927; **116**: 227, 1927.

[2] P. A. M. Dirac, *Proc.* Roy. Soc., A. **117**, 610; **118**, 351, 1928.

uniform precession in space about the total angular momentum vector of the atom, which would remain fixed in direction and magnitude. This total angular momentum, which is given by the quantum vector **j**, is the resultant of the orbital moment **l** and the spin moment **s**. An assumption fundamental to the determination of possible values of **j** is this: in a given case the values of j must all be either integral or half-integral, depending on whether s is integral or half-integral. Since for a single electron we have assumed $s = \frac{1}{2}$, j must be half-integral, and, in fact, can have only the values $l + \frac{1}{2}$ and $l - \frac{1}{2}$. The two ways of combining **l** and **s** into a resultant j are shown in the

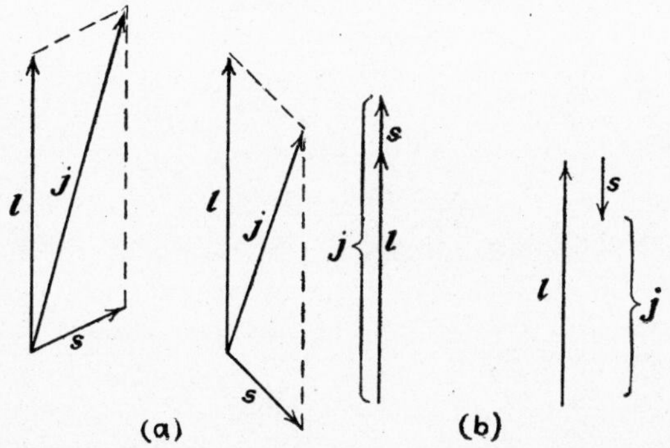

FIG. 16.—Composition of vectors **l** and **s** to form the resultant **j** for the case $l = 2$, $s = \frac{1}{2}$, $j = \frac{5}{2}$ or $\frac{3}{2}$, (a) according to the model in which the magnitudes of the vectors are $\sqrt{l(l+1)}$, $\sqrt{s(s+1)}$, and $\sqrt{j(j+1)}$, and (b) according to the model in which the magnitudes of the vectors are l, s, and j.

accompanying figure (Fig. 16), in which l has been given the value 2, so that j is equal to either $\frac{5}{2}$ or $\frac{3}{2}$. Inasmuch as $\sqrt{j(j+1)}$ differs only a little from j, and similarly for l and s, it is easily seen that, in general, the maximum and minimum values of the quantum number j are $l + s$ and $|l - s|$; for with j larger than $l + s$ or smaller than $|l - s|$ the quantum vectors cannot be combined.

In considering the energy term due to the interaction of electron spin and orbital motion, it will be found necessary to evaluate the quantity $sl \cos(\mathbf{sl})$. From the trigonometric equation connecting three sides and one angle of a plane triangle we obtain, with the introduction of the magnitudes $\sqrt{j(j+1)}$, etc., of the vectors in terms of the quantum numbers,

$$sl \cos(\mathbf{sl}) = \frac{j(j+1) - s(s+1) - l(l+1)}{2}. \tag{1}$$

Equation 1 is the equation given by the quantum mechanics for sl cos (**sl**), and for this reason it is to be accepted as correct; the fact that we have also obtained it from our model should not be interpreted to mean that the model will in all cases be in agreement with the quantum mechanics. It has in the past been customary to use the convention of giving the quantum vectors **j**, **l**, and **s** in the vector model the magnitudes j, l, and s. With this model there would result the incorrect relation

$$sl \cos (\mathbf{sl}) = \frac{j^2 - s^2 - l^2}{2}.$$

It was then said that the model corresponded only roughly to actual atoms, and that it was necessary to introduce certain quantum mechanics corrections; namely, to replace j^2 by $j(j+1)$, and so on, so as to obtain the correct Equation 1. The composition of vectors according to this model is shown in Figure 16*b*.

14b. Selection Rule for j.—It was found empirically that j can change during a quantum jump only by $+1$, 0, or -1. This selection rule is given by the quantum mechanics, and may also be derived by means of the correspondence principle, as will be shown in Chap. VIII. The selection rule for j is not rendered invalid by perturbing external electric fields, as is that for l. It will be shown later, however, that it is affected by external magnetic fields.

The name "inner quantum number" originally given j by Sommerfeld is less desirable than the more descriptive name "total angular momentum quantum number"; it is, moreover, convenient and desirable to reserve the letter j for this one use, and to refer to the total angular momentum quantum number as "the quantum number j."

14c. Term Symbols.[1]—It is now customary to designate states of an atom by the use of the capital letters $S, P, D, F, \ldots$ corresponding to the orbital momentum given by $l = 0, 1, 2, 3, \cdots$, while small letters $s, p, d, f, \ldots$ are retained for individual electrons; evidently in the case of alkali-like atoms we need merely to replace the small letters by capitals to obtain the atomic state from the state of the valence electron. Furthermore, the index $2s + 1$ ($=2$, with $s = \frac{1}{2}$) is written above and to the left of the atomic term symbol, to indicate the doublet character of the

[1] Term symbols are further discussed in Sec. 21*c*.

levels, and the value of j is written as a subscript. The index 2 is used with S levels even though only one level exists. The terms

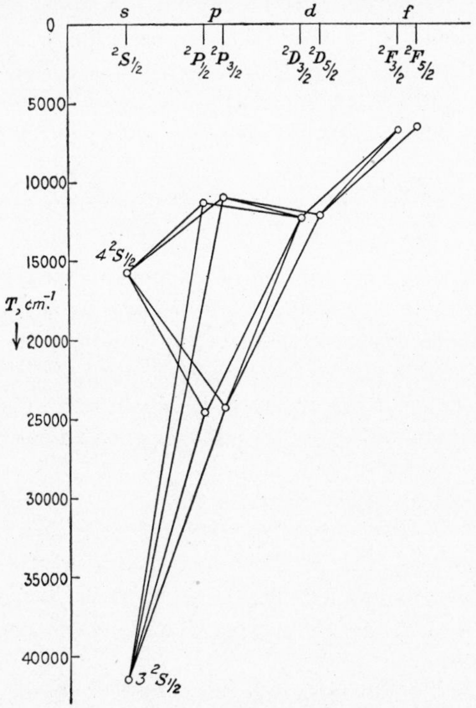

FIG. 17.—Term scheme of sodium, showing fine structure of levels and allowed transitions. (The F levels should read $^2F_{5/2}$ and $^2F_{7/2}$.)

of alkali-like atoms, and the corresponding symbols, are given by the following scheme:

	j =	½	3/2	5/2	7/2	9/2
l = 0.	s	$^2S_{1/2}$				
1.	p	$^2P_{1/2}$	$^2P_{3/2}$			
2.	d	. . .	$^2D_{3/2}$	$^2D_{5/2}$		
3.	f	. . .	. . .	$^2F_{5/2}$	$^2F_{7/2}$	
4.	g	. . .	. . .	. . .	$^2G_{7/2}$	$^2G_{9/2}$

The value of the total quantum number n may be written before this symbol; thus, the two components of the yellow sodium line (which we have called $3s - 3p$) are $3^2S_{1/2} - 3^2P_{1/2}$ and $3^2S_{1/2} - 3^2P_{3/2}$.[1]

The transitions allowed by the selection rules for l and j are shown in Figure 17. It will be seen that only lines due to transitions involving an s state have two components, all others having three. The name doublets refers not to the number of components of the spectral lines but to the multiplicity of the energy levels.

15. THE ENERGY CHANGE DUE TO THE SPINNING ELECTRON

Through the introduction of the magnetic electron the expression for the energy is naturally changed somewhat; a correction term is added. For a Kepler ellipse with quantum numbers n and l in the field due to the nuclear charge Ze this term is

$$W_s^1 = \frac{Rhc\alpha^2Z^4}{n^3l(l + \frac{1}{2})(l + 1)} ls \cos (\mathbf{ls}), \tag{2}$$

in which α, the Sommerfeld fine-structure constant, is $2\pi e^2/hc$. If a penetrating orbit such as that of Section 9 is being treated, the correction term is

$$W_s^1 = \frac{Rhc\, \alpha^2Z_i^2z^2}{n^{*3}l(l + \frac{1}{2})(l + 1)} ls \cos (\mathbf{ls}). \tag{3}$$

Introducing the value of $ls \cos(\mathbf{ls})$ there is obtained in the second case

$$W_s^1 = \frac{Rhc\, \alpha^2Z_i^2z^2}{n^{*3}l(l + \frac{1}{2})(l + 1)} \cdot \frac{j(j + 1) - l(l + 1) - s(s + 1)}{2} \tag{4}$$

Since j can assume only the values $l + \frac{1}{2}$ and $l - \frac{1}{2}$, this becomes

$$W_s^1 = \frac{Rhc\, \alpha^2Z_i^2z^2}{n^{*3}l(l + \frac{1}{2})(l + 1)} \cdot \frac{\pm(l + \frac{1}{2}) - \frac{1}{2}}{2}. \tag{5}$$

Each of the previously considered energy states of the atom is now split into two, which differ slightly in energy. But states with $l = 0$ are not split, they are only displaced. For with $l = 0$ the correction term has a finite value only for $j = l + \frac{1}{2}$; the

[1] Before the development of this nomenclature it was customary to represent alkali-like levels by using the subscript 2 for states with $j = l - \frac{1}{2}$ and 1 for those with $j = l + \frac{1}{2}$; thus $^2P_{1/2}$ was written p_2; $^2P_{3/2}$, p_1; $^2D_{3/2}$, d_2; $^2D_{5/2}$, d_1; etc. Sommerfeld introduced the use of $j + \frac{1}{2}$ as subscripts, writing p_1, p_2, d_2, d_3, etc. for the above terms. We shall use the capital letter symbols in all fine-structure considerations. For convenience in printing, the "half-integral" values of j are sometimes written $1\frac{1}{2}$, $2\frac{1}{2}$, etc.

case of $j = l - \frac{1}{2}$ gives an infinitely large correction term, corresponding to a non-existent state. This result is in complete agreement with the above-mentioned facts, that in the alkali spectra the s terms are single, and all others are double. This result regarding the multiplicity of terms may also be obtained very simply directly from the vector model. With $l = 1, 2, 3, \cdots$ there are two possible values for j, $l + \frac{1}{2}$ and $l - \frac{1}{2}$, but for $l = 0$ only one, $j = s = \frac{1}{2}$. From Equation 5 the doublet separation of the levels, expressed in wave-numbers, is found to be

$$\Delta\nu = \frac{R\alpha^2 Z_i^2 z^2}{n^{*3} l(l+1)} \qquad (5a)$$

It can be seen from the equation that the state with $j = l - \frac{1}{2}$ has a smaller energy than that with $j = l + \frac{1}{2}$; the level with the greater value of j lies higher. This also is in agreement with the observed fine-structure levels.

The derivation of Equations 2 to 5 representing the interaction of spin and orbital motion of the electron seems, at first sight, not to be difficult. The electron moves with velocity $\mathbf{v}$ in the electric field of the nucleus, thus producing according to electromagnetic theory a magnetic field

$$\mathbf{H} = \frac{1}{c}\mathbf{F} \times \mathbf{v}.$$

If the effective nuclear charge is Ze the field at the electron is

$$\mathbf{F} = \frac{Ze}{r^3}\mathbf{r},$$

in which $\mathbf{r}$ is the radius vector. (This formula also follows directly from the law of Biot and Savart. Relative to the electron the nucleus is moving with the velocity $\mathbf{v}$, and is equivalent to a current $Ze\mathbf{v}$, which produces at the electron a magnetic field of the above magnitude.) The angular momentum of the electron is

$$m_0\mathbf{r} \times \mathbf{v} = \mathbf{l}\frac{h}{2\pi},$$

and hence

$$\mathbf{H} = \mathbf{l}\cdot\frac{h}{2\pi m_0 c}\cdot\frac{Ze}{r^3}.$$

Now a magnetic electron in a magnetic field undergoes a Larmor precession about the field direction, with an angular velocity equal to the product of the field strength and the ratio of the magnetic and the mechanical moment of the spinning electron:[1]

$$\omega_H = \frac{e^2}{m_0{}^2c^2} \cdot \frac{Z}{r^3} \cdot \frac{1h}{2\pi}.$$

L. H. Thomas[2] has further remarked that the rigorous relativistic treatment of the motion of the spinning electron leads to a precession of the electron axis arising from the relativity theory, in addition to the magnetic precession. This "Thomas precession" is just half as great as the magnetic precession, and has the opposite sign. The derivation of this relativistic precession cannot be given here on account of its difficult nature. With both precessions the actual angular velocity of the electron axis becomes

$$\omega = \omega_H + \omega_T = \frac{1}{2}\frac{e^2}{m_0{}^2c^2} \cdot \frac{Z}{r^3} \cdot \frac{1h}{2\pi}.$$

Just as in the theory of the Zeeman effect, the energy of such a precessional motion is equal to the product of the angular velocity and the projection of the mechanical moment of the precessing system on the axis of precession; *i.e.*, on **H** or **l**:

$$W_s{}^1 = \frac{1}{2}\frac{e^2h^2}{4\pi^2m_0{}^2c^2} \cdot \frac{Z}{r^3}sl \cos(\mathbf{sl}). \qquad (6)$$

In general, the factor Z/r^3 is not constant during the motion of the electron. Since the energy $W_s{}^1$ is only a very small fraction of the total energy of the moving electron the perturbation theory states that the actual correction term is obtained by taking the average value of the perturbation energy (6) over the unperturbed motion. In this case the average of Z/r^3 is needed. For a Kepler orbit Z is constant; and the average value of Z/r^3 according to the quantum mechanics (Sec. 7) is

$$Z\overline{\left(\frac{1}{r^3}\right)} = \frac{64\,\pi^6\,m_0{}^3e^6\,Z^4}{h^6n^3l(l + \frac{1}{2})(l+1)}. \qquad (7)$$

15a. The Landé Doublet Formula.—An approximate value of $\overline{\left(\frac{Z}{r^3}\right)}$ for a penetrating orbit can be obtained by a method which is an extension of that used in Section 10. It was assumed there that the orbit consists of two nearly complete elliptical segments, one in the inner region, with effective nuclear charge Z_ie and segmentary principal quantum number n_i, and one in the outer

[1] See Footnote 3 on p. 69.
[2] L. H. Thomas, *Nature*, **107**: 514, 1926.

region, with ze and n^* for these quantities. The average value of Z/r^3 for each of these segments is given by introducing these values for Z and n in Equation 7. The times τ_i and τ_o that the electron spends in traversing the two segments of its orbit are given in Equation 21, Chap. II, as

$$= \frac{n_i^3 h^3}{4\pi^2 m_0 Z_i^2 e^4} \text{ and } \tau_o = \frac{n^{*3} h^3}{4\pi^2 m_0 z^2 e^4}.$$

From this we find for the average value of Z/r^3 in the entire orbit the expression

$$\overline{\left(\frac{Z}{r^3}\right)} = \frac{\tau_i \overline{\left(\frac{Z_i}{r_i^3}\right)} + \tau_o \overline{\left(\frac{z}{r_o^3}\right)}}{\tau_i + \tau_o}.$$

Since Z_i is much larger than z, τ_i is small compared with τ_o, while $\overline{\left(\frac{z}{r_o^3}\right)}$ is very small compared with $\overline{\left(\frac{Z_i}{r_i^3}\right)}$. Neglecting these small quantities, we obtain[1]

$$\overline{\left(\frac{Z}{r^3}\right)} \cong \frac{\tau_i}{\tau_o} \overline{\left(\frac{Z_i}{r_i^3}\right)} = \frac{64\pi^6 m_0^3 e^6 Z_i^2 z^2}{h^6 n^{*3} l(l + \frac{1}{2})(l + 1)}. \tag{8}$$

From Equations 7 and 8 and Equation 6 there result Equations 2 and 3 for the interaction energy between spin moment and orbital motion.

15b. Doublet Separations in Isoelectronic Sequences.—If the orbit of the outer electron deviates only a little from a hydrogen-like orbit in a field due to an effective nuclear charge $Z_{eff}e$, it is often convenient to represent the doublet separation by the equation

$$\Delta\nu = 5.82 \frac{(Z - S_0)^4}{n^3 l(l + 1)} \text{ cm.}^{-1} \tag{9}$$

in which S_0 is a screening constant arising from the shielding effect of the inner electrons in the atom.[2] The constant $R\alpha^2$

[1] This equation was obtained by formal methods and applied in this connection by A. Landé, *Z. f. Phys.*, **25**: 46, 1924, before the introduction of the spinning electron.

[2] The applicability of this equation to optical doublets was discovered empirically by R. A. Millikan and I. S. Bowen, *Phys. Rev.*, **23**: 764, 1924; **24**: 209, 233, 1924, and A. Landé, *Z. f. Phys.*, **25**: 46, 1924. The equation is the same as that derived by A. Sommerfeld for the hydrogen fine structure and applied by him to X-ray doublets. At that time (1924) it was believed that the relativistic change of mass of the electron provided a satisfactory theoretical basis for the equation; the work of Millikan and Bowen and of Landé showed, however, that its validity was a great riddle.

has been replaced by its numerical value. The use of this equation is especially to be recommended when the orbit of the valence electron is not supposed to penetrate the inner electron shells; that is, when the effective quantum number n^* lies close to the integer representing n. This condition is fulfilled in the case of the p orbits of lithium (for which $n^* = 1.96$ in the lowest state ($n = 2$)) and of the lithium-like ions. The experimental values of $\Delta\nu$ for this doublet level ($2^2P_{1/2} - 2^2P_{3/2}$) for Li, Be^+, B^{+2}, C^{+3}, N^{+4}, and O^{+5} are given in the accompanying table.

TABLE I.—THE DOUBLET SEPARATION $2^2P_{1/2} - 2^2P_{3/2}$ FOR LITHIUM-LIKE ATOMS[1]

Atom	$\Delta\nu$	$Z - S_0$	S_0
Li	0.338 cm.$^{-1}$	0.981	2.019
Be^+	6.61	2.063	1.937
B^{+2}	34.4	3.116	1.884
C^{+3}	107.4	4.142	1.858
N^{+4}	259.1	5.162	1.838
O^{+5}	533.8	6.184	1.816

[1] This table is taken from I. S. BOWEN and R. A. MILLIKAN, *Phys. Rev.*, **27**: 144, 1926.

The values of S_0 calculated from them correspond closely to complete screening by the two inner electrons; conversely, the substitution of $S_0 = 2$ in Equation 9 leads to theoretical values of $\Delta\nu$ which deviate only slightly from the observed ones. The less efficient screening as the atomic number increases is, furthermore, explicable; with increase in Z the size of the orbit of the outer electron decreases more rapidly than that of the two inner electrons, and the outer orbit begins to penetrate to a region of larger effective nuclear charge.

TABLE II.—THE DOUBLET SEPARATION FOR NON-PENETRATING ORBITS OF SODIUM-LIKE ATOMS[1]

Atom	Levels	$\Delta\nu$	$Z - S_0$	S_0
Mg^+	$3^2D_{3/2} - 3^2D_{5/2}$	0.99 cm.$^{-1}$	2.29	9.71
Al^{+2}	$3^2D_{3/2} - 3^2D_{5/2}$	2.28	2.82	10.18
Al^{+2}	$4^2D_{3/2} - 4^2D_{5/2}$	1.28	3.03	9.97
Al^{+2}	$4^2F_{5/2} - 4^2F_{7/2}$	0.38	2.66	10.34
Si^{+3}	$4^2F_{5/2} - 4^2F_{7/2}$	1.26	3.59	10.41

[1] I. S. BOWEN and R. A. MILLIKAN, *Phys. Rev.*, **24**: 209, 1924.

In Table II are given data for some doublets states of sodium-like ions. For these the screening constant is nearly 10 (within the experimental error), indicating complete screening by the two electrons in the K shell and the eight in the L shell, and again substantiating Equation 9. This equation can not be so satisfactorily applied, however, in case the orbit penetrates the inner electron shells. The large difference of the effective quantum number n^* from the value 3 in the case of the $3p$ orbits of sodium-like atoms (Table III) shows that the orbits penetrate the L shell; and, similarly, the values of S_0 obtained from the doublet separations are much smaller than 10. For these states the Landé formula

$$\Delta\nu = 5.82\frac{Z_i^2 z^2}{n^{*3}l(l+1)} \text{ cm.}^{-1}, \tag{10}$$

corresponding to Equation 5a, may be used. It leads to values of S_i, the screening constant effective in the region inside the L shell, which are about 2 for the ions with Z large, indicating that the orbit penetrates the L shell completely from the region with $z = Z - 10$ to that with $Z_i = Z - 2$. The penetration is evidently not complete in the case of sodium.

TABLE III.—THE DOUBLET SEPARATION $3^2P_{1/2} - 3^2P_{3/2}$ FOR SODIUM-LIKE ATOMS

Atom	$\Delta\nu$[1]	S_0	n^*	Z_i	$S_i = Z - Z_i$
Na	17.18 cm.$^{-1}$	7.450	2.12	7.59	3.41
Mg^+	91.55	6.606	2.27	9.56	2.44
Al^{+2}	234.00	6.180	2.38	10.90	2.10
Si^{+3}	461.84	5.916	2.46	12.10	1.90
P^{+4}	794.82	5.741	2.51	13.15	1.85
S^{+5}	1,267.10	5.596	2.56	14.20	1.80
Cl^{+6}	1,889.5	5.504			

[1] I. S. BOWEN and R. A. MILLIKAN, *Phys. Rev.*, **25**: 295, 1925.

16. THE FINE STRUCTURE OF HYDROGEN AND IONIZED HELIUM

An atom of hydrogen or of singly ionized helium consists of the nucleus and one electron, so that the considerations of the previous sections regarding fine structure should apply to its spectrum also. The main energy term is (Chap. II)

$$W_n = -\frac{RhcZ^2}{n^2}, \tag{11}$$

and depends only on the principal quantum number n. The states with different values of l will as a first approximation all have just this energy; for, in contradistinction to the other alkali-like atoms, there can occur no interaction with the electrons of the atom core (penetration, polarization, etc.). If, however, the relativistic change in mass with velocity of the electron be considered, there is found an energy correction term

$$W_l^1 = \frac{Rhc\alpha^2 Z^4}{n^3}\left(\frac{3}{4n} - \frac{1}{l + \frac{1}{2}}\right), \tag{12}$$

splitting the original level of Equation 11 into n levels ($s, p, d, f,$ etc.). The correction term due to the electron spin is, from Equation 2,

$$W_s^1 = \frac{Rhc\alpha^2 Z^4}{n^3 l(l + \frac{1}{2})(l + 1)} \cdot \frac{\pm(l + \frac{1}{2}) - \frac{1}{2}}{2}; \tag{13}$$

combining these, we obtain

$$W^1 = W_l^1 + W_s^1 = \frac{Rhc\alpha^2 Z^4}{n^3}\left(\frac{3}{4n} - \frac{1}{l + 1}\right) \quad \text{for } j = l + \tfrac{1}{2} \tag{14a}$$

and

$$W^1 = W_l^1 + W_s^1 = \frac{Rhc\alpha^2 Z^4}{n^3}\left(\frac{3}{4n} - \frac{1}{l}\right) \quad \text{for } j = l - \tfrac{1}{2} \tag{14b}$$

As a result of Equations 14a and 14b certain levels coincide; namely, those with the same value of j. This is illustrated in Figure 18, showing the fine structure of the level with $n = 3$. Instead of the five levels shown by sodium there appear only three, which arise in this way: the relativistic energy correction splits the term into three, represented by the dashed lines; these have different values of l. The magnetic effect of the spinning electron then splits each of these except that with $l = 0$ into two; and the energy correction terms are just of the right size to bring levels with the same j into coincidence.[1] In the figure these levels are shown slightly separated, for clearness.

On account of the smallness of the separation for large values of n only the fine structure of the level $n = 2$ has been experi-

[1] Equation 12 was first derived by W. PAULI, with the quantum mechanics (*Z. f. Phys.*, **36**: 336, 1926), and Equation 13 by W. HEISENBERG and P. JORDAN (*Z. f. Phys.*, **37**: 266, 1926). G. E. UHLENBECK and S. GOUDSMIT had previously, from formal considerations, become convinced of the correctness of these equations and had used them.

mentally determined for hydrogen. This level is double ($^2P_{3/2}$ and $^2P_{1/2} = {}^2S_{1/2}$), with a theoretical separation $\Delta\nu = R\alpha^2/2^4 = 0.364$ cm.$^{-1}$. In combining with higher states to form the Balmer series this separation is retained. In the case of the first few lines of the series an apparently too small separation is observed; this is completely explained by taking into consideration the fine structure of the levels with $n = 3, 4, \cdots$ The separation of succeeding lines in the Balmer series approaches more and more accurately the separation for the level $n = 2$. Taking into account the fine structure of the levels with $n = 3$, 4, and 5, the apparent separations to be theoretically expected for H_α, H_β, and H_γ are given in Table IV. The agreement of the experimental values with these is especially satisfactory in the case of H_γ.

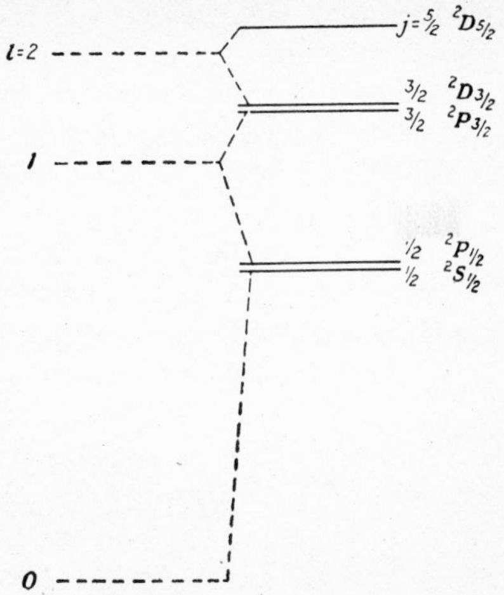

FIG. 18.—Fine structure of the state $n = 3$ for hydrogen and ionized helium. Levels with the same value of j, represented here as slightly separated, are actually coincident.

TABLE IV.—DOUBLET SEPARATIONS OF H_α, H_β, AND H_γ

	H_α	H_β	H_γ
Theoretical	0.320 cm.$^{-1}$	0.345 cm.$^{-1}$	0.354 cm.$^{-1}$
Experimental:			
Houston[1]	0.315	0.331	0.353
Kent, etc.[2]	0.318	0.335	0.354

[1] W. V. HOUSTON, *Astrophys. Jour.*, **64**: 81, 1926.
[2] N. A. KENT, L. B. TAYLOR, and H. PEARSON, *Phys. Rev.*, **30**: 266, 1927.

Comparison with experiment is more easily made for ionized helium; for the fine-structure separations increase with Z^4, or sixteen-fold in this case. In Figure 19 are represented the energy levels for $n = 4$ and $n = 3$; the transitions allowed by the selection rules for l and j are also indicated. It is seen that this line, λ4686 of ionized helium, has thirteen components, of which five pairs coincide, leaving effectively eight. This result is in complete agreement with Paschen's observations of the fine structure of this line.[1] From the fine-structure separations

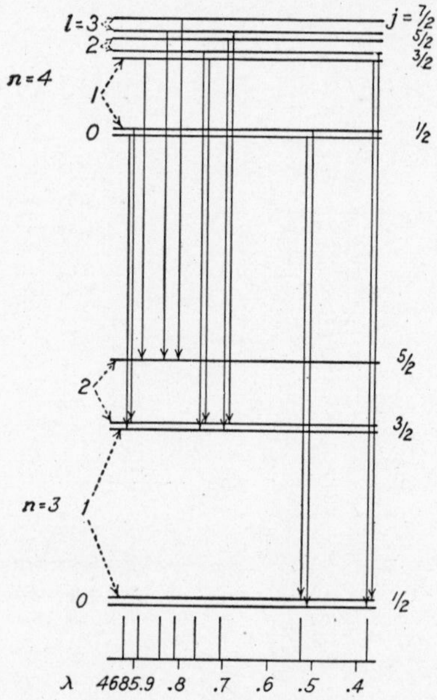

FIG. 19.—Fine structure of the line He^+ λ4686, corresponding to the transition from $n = 4$ to $n = 3$.

for ionized helium Paschen obtained the experimental value 5.82 $cm.^{-1}$ for the numerical constant in the fine-structure equation.[2]

[1] Formerly the fine structure of hydrogen and ionized helium was explained as resulting entirely from the relativistic change of mass (Sommerfeld). The old quantum theory gave Equations 14*a* and 14*b* directly (in terms of the azimuthal quantum number *k*) without the use of the spinning electron. That the spectra could be explained as due to coinciding doublets was suggested formally from analogy with alkali-like spectra by J. C. SLATER, (*Proc. Nat. Acad.* **11**: 732, 1925) and by S. GOUDSMIT and G. E. UHLENBECK (*Physica* **5**: 266, 1925). The selection rules of the new theory differ from those of the old, and, as a consequence, more transitions are allowed. These explain the occurrence of components (of λ4686 of He^+, for example) which are found by experiment but which were not allowed by the old theory. Further facts indicating the superiority of the new theory are discussed by A. SOMMERFELD and A. UNSÖLD (*Z. f. Phys.*, **36**: 259, 1926 and **38**: 237, 1926).

[2] F. PASCHEN, *Ann. d. Phys.*, **82**: 689, 1927.

CHAPTER V

THE VECTOR MODEL FOR ALKALI-LIKE ATOMS

The introduction of the spinning electron has caused the picture representing the motion of the electron (the classical picture involving precessing orbits) to become too complicated to be visualized in all but the simplest cases; this complication is especially pronounced in the description of the magnetic properties of the atom. For discussing these properties it is, fortunately, not necessary to describe the motion of the electron in detail. It is sufficient to know what mechanical and magnetic moments the atom has; one can then use the vector model of the atom, with which it is shown, by vectors and their quantum numbers alone, which angular momenta occur in the atom, and how they are combined. For alkali-like atoms, with one electron to be considered, the vector model consists of the two vectors $\mathbf{l}$ and $\mathbf{s}$ and their resultant $\mathbf{j}$, about which $\mathbf{l}$ and $\mathbf{s}$ precess with constant angular velocity. This model has already been used in discussing the fine structure and the doublet separation.

For most purposes this model leads to conclusions which are identical with those obtained from the quantum mechanics and which are verified by experiment. Some problems, however, cannot be treated with the aid of the vector model; the formulas given by the quantum mechanics are of course then to be applied without our attempting to describe them in terms of a visualizable model. (Examples: the transition from weak to strong magnetic fields (Sec. 28*a*); the transition from one coupling scheme to another (Sec. 29*a*); etc.)

17. THE ZEEMAN EFFECT

17a. The Magnetic Moment of the Atom. The Landé *g*-factor.—The magnetic moment of an alkali-like atom in a given stationary state is easily obtained from the vector model. The mechanical moment of the orbital motion is $\mathbf{l}\frac{h}{2\pi}$, and the corresponding magnetic moment $\mathbf{l}\frac{h}{2\pi}\cdot\frac{e}{2m_0c}$. For according to elementary electrodynamics the magnetic moment of a circuit is equal to the product of the current and the area of the circuit, divided by c:

$$\mu = \frac{IA}{c}.$$

For an electron in a Kepler ellipse the angular momentum $p = m_0r^2\dot{\psi}$ is a constant, with the value $kh/2\pi$. In terms of τ, the time required for one revolution of the electron in its orbit, I and A are given by the equations

$$I = \frac{e}{\tau}, \quad A = \int_0^{2\pi}\frac{r^2}{2}d\theta = \int_0^{\tau}\frac{p}{2m_0}dt = \frac{\tau}{2m_0}p,$$

so that the magnetic moment is found to be equal to $e/2m_0c$ times the mechanical moment:

$$\mu = \frac{e}{2m_0c}p = \frac{eh}{4\pi m_0c}k.$$

This relation is retained in the quantum mechanics.

Just as $h/2\pi$ is the quantum unit of mechanical moment, so is $eh/4\pi m_0c$ the quantum unit of magnetic moment.[1] It is called the "Bohr magneton," and is equal to 0.918×10^{-20} erg gauss.$^{-1}$

If the magnetic moment of the orbital motion of an electron is resolved into a component along **j** and one perpendicular to **j**, then the latter will not be observable on account of the precession of **l** about **j**, for this component is continuously changing direction and its average value is zero. The component along **j** alone contributes to the observable magnetic moment of the atom. The spinning electron has been given the mechanical moment $\mathbf{s}\cdot\frac{h}{2\pi}$ and the magnetic moment $2\cdot\mathbf{s}\cdot\frac{h}{2\pi}\cdot\frac{e}{2m_0c}$. Of this magnetic moment also only the component along **j** is effective. The magnetic moment of the entire atom is, accordingly, a vector parallel to **j**, of magnitude

$$j\cdot\frac{h}{2\pi}\cdot g\frac{e}{2m_0c} = [l\cos(\mathbf{lj}) + 2s\cos(\mathbf{sj})]\frac{h}{2\pi}\frac{e}{2m_0c}. \quad (1)$$

[1] For the quantum mechanical discussion of the Bohr magneton, see Condon and Morse, Secs. 32 and 44.

Here g is the "Landé g-factor,"[1] by definition the ratio of magnetic to mechanical moment when these are in the quantum units $\frac{h}{2\pi}\frac{e}{2m_0c}$ and $\frac{h}{2\pi}$, respectively. The evaluation of the cosines with the use of the vector magnitudes $\sqrt{j(j+1)}$, $\sqrt{l(l+1)}$, and $\sqrt{s(s+1)}$ gives directly

$$g = 1 + \frac{j(j+1) + s(s+1) - l(l+1)}{2j(j+1)}. \qquad (2)$$

Thus in order to discuss its magnetic properties the atom can be described as a magnetic top with the mechanical moment **j** and the magnetic moment **j**g, both in quantum units.

17b. The Zeeman Effect and the Magnetic Quantum Number m.—It was found by Zeeman in 1896 that spectral lines in general are split into a number of components by the application of an external magnetic field to the emitting atoms.[2] In some cases this splitting is of a simple type shown by Lorentz to be explicable on the basis of the classical theory; the phenomenon is then called the "normal Zeeman effect." In general, however, the splitting is more complicated; there occurs the "anomalous Zeeman effect." We shall see that the anomalous Zeeman effect results from the presence of the two quantum vectors **l** and **s**, for one of which, **s**, the ratio of magnetic to mechanical moment is just twice that for the other. The normal Zeeman effect occurs only when **s** does not contribute to the mechanical and magnetic moments of the atoms.

In an external magnetic field a magnetic top carries out a precession about the field direction, in accordance with Larmor's theorem of classical mechanics.[3] The angular velocity ω of this precession is equal to the product of the field strength H and the ratio of magnetic to mechanical moment:

$$\omega = Hg\frac{e}{2m_0c}. \qquad (3)$$

[1] It is given this name on account of its introduction by A. Landé (*Z. f. Phys.*, **5**: 231, 1921) to account formally for the anomalous Zeeman effect.

[2] Zeeman-effect phenomena are discussed at length by E. Back and A. Landé, "Zeemaneffekt und Multiplettstruktur," J. Springer, Berlin, 1925.

[3] Larmor's theorem results from the neglect of terms proportional to H^2, H^3, etc. A derivation of the theorem is given by J. H. Van Vleck, "Quantum Principles and Line Spectra," *Bull.*, National Research Council, No. 54, p. 300, 1926.

The energy of the precession is the product of this angular velocity and the projection of the mechanical moment on the precession axis, in this case the field direction:

$$W_m^1 = \omega \cdot j \frac{h}{2\pi} \cos (\mathbf{jH}). \tag{4}$$

The projection of **j** on **H** is a new quantum vector **m**, corresponding to the magnetic quantum number m. The extreme values of m are $+j$ and $-j$; altogether there are $2j + 1$ different values possible, and $2j + 1$ angles between **j** and **H**. As was stated in

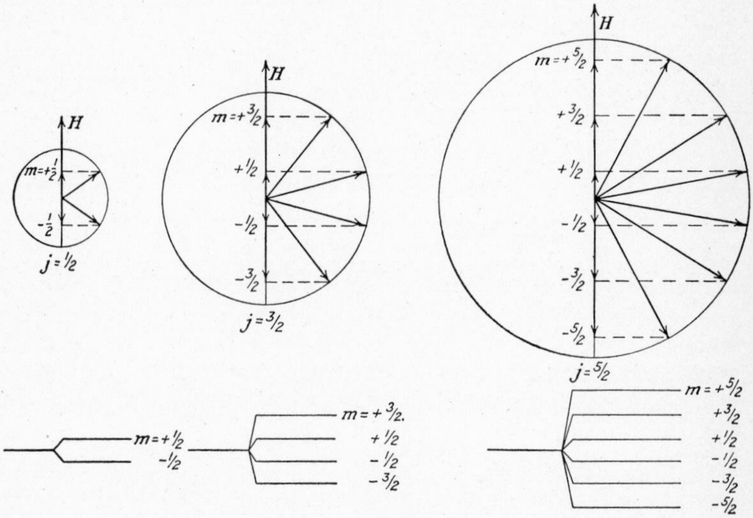

FIG. 20.—Orientations of the vector j in a weak magnetic field, and the corresponding Zeeman splitting of the energy levels.

Chap. I, we must take m as the magnitude of **m** in order to cause the model to agree with the quantum mechanics equations. The energy in terms of m then becomes

$$W_m^1 = Hg \frac{e}{2m_0c} \cdot \frac{h}{2\pi} m. \tag{5}$$

For simplification it is customary to introduce a new unit, the Lorentz unit, which is the quantity $\frac{he}{4\pi m_0 c} H$; in terms of this unit the energy is

$$W_m^1 = mg. \tag{6}$$

It is to be observed that the proportionality of the magnetic energy to field strength is included in this unit.

Equations 1 and 5 show how each level of an alkali atom splits up in an external magnetic field. The possible orientations of the quantum vector **j** and the corresponding energy levels are also represented in Figure 20 for **j** $= 1/2$, $3/2$, and $5/2$. The values of g for various terms of an alkali-like atom calculated from Equation 2 are given in Table I, and the corresponding Zeeman-effect separations according to Equation 6 in Table II.

TABLE I.—THE g-FACTOR FOR ALKALI-LIKE ATOMS

		$j = 1/2$	$3/2$	$5/2$	$7/2$	$9/2$	$11/2$
^2S	$l = 0$	2					
^2P	1	$2/3$	$4/3$				
^2D	2	..	$4/5$	$6/5$			
^2F	3	..	..	$6/7$	$8/7$		
^2G	4	..	..	..	$8/9$	$10/9$	
^2H	5	..	..	..	..	$10/11$	$12/11$

TABLE II.—ZEEMAN-EFFECT SEPARATIONS mg FOR TERMS OF ALKALI-LIKE ATOMS

$^2S_{1/2}$	.....	.....	.....	$+1$	-1			
$^2P_{1/2}$	.....	.....	.....	$+1/3$	$-1/3$			
$^2P_{3/2}$	.....	.....	$+6/3$	$+2/3$	$-2/3$	$-6/3$		
$^2D_{3/2}$	.....	.....	$+6/5$	$+2/5$	$-2/5$	$-6/5$		
$^2D_{5/2}$	.....	$+15/5$	$+9/5$	$+3/5$	$-3/5$	$-9/5$	$-15/5$	
$^2F_{5/2}$	.....	$+15/7$	$+9/7$	$+3/7$	$-3/7$	$-9/7$	$-15/7$	
$^2F_{7/2}$	$+28/7$	$+20/7$	$+12/7$	$+4/7$	$-4/7$	$-12/7$	$-20/7$	$-28/7$

It is seen that splitting depends only on the mechanical and magnetic moments of the atom and is independent of the main electronic motion represented by the principal quantum number n. This causes all levels of a series to have the same splitting and hence all lines of a line series to show the same Zeeman effect. This is the rule found empirically by Preston, and called "Preston's rule."

17c. Selection and Polarization Rules.—The quantum mechanics as well as the correspondence principle (Chap. VIII) leads to the rule that the quantum number m must change during a transition by $+1$, 0, or -1. The transitions for which m changes by 0 result in spectral lines which are linearly polarized with the electric vector parallel to the direction of the external magnetic field **H**. When m changes by $+1$ or -1, the emitted line is circularly polarized in the plane perpendicular to **H**, the sense of the polarization being in one case right handed and in the other left handed. The types of polarization are customarily indicated by the symbols π (parallel) and σ (perpendicular).[1]

17d. The Sodium D-lines as an Example.—The sodium D-lines correspond to the transitions $^2P_{3/2} - {^2S_{1/2}}$ and $^2P_{1/2} - {^2S_{1/2}}$. The Zeeman separations of the individual levels are indicated in Figure 21. On the left are shown the lines in the absence of an external field, and on the right the transitions which are allowed by the selection rule for m in the presence of an external field. The positions of the lines as they would be observed in a spectral apparatus are indicated at the bottom of the figure; those linearly polarized being represented by dotted lines, and those circularly polarized by full lines. The line $^2P_{3/2} - {^2S_{1/2}}$ is split into six components (two π and four σ), and $^2P_{1/2} - {^2S_{1/2}}$ into four (two π and two σ). The nature of the light observed in different directions relative to the field may be deduced by assuming the π-components to be produced by a linear oscillator parallel to **H** and the σ-components by circular rotators in the plane perpendicular to **H**. The intensity of the light emitted by the linear oscillator in the field direction is zero; hence, if observations be made in this direction only the σ-components will appear, and they will be circularly

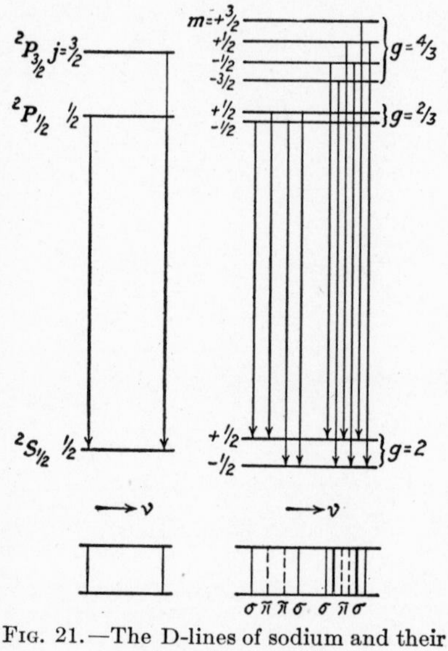

FIG. 21.—The D-lines of sodium and their anomalous Zeeman effect.

[1] The conception that the Zeeman splitting of spectral lines arises from a splitting of spectral terms was first pronounced by VAN LOHUIZEN (*Proc.*, Amsterdam Acad., **22**: 190, 1919), and was developed by A. SOMMERFELD (*Ann. d. Phys.*, **63**: 221, 1920). The g-factor was introduced in 1921 by A. LANDÉ (*Z. f. Phys.*, **5**: 231, 1921), who published an equation equivalent to Equation 2 for its calculation. Landé's work found experimental substantiation in the accurate Zeeman-effect measurements of H. GIESELER (*Ann. d. Phys.*, **69**: 147, 1922) and E. BACK (*Z. f. Phys.*, **15**: 206, 1923), and led in a short time to the analysis of a number of spectra.

polarized. Observations made in the plane perpendicular to the field direction will show the π-components linearly polarized parallel to **H**, and the σ-components linearly polarized in the plane perpendicular to **H**. In intermediate directions the π-components will appear with reduced intensity, and the σ-components will be elliptically polarized.

The Zeeman effects of all lines in the spectra of alkali-like atoms are anomalous. If s were equal to 0 for two states, the corresponding transition would show the normal Zeeman effect. Such states with $l = 3$ and $l = 2$ are shown in Figure 22, with the levels into which they are split by a magnetic field. The various transitions corresponding to the allowed changes $+1$, 0, and -1 in m are indicated; there are five of each. Since $g = 1$ for each state these groups of five coincide, and only three lines, two σ-components and one π-component, occur. The π-component is not shifted from the position of the original line, and the σ-components are one Lorentz unit to the right and to the left.

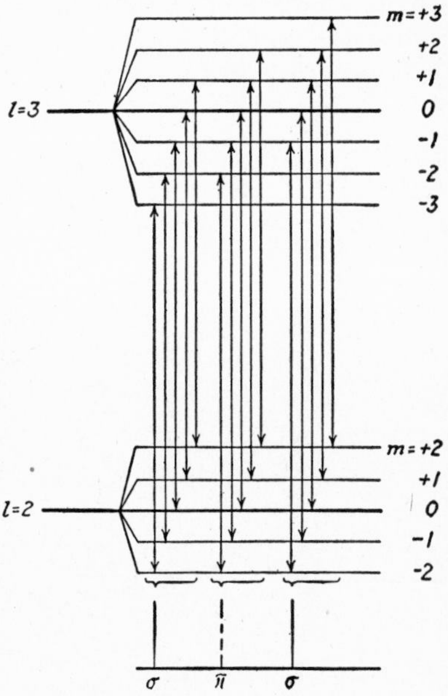

FIG. 22.—The normal Zeeman effect, shown by transitions between states for which $s = 0$ and $g = 1$.

18. THE PASCHEN-BACK EFFECT

Let us now return to the vector model of the atom. In the treatment of the Zeeman effect it was mentioned that the total moment **j** of the atom precesses about the external magnetic field. Before that it was also stated that the vectors **s** and **l**, the spin moment and the orbital moment, precess similarly about **j**. In our treatment of the Zeeman effect it was implicitly assumed that the precession about **j** is much faster than that of **j** about **H**; for in the derivation of the equation for g it was assumed that the precession about **j** is sufficiently fast for the components normal to **j** to average to zero, and have no externally appreciable influence. But if the precession of **j** about **H** is of the same magnitude as or is larger than that of **l** and **s** about **j** there can be no such averaging to zero. In this case the atom can no longer be represented by a simple magnetic top with the mechanical moment **j** and the magnetic moment **j**g, but consideration must be taken of two magnets, that of the spinning electron and that of the orbital motion.

It will be shown in Chap. VIII that with our model the doublet separation of a level is a measure of the frequency of precession

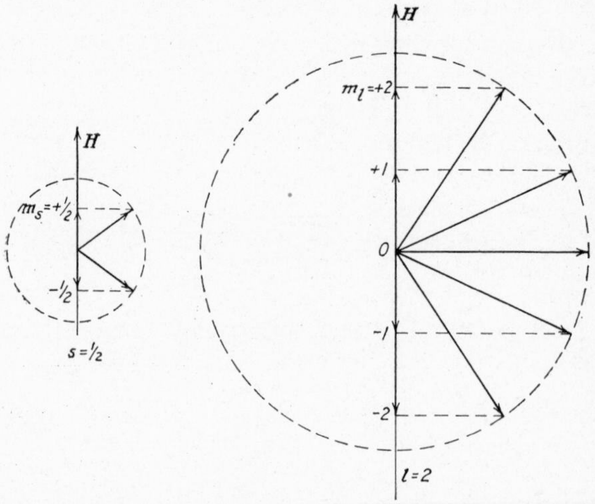

FIG. 23.—Orientation of the vectors **s** and **l** in a strong magnetic field (Paschen-Back effect).

of **s** and **l** about **j**; the energy difference divided by h gives the order of magnitude of this frequency. Similarly, the Zeeman separation of a level gives the order of magnitude of the frequency of the Larmor precession about the external field. If the field strength H is so large that the Zeeman separation becomes of the same order of magnitude as the doublet separation of the two levels, the spectrum will show a new phenomenon, the Paschen-Back effect.

We shall here discuss only the case when the external field is very strong. Then the spin moment of the electron can be treated as though the magnetic field produced by the orbital motion vanished, for it can be neglected in comparison with the external field. Similarly, the orbit behaves as though the electron were not itself a small magnet, and interacts only with the external field. This means that the electron spin moment **s** and the orbital moment **l** orient themselves independently of each other with respect to the external field. The projection of the orbital moment on the field direction is $\mathbf{m}_l$, and is given by the quantum number m_l, which may have values from $-l$ to $+l$, that of the spin moment is $\mathbf{m}_s$, for which m_s may have values $-\frac{1}{2}$ and $+\frac{1}{2}$. In conformity with Chap. I the vectors $\mathbf{m}_l$ and $\mathbf{m}_s$ are assumed to have the magnitudes m_l and m_s, respectively. The orientations of **l** and **s** are illustrated for one state in Figure 23. **l** and **s** carry out their own Larmor precessions about the field direction, **s** with twice the angular velocity of **l**, since the ratio of magnetic to mechanical moment is twice as large for **s** as for **l**. It will be shown in Chap. VIII that m_s can not change during a transition (that is, $\Delta m_s = 0$), and that the selection and polarization rules for m are now valid for m_l.

The magnetic energy of the atom now consists of two parts, that due to the orbital precession and that due to the electron precession:

$$W_m{}^1 = m_l \cdot \frac{h}{2\pi}\frac{e}{2m_0c}H + 2m_s \cdot \frac{h}{2\pi}\frac{e}{2m_0c}H,$$

or, in the usual units,

$$W_m{}^1 = m_l + 2m_s. \tag{7}$$

The interaction energy between **s** and **l** has the value

$$W_s{}^1 = a \cdot ls \cos(\mathbf{ls}) \tag{8}$$

in which from Equation 3, Chap. IV,

$$a = \frac{Rhc\alpha^2 Z_i{}^2 z^2}{n^{*3} l(l + \frac{1}{2})(l + 1)}. \tag{9}$$

$\cos(\mathbf{ls})$ is no longer constant and to determine the energy $W_s{}^1$ its average value $\overline{\cos(\mathbf{ls})}$ must be calculated. It can be easily shown with elementary principles of trigonometry that if two vectors **l** and **s** precess uniformly and independently about a direction **H** the relation $\overline{\cos(\mathbf{sl})} = \cos(\mathbf{sH})\cos(\mathbf{lH})$ is true, so that we may write

$$sl\,\overline{\cos(\mathbf{sl})} = m_s\,m_l. \tag{10}$$

The sum of the magnetic and the interaction energy, which together determine the separations of the level, is thus[1]

$$W_m^1 + W_s^1 = m_l + 2m_s + am_s \cdot m_l. \tag{11}$$

It is to be remembered that this expression is valid only when the external field is so large that W_m^1 is large compared with W_s^1.

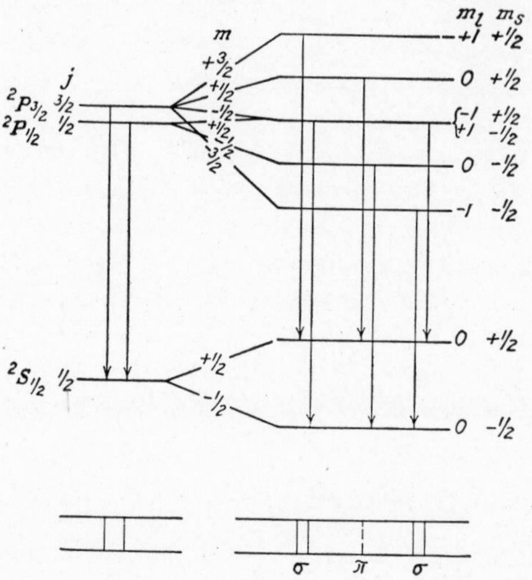

FIG. 24.—The Paschen-Back effect for the sodium D-lines.

Figure 24 shows the Paschen-Back effect for the sodium D-lines. From the diagram below it is seen that the lines form nearly a normal triplet, such as would be expected for the Zeeman effect from the classical theory. The two σ-components of the triplet are, however, themselves split, the separation arising from the interaction term W_s^1, and in this case (the sodium D-lines) being two-thirds as large as the original doublet separation. If the field energy W_m^1 alone had been taken into consideration the normal Zeeman triplet would have been obtained. The rarely occurring transitions for which m_s changes give rise to very weak components at twice the normal distance from the center.

[1] The last term in this equation is in different units from the two others. a is usually expressed in cm.$^{-1}$, so as to give the term separations directly in frequency units; in these units its value is

$$a = \frac{R\alpha^2 Z_i^2 z^2}{n^{*3} l(l + \frac{1}{2})(l + 1)} = \frac{5.82 Z_i^2 z^2}{n^{*3} l(l + \frac{1}{2})(l + 1)}.$$

The Paschen-Back effect can be observed experimentally only for very narrow doublets, such as the lithium doublet with $\Delta\nu = 0.34$ cm.$^{-1}$ (Table I, Chap. IV), since the ordinarily available field strengths of at most 43,000 gausses produce a splitting of only $\Delta\nu = 2.21$ cm.$^{-1}$ for $g = 1$.

The problem of the motion of the quantum vectors **s** and **l** can also be handled rigorously for cases lying in between the two we have considered; that is, when the external magnetic field is neither very strong nor very weak in comparison with the internal fields. The treatment cannot be given here. It is worthy of mention that when the external field becomes of the same order of magnitude as the internal, the precession of **s** and **l** about **j** will be no longer uniform. As a result of this, spectral lines will occur which are ordinarily forbidden; that is, the selection rule for j will be violated, as was mentioned on page 56. This was discovered experimentally by Paschen and Back[1] in the case of some lines in the zinc spectrum.

19. THE TRANSITION BETWEEN WEAK AND STRONG MAGNETIC FIELDS

The number of levels into which a given state is split is just the same in a weak field as in a strong one. This number is called the "quantum weight" or the "a priori probability" of the state. In a weak field a level with the quantum number l is split into

$$2(l + \tfrac{1}{2}) + 1 + 2(l - \tfrac{1}{2}) + 1 = 4l + 2$$

levels; for in the case of an alkali-like atom a state with the quantum number l consists always of two levels, one with $j = l + \frac{1}{2}$ and one with $j = l - \frac{1}{2}$, which can each have $2j + 1$ orientations in an external magnetic field. In a strong field l alone has $2l + 1$ orientations and for each of these s has $2s + 1$, giving altogether

$$(2l + 1)(2s + 1) = 4l + 2$$

different levels.

In a weak field each of these states is characterized by the quantum numbers j and m, since the others (l and s) retain their original values. In a strong field the magnetic states are, however, given by m_l and m_s. We may now inquire which of the states with j and m goes over during a slow mechanical

[1] F. Paschen and E. Back, *Physica*, **1** : 261, 1921.

transformation (increase in H) into a given state with certain values of m_l and m_s, and, conversely, what values of m_l and m_s arise from a state with given j and m.

As a first rule it is found that the total projection of the mechanical moment on **H** does not change. In a weak field this projection is **m**, in a strong field it is $\mathbf{m}_l + \mathbf{m}_s$. But there are states having the same value of m, one with $j = l + \frac{1}{2}$ and one with $j = l - \frac{1}{2}$. For such states it is found that the transition occurs so that as the field strength increases the levels do not cross. With the aid of these rules the connecting lines in Figure 24 have been drawn. The derivation of the rules can be rigorously carried out only with the help of the quantum mechanics.

20. THE STARK EFFECT

In 1913, J. Stark[1] discovered that the Balmer lines emitted by hydrogen atoms in an electric field are split into several components, some of which are polarized with the electric vector parallel to the field (the π-components) and the others polarized in the plane normal to the field (the σ-components). The study of the structure, polarization, and intensities of the Stark effect lines of hydrogen and other elements was rapidly and carefully carried out by Stark and other investigators.[2] The discovery of this new phenomenon at the time at which the old quantum theory was being developed excited great interest, and its theoretical explanation was immediately attempted. In distinction to the normal Zeeman effect, the Stark effect can not be accounted for by the classical theory. The quantization of a hydrogen-like atom in an electric field by Schwarzschild[3] and Epstein[4] and the consequent explanation of the observed Stark effect of hydrogen and ionized helium in all its details was one of the most striking successes of the old quantum theory; the equations found by them for the first-order Stark effect are still valid, since they are also given by the quantum mechanics.

The Stark effect is not of so much interest to spectroscopists as the Zeeman effect because it does not depend in a simple way on

[1] J. Stark, *Berliner Sitzungsber.*, November, 1913; *Ann. d. Phys.*, **43**: 965, 983, 1919.

[2] J. Stark, *Göttinger Nachr.*, November, 1914; Lo Surdo, *Accad. dei Lincei*, **23**: 83, 117, 143, 252, 326, 1914, etc.

[3] K. Schwarzschild, *Berliner Sitzungsber.*, April, 1916.

[4] P. S. Epstein, *Ann. d. Phys.*, **50**: 489, 1916.

the nature of the spectral state and so can not be used in unravelling spectra.

20a. The First-order Stark Effect of Hydrogen and Ionized Helium.—The energy of an atom in an electric field of strength F can be written

$$W = W_0 + AF + BF^2 + \cdots$$

in which W_0 represents the energy of the atom in the absence of the field. The term AF, linear in the field strength, is called the "energy of the first-order Stark effect;" similarly BF^2 gives the second-order Stark effect, and so on.

The first-order Stark effect energy may be considered as the energy of a permanent electric dipole in the electric field. The electric moment of a system composed of a nucleus about which an electron describes a Kepler ellipse is given by

$$\mu = \frac{3}{2}e\epsilon a,$$

in which a is the semimajor axis of the ellipse and ϵ its eccentricity. The field energy of such a system having the angle β between the major axis and the field direction is

$$\mu F \cos \beta = \frac{3}{2}e\epsilon aF \cos \beta.$$

This equation could be used to obtain the first-order Stark effect for the various levels of hydrogen and ionized helium if the values of ϵ and β could be calculated. It was shown in Chap. III that the semimajor axis a is determined by the main energy term; that is, by the principal quantum number n. In that chapter it was also shown how the introduction of a second quantum number k suffices to determine the eccentricity. This treatment is no longer valid, however; in an electric field the eccentricity changes with the time, and so does the angle β. It was shown by Bohr[1] that the consideration of the perturbing influence of the electric field leads to the introduction of new quantum numbers and the evaluation of the product $\epsilon \cos \beta$. The resultant energy term is

$$W^1 = -\frac{3h^2}{8\pi^2 m_0 eZ}n(n_2 - n_1)F, \qquad (13)$$

in which n is the principal quantum number and n_1 and n_2 are new quantum numbers, which can assume the values

$$0 \leqq n_1 \leqq n - 1, \quad 0 \leqq n_2 \leqq n - 1. \qquad (14)$$

[1] N. Bohr, "Über die Quantentheorie der Linienspektren," p. 98.

Equation 13 is the same as that derived earlier by Schwarzschild and Epstein, who used different coordinate systems in solving the problem. This equation results also from the application of the quantum mechanics, as was shown by Schrödinger.[1]

It is seen that the Stark-effect levels in a hydrogen-like atom are all shifted by integral multiples of a fundamental amount from the original level. For the first four levels of hydrogen these multiples are shown in Table III, as well as by Figure 25.

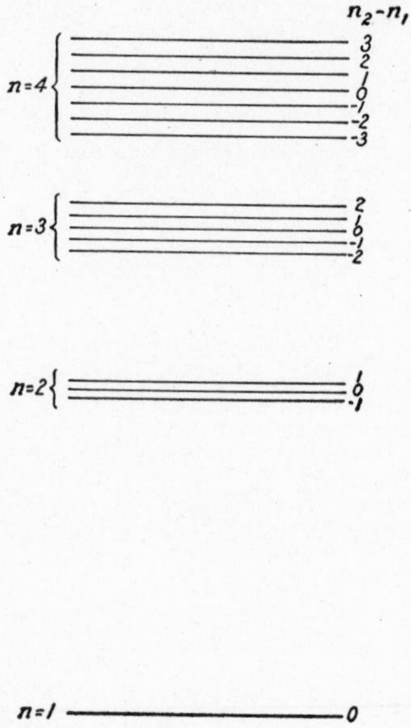

FIG. 25.—Stark-effect levels for the first four states of hydrogen, showing relative separations.

The total number of orbits with a given value of n has not been changed by the change in quantization; before there were n values possible for l; namely, 0, 1, 2, $\cdots$ $n - 1$, and for each one there were $2l + 1$ values of the magnetic quantum number m, making a total of n^2 orbits. With Stark-effect quantization there are n possible values for n_1, and for each of these there are n values of n_2, or again a total of n^2.

The selection and polarization rules are most easily expressed in terms of a third quantum number n_3, such that

$$n_3 = n - 1 - n_1 - n_2. \tag{15}$$

[1] E. SCHRÖDINGER, *Ann. d. Phys.*, **80**: 437, 1926.

Only transitions for which $\Delta n_3 = 0$ or ± 1 take place. Those with $\Delta n_3 = 0$ lead to the emission of spectral lines linearly polarized parallel to the field and those with $\Delta n_3 = \pm 1$ to lines circularly polarized in the plane normal to the field. The transitions with $\Delta n_3 = 1$ give light circularly polarized in one sense, those with $\Delta n_3 = -1$ in the opposite sense. It is seen from Table III that every Stark-effect level has a negative

TABLE III.—VALUES OF QUANTUM NUMBERS FOR THE STARK EFFECT IN HYDROGEN

n	n_1	n_2	$n_2 - n_1$	$n(n_2 - n_1)$	n_3
1	0	0	0	0	0
2	1	1	0	0	−1
		0	1	2	0
	0	1	−1	− 2	0
		0	0	0	1
3	2	2	0	0	−2
		1	1	3	−1
		0	2	6	0
	1	2	−1	− 3	−1
		1	0	0	0
		0	+1	3	1
	0	2	−2	− 6	0
		1	−1	− 3	1
		0	0	0	2
4	3	3	0	0	−3
		2	1	4	−2
		1	2	8	−1
		0	3	12	0
	2	3	−1	− 4	−2
		2	0	0	−1
		1	1	4	0
		0	2	8	1
	1	3	−2	− 8	−1
		2	−1	− 4	0
		1	0	0	1
		0	1	4	2
	0	3	−3	−12	0
		2	−2	− 8	1
		1	−1	− 4	2
		0	0	0	3

value of n_3 for every positive value. As a result a transition $\Delta n_3 = -1$ occurs for every transition $\Delta n_3 = 1$, and the superposition of the two oppositely polarized waves emitted by a large number of excited atoms leads to radiation which appears to be unpolarized when viewed along the direction of the field. This is in contradistinction to the polarization phenomena

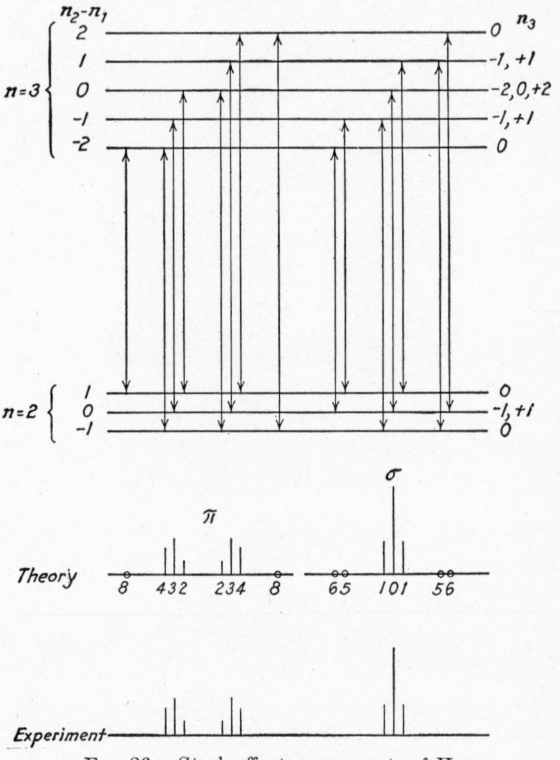

FIG. 26.—Stark-effect components of H_α.

shown in the Zeeman effect, where the right-handed and left-handed types of polarization occur in different components.

The possible transitions for the first Balmer line H_α are shown in Figure 26. Below there is shown, diagrammatically, the positions of the expected σ- and π-components arranged on a frequency scale. The heights of the lines give the relative intensities calculated for them by Schrödinger with the use of the quantum mechanics. There are also represented the experimental results[1] for this line. It is seen that the agreement is excellent; the only theoretical features not reproduced in experiment are the extremely weak outermost components whose intensities are, no doubt, so small as to cause them to escape observation.

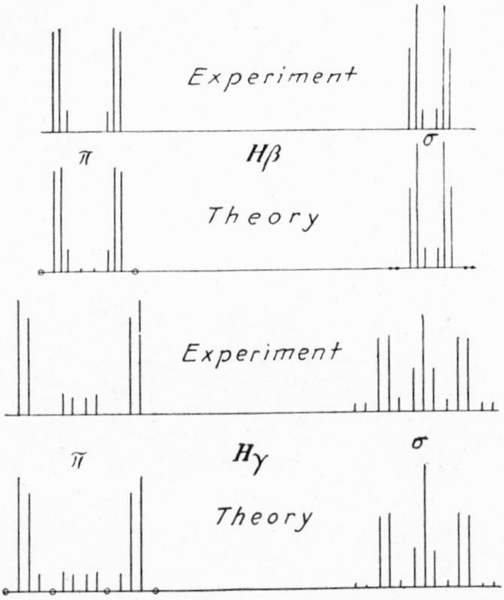

FIG. 27.—Comparison of theoretical and observed intensities for Stark-effect components of H_β and H_γ.

Similar results are obtained with the other Balmer lines, as is shown by Figure 27.[2]

20b. The Second-order Stark Effect.—The existence of a Stark-effect displacement proportional to the square of the field strength and not symmetrical relative to the unshifted

[1] The observed intensities are as reported by J. S. FOSTER and M. L. CHALK, *Proc.*, Roy. Soc., A **123**: 108, 1929. Their measurements are also incorporated in Figure 27. The weaker components of H_γ (not measured by Foster and Chalk) are given in Figure 27 as reported by Stark.

[2] The energy levels of a hydrogen-like atom in an electric field have been discussed with the quantum mechanics and with consideration of the relativity and spin corrections by R. SCHLAPP, *Proc.*, Roy. Soc., A **119**: 313, 1928 and V. ROJANSKY, *Phys. Rev.*, **33**: 1, 1929. It is of interest that even for very small field strengths a first-order Stark effect is shown by hydrogen-like atoms, in contradistinction to non-hydrogen-like atoms (discussed in the following section). This arises from the coincidence in energy value of hydrogen-like states with the same j and different l in the absence of a field. Since the level with $j = n - \frac{1}{2}$ is not shared with any other state, this level, however, shows only a second-order Stark effect.

line was shown experimentally by Takamine and Kokubu[1] in the case of the center σ-component of H_γ. Their results were discussed by Sommerfeld,[2] who showed them to be in approximate accordance with an expression derived by Epstein with the old quantum theory. Wentzel,[3] Waller,[4] and Epstein[5] have found with the quantum mechanics that the energy change W^2 of the second-order Stark effect is given by

$$W^2 = -\frac{h^6}{16(2\pi)^6 m_0{}^3 e^6 Z^4} n^4\{17n^2 - 3(n_2 - n_1)^2 - 9n_3{}^2 + 19\}F^2, \quad (16)$$

in which n_1, n_2, and n_3 are the Stark-effect quantum numbers previously introduced. This expression differs from that of the old quantum theory in the inclusion of the number 19 and in the values given to n_3 (formerly n_3 was taken as $n - n_1 - n_2$). The new expression is also in better agreement with experiment than the old.[6]

Equation 16 furthermore provides theoretical values for the electrical polarizability of hydrogen, singly ionized helium, doubly ionized lithium, etc. The second-order Stark effect energy can be considered as the field energy of an electric dipole of moment $\mu = \alpha F$ induced in the atom by the electric field. The energy of such an induced dipole is $-\frac{1}{2}\alpha F^2$; from Equation 16 the polarizability of a hydrogen-like atom is, then,

$$\alpha = \frac{h^6}{32(2\pi)^6 m_0{}^3 e^6 Z^4} n^4\{17n^2 - 3(n_2 - n_1)^2 - 9n_3{}^2 + 19\}. \quad (17)$$

From this there are obtained the following values for ions in the normal state:

	H	He^+	Li^{++}
$\alpha =$	0.666×10^{-24}	0.0416×10^{-24}	0.0082×10^{-24}.

These values can be used in calculating the contribution of polarization of the atom core to the quantum defects of states in which there is one non-penetrating orbit, in the way discussed

[1] TAKAMINE and KOKUBU, *Mem. Coll. Sci. Kyoto*, **3**: 271, 1919.

[2] A. SOMMERFELD, *Ann. d. Phys.*, **65**: 36, 1921.

[3] G. WENTZEL, *Z. f. Phys.*, **38**: 518, 1926.

[4] I. WALLER, *ibid.*, **38**: 635, 1926.

[5] P. S. EPSTEIN, *Nature*, **118**: 444, 1926; *Phys. Rev.*, **28**: 695, 1926.

[6] Wentzel points out that the measurements of TAKAMINE and KOKUBU and of M. KIUTI (*Japanese Jour. Phys.*, **4**: 13, 1925) on the center σ-component of H_γ indicate a shift about 20 per cent larger than that given by the old quantum theory, but in good agreement with Equation 16.

in Chap. III. Wentzel and Waller showed that these calculated quantum defects for helium and singly ionized lithium lie about midway between the quantum defects observed for singlet and triplet terms. Equation 17 can also be used with the introduction of suitably chosen effective nuclear charges in calculating polarizabilities of many-electron atoms and ions. The values of α used in Chap. III were obtained in this way.[1]

An expression for the third-order Stark effect of hydrogen-like atoms has been derived by S. Doi,[2] and the effect has been observed by Ishida and Hiyama,[3] whose measurements, however, are not sufficiently accurate to provide more than a rough check of the theory.

20c. The Stark Effect of Non-hydrogen-like Atoms.—An atom with an outer electron moving in a penetrating orbit would show no first-order Stark effect; for during the precession of the orbit the electric-moment vector would assume various

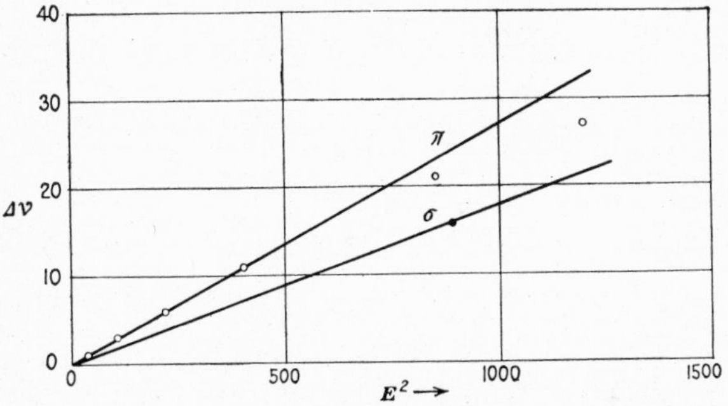

FIG. 28.—The calculated and observed Stark-effect shift for the parhelium line λ3613.6.

orientations in the orbital plane, leading to a time-averaged moment of zero. But when the field energy of the electric moment became greater than the energy contribution of the inner segment of the orbit the nature of the quantization would be changed. The orbit would then approximate a hydrogen-like orbit in an electric field, and the atom would show a first-order Stark effect, with the penetration into the inner region of the atom exerting only a secondary energy change.

[1] LINUS PAULING, *Proc.*, Roy. Soc., A **114**: 181, 1927; see also J. H. VAN VLECK, *Proc.*, Nat. Acad., **12**: 662, 1926.

[2] S. DOI, reported by Ishida and Hiyama.

[3] Y. ISHIDA and S. HIYAMA, *Sci. Papers Tokyo*, **9**: 1, 1928.

The deductions drawn from this model are substantiated by the quantum mechanics and by experiment. Spectral lines from many-electron atoms show, in general, only a second-order Stark effect, arising from the induction by the field of an electric moment in the atom. The quantum mechanics permits the calculation of the magnitude expected for the effect in some cases. In Figure 28 there is shown the wave-number shift of the π- and σ-components of the parhelium line $5p^1P_1 - 2s^1S_0$ plotted against the square of the field strength; the solid lines represent the shifts calculated by Unsöld,[1] the points those measured by Stark[2] and Foster.[3] The agreement is satisfactory for low field strengths. At higher field strengths the experimental points for the π-component show a curvature, indicating an approach to proportionality with a lower power of F than the second. This is to be anticipated, for the largest observed Stark-effect shift of 25.4 cm.$^{-1}$ is already larger than the field-free $5d^1D_2 - 5p^1P_1$ separation of 24.3 cm.$^{-1}$, and the upper state is approaching quantization in Stark-effect coordinates rather than in the polar coordinates of a penetrating orbit. For still higher field strengths the first-order Stark effect should be observed. This is shown distinctly at lower field strengths by lines with ^1D as the upper state, for the $^1D - {}^1F$ separation is smaller than the $^1P - {}^1D$ separation.[4]

[1] A. Unsöld, *Ann. d. Phys.*, **82**: 355, 1927.

[2] J. Stark, "Elektrische Spektralanalyse," Leipzig, 1914.

[3] J. S. Foster, *Phys. Rev.*, **23**: 667, 1924.

[4] Further papers dealing with the Stark effect in many-electron atoms are the following: R. Becker, *Z. f. Phys.*, **32**: 332, 1925; W. Thomas, *ibid.*, **34**: 586, 1925; J. S. Foster, *Proc.*, Roy. Soc., A **114**: 47, 1927; **117**: 137, 1927; J. Dewey, *Phys. Rev.*, **28**: 1108, 1926; **30**: 770, 1927; Y. Ishida and G. Kamijima, *Sci. Papers Tokyo*, **9**: 117, 1928.

CHAPTER VI

THE VECTOR MODEL FOR ATOMS WITH TWO VALENCE ELECTRONS

Equations correctly describing the spectral phenomena shown by atoms with two or more valence electrons can be obtained with the aid of the quantum mechanics; but not always, in fact not often, simply. Many of these equations can, however, be easily obtained from a vector model of the atom similar to that discussed in the previous chapter, and for clarity as well as convenience the use of the model is to be recommended. It is found that in some relatively few cases the model does not permit the derivation of the correct equations, and that it is, consequently, sometimes necessary to refer to the quantum mechanics for more than verification. In other cases the model can be made to lead formally to the correct equations, but by a definitely incorrect procedure; an example of this will be given in the following discussion of resonance energy.

In the vector model the orbital moment of each electron (the ith) is replaced by the quantum vector $\mathbf{l}_i$, and its spin moment by $\mathbf{s}_i$. Under varying circumstances these combine to form resultant vectors, in terms of which the properties of the atom may be expressed.

21. THE FINE STRUCTURE OF THE SPECTRA OF ATOMS WITH TWO VALENCE ELECTRONS

21a. Two *s* Electrons. Resonance Energy.[1]—We shall begin with the simplest case, when both of the two electrons have $l_i = 0$. Each electron is then in an *s* state. For a reason to be given later (Chap. IX) we shall assume that the principal quantum numbers for the two orbits are different.

The total moment of the atom, which was called **j**, now consists of the spin moments of the two electrons only; it can have in this case then only the values corresponding to $j = \frac{1}{2} + \frac{1}{2} = 1$ and

[1] See CONDON and MORSE, Secs. 48, 49, 50, for the derivation of the quantum mechanics expressions for the resonance energy.

$j = \frac{1}{2} - \frac{1}{2} = 0$. Thus the atom can assume only two different states, represented in Figure 29; these may be designated by saying that the two vectors are either parallel or opposed.[1] Experience shows that these two states in general differ greatly in energy. This is not explicable with our model, in which the two states differ only in the relative orientation of the spin axes of the two electrons, as can be seen from the following argument. The interaction energy of the electron spin and its orbital motion gave in the case of a single electron the doublet separation

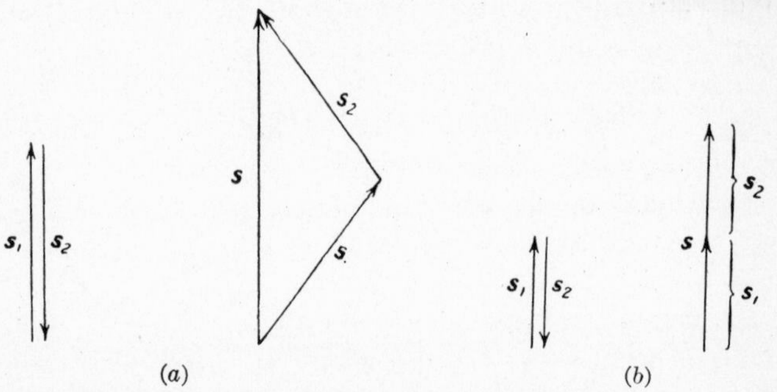

FIG. 29.—The formation of a resultant spin moment vector **s** from two electron spin vectors $\mathbf{s}_1$ and $\mathbf{s}_2$, (a) when the vector magnitudes are taken to be $\sqrt{s(s+1)}$, $\sqrt{s_1(s_1+1)}$, and $\sqrt{s_2(s_2+1)}$; (b) when they are taken to be s, s_1 and s_2.

The interaction energy of the spin of one electron and the orbital motion and spin of another electron is certainly to be expected to be smaller than this, since a calculation similar to that used for the doublet separation shows that it is proportional to a lower power of the effective nuclear charge. The energy difference of the two possible states, $j = 1$ and $j = 0$, would thus be expected to be at the most of the same order of magnitude as that of the doublets in the alkali spectra.

It has been shown by Heisenberg,[2] however, that there occurs as a result of the presence of the two electrons a *resonance*

[1] The convenient use of "parallel" is not to be interpreted as signifying that the relative orientations of the vectors $\mathbf{s}_1$ and $\mathbf{s}_2$ conform to the usual meaning of this word. If the quantum vectors be given the magnitudes s_1, s_2, and j, this interpretation is justified to some extent, but with the more generally satisfactory magnitudes $\sqrt{s_1(s_1+1)}$, $\sqrt{s_2(s_2+1)}$, and $\sqrt{j(j+1)}$, it is not (see Fig. 29*a*).

[2] W. HEISENBERG, *Z. f. Phys.*, **38**: 411, 1926; **39**: 499, 1926; **41**: 239, 1926. The resonance phenomenon was discovered independently by P. A. M. DIRAC, *Proc.*, Roy. Soc., A **112**: 661, 1926.

phenomenon characteristic of the quantum mechanics, and that the large energy difference of the states with $j = 0$ and with $j = 1$ is due to it. Classically, two systems which are coupled together are said to resonate when for each a frequency of the mechanical motion is nearly independent of the amplitude of the motion, and this frequency is nearly the same for the two systems. These requirements are satisfied only by two harmonic oscillators or by systems with approximately simple harmonic motion. As a familiar illustration we may mention two similar pendulums suspended near each other from a support which is not rigid. If one pendulum be set in oscillation with a large amplitude, its oscillational energy will be transmitted by small impulses through the support to the other pendulum, and in time the first will come to rest and the second will oscillate with the original amplitude. As this process is repeated the energy of the system fluctuates back and forth from one pendulum to the other; we may say that the two pendulums change places regularly.

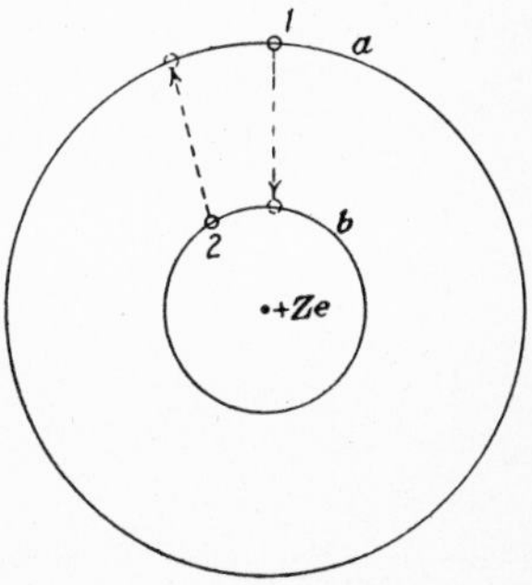

FIG. 30.—Diagrammatic representation of transitions in a two electron atom giving rise to the resonance phenomenon.

This phenomenon is of great importance in the quantum mechanics, and occurs very often. There are two ways of representing an atom with two electrons in different quantum states, if we ignore the interaction between the charges of the electrons. One corresponds to the first electron in the orbit a of energy W_a and the second electron in orbit b of energy W_b; the second corresponds to the first and second electrons in orbits b and a, respectively. Now according to the quantum mechanics the frequency associated with the transition of an electron from a state of energy W_a to one of energy W_b or W_b to W_a is $\nu = \frac{W_a - W_b}{h}$. Hence as a result of the coupling of the two electrons through interaction of their charges resonance will occur, associated with the transition of one electron from a to b and of the other from b to a; the electrons will change places regularly, and it will no longer be possible to say that the first electron remains in the outer orbit and the second in the inner, as was predicted by the old quantum theory. In consequence, the energy of the system is changed in a definite way, depending on, although not arising from, the relative orientation of the spin vectors of the electrons. It has been shown by Heisenberg[1] and others that the phenomenon provides a quantitatively accurate explanation of the level-separations of many-electron atoms.

In order to continue to make use of the vector model, the fiction may be adopted that, as a result of some effect not represented in the model, there exists a great interaction energy between the two electron spins; with this assumption a complete description can be given of the structure of spectra. It must not be forgotten, though, that this great interaction energy is in reality the energy of the Heisenberg-Dirac resonance phenomenon, and is to be attributed in reality to the charges of the two electrons and not to their magnetic moments.

This apparent interaction energy is assumed to be small in magnitude when the angle between the spin vectors of the two electrons is small. Its algebraic sign is such that the state with $j = 1$, for which the spin vectors are parallel, has a smaller energy than that with $j = 0$. The state with $j = 1$ is hence the more stable, and lies lower in the energy level diagram.

21b. One *s* Electron and One Other Electron.—The following picture represents one *s* electron and one other electron for which l is not zero. The vectors of one electron are $\mathbf{s}_1$ and $\mathbf{l}_1$ (here equal to zero), and of the other $\mathbf{s}_2$ and $\mathbf{l}_2$. We assume, in accordance with the above discussion, that the interaction energy between $\mathbf{s}_1$ and $\mathbf{s}_2$ is much greater than that between $\mathbf{s}_2$ and $\mathbf{l}_2$. This has the same influence on the second electron as a strong magnetic field had in the Paschen-Back effect; the vector $\mathbf{s}_2$ acts as though $\mathbf{l}_2$ were not present, and obeys only the influence of $\mathbf{s}_1$. $\mathbf{s}_1$ and $\mathbf{s}_2$, as in the previous case with $\mathbf{l}_2 = 0$, then form a resultant, the total spin moment vector $\mathbf{s}$ of the atom. The associated quantum number s can assume the values 1 or 0. The total moment $\mathbf{j}$ of the two electrons is then formed as the resultant of $\mathbf{s}$ and $\mathbf{l}_2$. For $s = 1$ the quantum number j can have the values

$$j = l_2 - 1,\ l_2,\ \text{and}\ l_2 + 1.$$

These three states differ in the orientation of $\mathbf{l}_2$ with respect to $\mathbf{s}_2$ and $\mathbf{s}_1$, and hence their energy differences can be calculated

[1] W. Heisenberg, *Z. f. Phys.*, **39**: 499, 1926; *ibid.*, **41**: 239, 1927; A. Unsöld, *Ann. d. Phys.*, **82**: 355, 1927; J. A. Gaunt, *Proc.*, Roy. Soc., **122**: 513, 1929; *Phil. Trans*, Roy. Soc., **228**: 151, 1929, etc.

in the same way as that of the alkali doublets. We shall show later that the separation of this triplet is of the same order of magnitude as that of the doublets. With $s = 0$, j can have only the one value

$$j = l_2,$$

so that the state is a singlet state. In accordance with the discussion at the end of the previous section we may expect the singlet-triplet distance to be large compared with the triplet separation, with the triplet state the more stable.

21c. Two Arbitrary Electrons. Term Symbols.—Now let us consider the general case when neither l_1 nor l_2 is zero. In coupling $\mathbf{s}_1$ and $\mathbf{s}_2$ there is now also strong coupling between $\mathbf{l}_1$ and $\mathbf{l}_2$. That there is a large interaction energy between the orbital moments can be seen from our model; the orbits interpenetrate each other and hence perturb each other strongly. For the composition of vectors this signifies that $\mathbf{l}_1$ and $\mathbf{l}_2$ should form a resultant which we shall call $\mathbf{l}$. The total moment $\mathbf{j}$ is composed as the resultant of $\mathbf{l}$ and $\mathbf{s}$.

The quantum number s can in this case also have only the values 1 and 0. l traverses the values

$$|l_1 - l_2| \leq l \leq l_1 + l_2.$$

For the case $s = 1$ this leads to triplets; the quantum number j can in general for a given l have three values

$$j = l - 1,\ l,\ \text{and}\ l + 1.$$

For $l = 0$ there is, however, only one resultant, with $j = s = 1$. This state also is customarily called a "triplet state" or "triplet term" since s has the value 1, even though the state is in reality not threefold.

When $s = 0$ all the states are single and are called "singlets."

As was mentioned in Chap. IV, the symbols S, P, D, F, etc. are used for the terms having the resultant $l = 0, 1, 2, 3$, etc. All of the symbols shown in Table I are needed to account for observed spectra.

TABLE I.—TERM SYMBOLS

l = ...	0	1	2	3	4	5	6	7	8	9	
Symbol...........	*S*	*P*	*D*	*F*	*G*	*H*	*I*	*K*[1]	*L*	*M*	
l = ...	10	11	12	13	14	15	16	17	18	19	20
Symbol...........	*N*	*O*	*Q*	*R*	*T*	*U*	*V*	*W*	*X*	*Y*	*Z*

[1] The letter *J* is omitted in accordance with the German practice.

It is to be noted that these symbols tell nothing of the actual electronic states in the atom, giving only values of the resultant quantum vectors. For example, if there is one electron in a p orbit ($l_1 = 1$) and another in a d orbit ($l_2 = 2$), then l can have among others the value 3 and the state is given the symbol F, and indeed ^3F for $s = 1$ (triplet F) and ^1F for $s = 0$ (singlet F). To the right there may be further written a subscript giving the value of j. The combination of a p and a d electron gives the states shown in Table II.

TABLE II.—STATES ARISING FROM A p AND A d ELECTRON

	$s = 0$, singlets			$s = 1$, triplets				
$j =$	1	2	3	0	1	2	3	4
$l = 1$..................	$^1P_1$	...	...	$^3P_0$	$^3P_1$	$^3P_2$		
2..................	...	$^1D_2$	...	...	$^3D_1$	$^3D_2$	$^3D_3$	
3..................	...	...	$^1F_3$	...	...	$^3F_2$	$^3F_3$	$^3F_4$

Similar term symbols are used in the case of atoms containing many electrons outside of completed shells; the value of the resultant l is given by the symbol of Table I, the multiplicity is given by the superscript $2s + 1$ written to the left, and the value of j is appended as a subscript. If it is desired to mention the states of the individual electrons, their symbols are written before the term symbol; thus to show that the terms of Table II are derived from one p and one d electron we would write $pd\,^1P_1$, $pd\,^3P_0$, etc. If it were further desired to indicate the values of the principal quantum number n for each electron, this could be introduced in the usual way; as, for example, $3p3d\,^1P_1$, $3p4d\,^1P_1$, etc. It is often desirable to express the fact that the principal quantum numbers for certain electrons are different, even though they be not explicitly stated; for, as will be shown in Chap. IX, the allowed terms often depend on this difference. This difference is indicated by placing a point between symbols representing electrons of different n; thus $3p3d\,^1P_1$ or $4p4d\,^1P_1$ would be $pd\,^1P_1$, while $3p4d\,^1P_1$ or $4p6d\,^1P_1$ would be $p \cdot d\,^1P_1$. If two or more electrons have the same values of n and l_i the fact is indicated by means of an exponent; an atom in which seven electrons with $n = 4$ and $l_i = 3$, two with $n = 5$ and $l_i = 2$, and one with $n = 6$ and $l_i = 1$ combined to give a state with $s = 3/2$, $l = 16$, and $j = 33/2$ would have the symbol $4f^7 5d^2 6p^4 \, {}^4V_{3\frac{3}{2}}$ or $f^7 \cdot d^2 \cdot p \; {}^4V_{3\frac{3}{2}}$.[1] On account of the length of these symbols they are sometimes replaced by abbreviations such as those given below.

Configuration	Designation[1]
s^2p^{n-2}	*a*
sp^{n-1}	*b*
p^n	*c*
$s^2p^{n-3} \cdot s$	*k*
$s^2p^{n-3} \cdot p$	*m*
$s^2p^{n-3} \cdot d$	*n*
$s^2p^{n-3} \cdot f$	*q*
	etc.

[1] These were introduced by I. S. Bowen.

21d. Selection Rules. The selection rule for l in the case of alkali-like atoms stated that l could change by $+1$ or -1 during a transition. For many-electron atoms the resultant l may change by 0 as well as $\pm$ 1. Usually during a transition only one electron jumps; *i.e.*, changes its quantum numbers n and l_i; for this electron the selection rule that l_i must change by $+1$ or -1 is valid. At times, however, as was discovered by Russell and Saunders,[2] two electrons may jump simultaneously. It has been shown theoretically by Heisenberg[3] that in this case l_i for one of them must change by ± 1, and for the other by ± 2. This rule is empirically verified.[4]

[1] Russell and Saunders first suggested the use of capital letters only for terms, with the multiplicity indicated by an exponent at the left. Sommerfeld had previously written j as a subscript, and Grimm and Sommerfeld wrote the quantum numbers of the valence electron before the term symbol. The complete symbols described above were introduced by Hund. There has been introduced recently the use of capital letters S, L, and J for the resultant quantum numbers s, l, j, small letter symbols being restricted to quantum numbers of the individual electrons. In our treatment there is no confusion, since quantum numbers and quantum vectors for the individual electrons are always written with a subscript, whereas the resultants have none. (See "Report of the Committee on Notation in Line Spectra," *Phys. Rev.*, **33**: 900, 1929.)

[2] H. N. Russell and F. A. Saunders, *Astrophys. Jour.*, **61**: 38, 1925.

[3] W. Heisenberg, *Z. f. Physik*, **32**: 841, 1925.

[4] H. N. Russell, *Science*, **69**: 512, 1924, and O. Laporte, *Z. f. Phys.*, **23**: 135, 1924, express the following empirical selection rule: the sum of the changes in all the l_i's must be odd. This includes some transitions in addition to those allowed by the Heisenberg rule. The observed combinations are, however, almost without exception included under the latter.

The empirical rule[1] that transitions will occur only from a state for which the l_i sum, $\sum_i l_i$, is odd to one for which it is even, or *vice versa*, is called the "Laporte rule." As a result of this rule, we may differentiate beween two groups of terms, for one of which, the even terms, the l_i sum is even, and for the others, the odd terms, the l_i sum is odd. Membership in one of these groups or the other was formerly indicated by the use of a prime, the primed and unprimed terms alternating in the following way:

	$l = 0$	1	2	3	4
Even terms, $\sum_i l_i$ even........	S	P'	D	F'	G
Odd terms, $\sum_i l_i$ odd..........	S'	P	D'	F	G'

Recently the custom has developed of omitting the primes; if it is desired to differentiate between the groups, a small superscript ° is added to the odd terms, following a suggestion of Russell. Thus $3s^2 2p\ {}^2P^\circ$ is a representative odd term in the new nomenclature.

The quantum number s will not change during a transition unless the interaction between **l** and **s** is large; that is, unless the separation of the triplet levels becomes of the same order of magnitude as the triplet-singlet distance. Usually, then, triplet-singlet intercombinations will appear not at all or only with small intensities.

21e. The Level Scheme of Calcium. Metastable States.—Figure 31*a* represents the level scheme of the calcium[2] atom. The lowest energy state is the state in which the two outer electrons are both in the 4*s* orbit, giving rise to the $4s^2\ {}^1S_0$ level. When both electrons are in the same *s* state only the singlet level occurs, the triplet being non-existent, as will be explained in Chapter IX.

In most of the excited states of calcium only one of the outer electrons is excited, the other one remaining in the 4*s* state. These excited states give rise to the series of levels

$$4s \cdot ns\ {}^1S_0 \text{ and } {}^3S_1,\ 4s \cdot np\ {}^1P_1 \text{ and } {}^3P_2,\ {}^3P_1,\ {}^3P_0, \text{ etc.}$$

[1] The quantum mechanical proof of this rule has been given by H. Weyl, "Gruppentheorie und Quantenmechanik," Leipzig, 1928, p. 181.

[2] H. N. Russell, *Astrophys. Journ.*, **66**: 191, 1927.

The level scheme shows that the triplet state is usually lower than the singlet state of the same configuration.

Removing the excited electron completely will leave a calcium ion with its outer electron in the 4*s* state. This explains the existence of a limit to which all these level series converge.

There also have been observed levels arising from the configurations $3d \cdot np$ and $3d \cdot nd$, with both outer electrons in excited

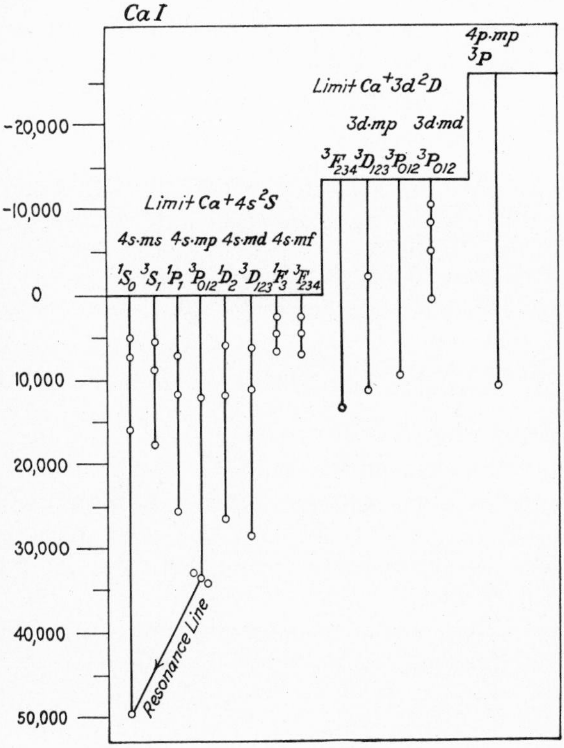

FIG. 31*a*.—Term diagram for CaI.

orbits, one of which is a 3*d* orbit. Removing the second electron will then give rise to a calcium ion with its outer electron in the 3*d* orbit. The series of levels $3d \cdot np$ and $3d \cdot nd$ will thus converge to a limit different from that for the levels considered above, this limit representing the 3*d* state of the calcium ion. The difference between these two level limits can be obtained directly from the known level scheme of Ca^+ and is in complete agreement with the calculations of these limits with the help of series formulas.

Only the lowest $4s4p\ ^3P$ state is drawn in the diagram as a triplet. Of this triplet the levels $^3P_2$ and $^3P_0$ are so-called *metastable states*. This means that when the atom is in either one of these states it will not drop to its normal state, $4s^2\ ^1S_0$, with the emission of radiation, for the selection rule for j forbids these transitions. An atom in one of these states can be brought into the nearby $4s4p\ ^3P_1$ state by means of collisions with other atoms, and from there it can drop to the normal state. Or the atom can absorb radiation and in that way be brought into a state of higher excitation, from which it might then drop to the lowest level with the emission of radiation.

Metastable states occur in all of the more complicated spectra. It has been shown experimentally that they have very long mean lives and that often absorption lines can be obtained with such a level as initial level. This shows that there can sometimes be a large concentration of the atoms in a metastable state. When the gas is very rarefied so that few collisions occur this concentration may become very high. In that case the "forbidden" spectral lines corresponding to transitions from the metastable states to the normal state of the atom will take place. For the strict formulation of the selection principles does not completely "forbid" such a transition, but states that its probability is extremely small and, under normal laboratory conditions, much smaller than for transitions due to collisions. These considerations led Bowen[1] to his famous explanation of the previously unclassified spectral lines emitted by nebulae, where indeed collisions are very rare. Bowen showed that the strong nebular lines arise from such "forbidden" transitions from metastable states in N_{II}, O_{II}, and O_{III}. The states involved are $2s^22p^2\ ^3P$, $2s^22p^2\ ^1D$, and $2s^22p^2\ ^1S$ for N_{II} and O_{III}, and $2s^22p^3\ ^4S$, $2s^22p^3\ ^2D$, $2s^22p^3\ ^2P$ for O_{II}. Combinations between these states are not allowed by the selection rule for the l_i's, for $\Delta l_i = 0$ throughout.

Inspired by Bowen's success, McLennan[2] identified the green auroral line $\lambda 5577.35$ with the forbidden transition $2s^22p^4\ ^1D_2 - 2s^22p^4\ ^1S_0$ in O_I.

Merrill[3] also interpreted some lines in stellar spectra in the same way. The spectrum of the southern variable star η Carinae consists essentially of known emission lines of H and

[1] I. S. Bowen, *Astrophys. Jour.*, **67**: 1, 1928.
[2] J. C. McLennan, *Proc. Roy. Soc.*, A **120**: 327, 1928.
[3] P. W. Merrill, *Astrophys. Jour.*, **67**: 391, 1928.

Fe_{II}. Most of the others were found to correspond to transitions in Fe_{II} forbidden by the Laporte rule. The selection rule for j was also not obeyed; the strongest component of a forbidden multiplet line was found to correspond to a value of Δj equal to that of Δl.

22. EQUATIONS FOR TRIPLET SEPARATIONS

The terms which are to be expected in general for singlet and triplet spectra are shown in Table III. Each singlet level

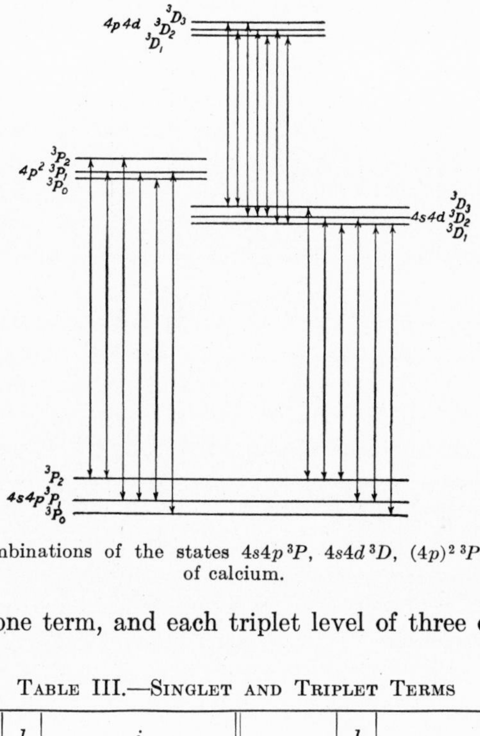

FIG. 31b.—Combinations of the states $4s4p\,^3P$, $4s4d\,^3D$, $(4p)^2\,^3P$, and $4p4d\,^3D$ of calcium.

consists of one term, and each triplet level of three except that with $l = 0$.

TABLE III.—SINGLET AND TRIPLET TERMS

	l	j						l	j					
^1S..........	0		1				^3S......	0	..	1				
^1P..........	1	..	1				^3P......	1	0	1	2			
^1D..........	2	..	..	2			^3D......	2	..	1	2	3		
^1F..........	3	..	..	..	3		^3F......	3	..	..	2	3	4	
^1G..........	4	..	..	..	..	4	^3G......	4	..	..	..	3	4	5

Lines resulting from transitions from one singlet level to another are single. The selection rule for j is that changes of

0, +1, and −1 are allowed (Sec. 14*b*); except that transitions from $j = 0$ to $j = 0$ do not occur. Thus $^3S - {}^3P$ consists of two lines, $^3S_1 - {}^3P_0$ and $^3S_1 - {}^3P_2$. The maximum number of components of a triplet-triplet line is seven. The combinations of the states $4s4p\,^3P$, $4s4d\,^3D$, $4p^{2\,3}P$, and $4p4d\,^3D$ of calcium are shown in Figure 31*b*, and the corresponding wave-lengths and wave-numbers are given in Table IV.

TABLE IV.—TRIPLET COMBINATIONS IN THE CALCIUM SPECTRUM

	$4p4d\,^3D_1$		$^3D_2$		$^3D_3$
$4s4d\,^4D_1$	λ5600.21		λ5591.82		
	17,856.48	*26.79*	17,883.27		
	13.97		*13.90*		
$^3D_2$	λ5604.59		λ5596.17		λ5583.68
	17,842.51	*26.86*	17,869.37	*39.96*	17,909.33
			21.92		*21.78*
$^3D_3$			λ5603.04		λ5590.48
			17,847.45	*40.10*	17,887.55
	$4p^2\,^3P_0$		$^3P_1$		$^3P_2$
$4s4p\,^3P_0$			λ4290.69		
			23,306.27		
			52.24		
$^3P_1$	λ4309.10		λ4300.33		λ4284.34
	23,206.70	*47.33*	23,254.03	*86.79*	23,340.82
			105.84		*105.92*
$^3P_2$			λ4319.99		λ4303.87
			23,148.19	*86.71*	23,234.90
	$4s4d\,^3D_1$		$^3D_2$		$^3D_3$
$4s4p\,^3P_0$	λ19310.3				
	5,177.3				
	52.2				
$^3P_1$	λ19506.8		λ19452.6		
	5,125.1	*14.4*	5,139.5		
	105.6		*106.7*		
$^3P_2$	λ19917.3		λ19864.3		λ19777.1
	5,019.5	*13.3*	5,032.8	*22.2*	5,055.0

Often the fine-structure separation of one state is so small as to be unresolved by the spectral apparatus; in this case triplet combinations have three components, and show just the fine structure of the other state.

In calculating the energy differences of the triplet levels of atoms with two valence electrons we shall at first take into consideration only the interaction of the spin of each electron and its own orbital motion. In case that one of the electrons is in an s orbit only the other will contribute to the fine-structure separations, and from Equation 2, Chap. IV, we find for the spin energy (introducing an effective nuclear charge $Z - S_1$)

$$W_s^{\,1} = \frac{Rhc\alpha^2(Z - S_1)^4}{n_1^3 l_1(l_1 + \tfrac{1}{2})(l_1 + 1)} \cdot l_1 s_1 \overline{\cos(\mathbf{l}_1\mathbf{s}_1)}, \tag{1}$$

in which the bar over cos $(\mathbf{l}_1\mathbf{s}_1)$ indicates that the average value of this quantity is to be taken.[1] Since the precessions of $\mathbf{s}_1$ about $\mathbf{s}$ and of $\mathbf{l}_1$ about $\mathbf{l}$ are uniform, the relation

$$\overline{\cos(\mathbf{l}_1\mathbf{s}_1)} = \cos(\mathbf{l}_1\mathbf{l})\cos(\mathbf{s}_1\mathbf{s})\cos(\mathbf{l}\mathbf{s}) \tag{2}$$

is true; and on calculating the values of these cosines from the vector model Equation 1 becomes

$$W_s^{\,1} = a_1\frac{j(j+1) - l(l+1) - s(s+1)}{2}, \tag{3}$$

in which

$$a_1 = \frac{Rhc\alpha^2(Z - S_1)^4}{n_1^3 l_1(l_1 + \tfrac{1}{2})(l_1 + 1)} \cdot \frac{s_1(s_1+1) + s(s+1) - s_2(s_2+1)}{2s(s+1)} \cdot \frac{l_1(l_1+1) + l(l+1) - l_2(l_2+1)}{2l(l+1)}. \tag{4}$$

In this case, with $l_2 = 0$ and, of course, $s_1 = s_2$, the equation is simplified to

$$a_1 = \frac{Rhc\alpha^2(Z - S_1)^4}{n_1^3 l_1(l_1 + \tfrac{1}{2})(l_1 + 1)} \cdot \tfrac{1}{2}. \tag{5}$$

If neither electron is an s electron the interaction energy is

$$W_s^{\,1} = \frac{Rhc\alpha^2(Z - S_1)^4}{n_1^3 l_1(l_1 + \tfrac{1}{2})(l_1 + 1)} l_1 s_1 \overline{\cos(\mathbf{l}_1\mathbf{s}_1)} + \frac{Rhc\alpha^2(Z - S_2)^4}{n_2^3 l_2(l_2 + \tfrac{1}{2})(l_2 + 1)} l_2 s_2 \overline{\cos(\mathbf{l}_2\mathbf{s}_2)}, \tag{6}$$

[1] For deeply penetrating orbits the Landé product $Z_i^2 z^2/n^{*3}$ can be used in place of $(Z - S_1)^4/n^3$.

which becomes on introducing the average values of the cosines

$$W_s^1 = (a_1 + a_2)\frac{j(j+1) - l(l+1) - s(s+1)}{2}, \tag{7}$$

in which a_1 is given by Equation 4 and a_2 by a similar equation in which the subscripts 1 and 2 have been interchanged.

From Equation 7 it is seen that the separations of adjacent levels in a triplet are proportional to successive differences of $j(j+1)$. Thus if $l = 1$, so that $j = 2$, 1, or 0, the separations ${}^3P_2 - {}^3P_1$ and ${}^3P_1 - {}^3P_0$ are in the ratio $(2 \times 3 - 1 \times 2)$:$(1 \times 2 - 0 \times 1)$ or 2:1. Similarly the ratio of ${}^3D_3 - {}^3D_2$ to ${}^3D_2 - {}^3D_1$ is 3:2, that of ${}^3F_4 - {}^3F_3$ to ${}^3F_3 - {}^3F_2$ is 4:3, and so on. The triplet separations of Table IV lead to the ratios shown in Table V for calcium, in approximate agreement with the expected result.

Table V.—Intervals for Calcium Triplets

State	Observed Interval Ratio
$4s4p\ {}^3P$	2.02 : 1
$4p^2\ {}^3P$	1.83 : 1
$4s4d\ {}^3D$	3.13 : 2
$4p4d\ {}^3D$	2.99 : 2

The triplet separations of magnesium-like atoms (Table VI) are in similarly good agreement with the theoretical ratio of 2:1, the deviation being about 3 per cent. Those for beryllium-like atoms, on the other hand, deviate considerably from this ratio, the most pronounced discrepancy being shown by $2s2p\ {}^3P$ of beryllium (Tables VII and VIII). It is probable that the failure to adhere to the interval rule is due to the fact that in case the effective nuclear charge is small the interaction between the spin of each electron and the orbital motion of the other, which has been neglected in deriving the rule, becomes of significance. This explanation will be further discussed in the following section.

In case that one electron is an s electron the triplet separation has been found to be given by Equation 3, in which the spin-orbit interaction of the other electron alone has been taken into consideration. The maximum value of j is $l_1 + 1$, the minimum $l_1 - 1$; introducing these values in Equations 3 and 5, the total width of the triplet is found to be

$$\Delta\nu = 5.82\frac{(Z - S_1)^4}{n_1^3 l_1(l_1 + 1)} \text{ cm.}^{-1} \tag{8}$$

This equation is identical with Equation 9, Chap. IV; the total triplet separation accordingly is given in this case by the same equation as the doublet separation for sodium-like atoms. In the last columns of Tables VI and VIII are given values of S_1 calculated with this equation. On comparing them with the values of S_0 for the corresponding alkali-like atoms (2^2P of Be^+, B^{+2}, etc. in Table I, Chap. IV; 3^2P of Mg^+, Al^{+2}, etc. in Table III, Chap. IV) it will be seen that the screening constants for doublets and triplets show closely the same variation with nuclear charge; in each atom the introduction of an *s* electron has increased the screening constant by about 0.30.

TABLE VI.—FINE STRUCTURE OF $3s3p\,^3P$ OF MAGNESIUM-LIKE ATOMS

Atom	$^3P_2 - {}^3P_1$	$^3P_1 - {}^3P_0$	Interval ratio	S_1
Mg	40.9 cm.$^{-1}$	19.9 cm.$^{-1}$	2.06	7.130
Al^+	125.5	61.8	2.03	6.549
Si^{+2}	263	131.	2.01	6.231
P^{+3}	467.9	228.6	2.05	6.042
S^{+4}	754.7	365.8	2.06	5.894
Cl^{+5}	1717.2		....	5.77

TABLE VII.—FINE STRUCTURE OF $2p^2\,^3P$ OF BERYLLIUM-LIKE ATOMS

Atom	$^3P_2 - {}^3P_1$	$^3P_1 - {}^3P_0$	Interval ratio	S_1
Be	2.03 cm.$^{-1}$	1.41 cm.$^{-1}$	1.44	2.25
B^+	22.2		....	2.20
C^{+2}	47.4	29.7	1.60	2.18
N^{+3}	124.5	72.8	1.71	2.17
O^{+4}	268.2	155.4	1.73	2.16

TABLE VIII.—FINE STRUCTURE OF $2s2p\,^3P$ OF BERYLLIUM-LIKE ATOMS

Atom	$^3P_2 - {}^3P_1$	$^3P_1 - {}^3P_0$	Interval ratio	S_1
Be	2.36 cm.$^{-1}$	0.67 cm.$^{-1}$	3.57	2.30
B^{+1}	22.8		....	2.18
C^{+2}	56.5	22.9	2.47	2.16
N^{+3}	143.8	61.7	2.33	2.13
O^{+4}	305.9	134.9	2.27	2.10

If the two electrons are alike, so that $l_1 = l_2$ and $a_1 = a_2$, Equation 7 gives for the total triplet separation

$$\Delta\nu = 5.82\frac{(Z - S_1)^4}{n_1{}^3 l_1(l_1 + 1)} \cdot \frac{(l + \frac{1}{2})}{(l_1 + \frac{1}{2})} \text{ cm.}^{-1} \tag{9}$$

and if $l_1 = l$, as, for example, in $p^2\,{}^3P$, this again reduces to Equation 8. The values of S_1 calculated in this way for $2p^2\,{}^3P$ of beryllium-like atoms (Table VII) are nearly the same as those found for $2s2p\,{}^3P$, so that each p electron is seen to screen the other by the same amount as the s electron, about 0.30.

23. THE SPECTRA OF HELIUM AND IONIZED LITHIUM

The spectrum of neutral helium consists of two term systems which combine with each other hardly at all.[1] One of these systems, which includes the normal state of the atom, is a singlet system, and the other consists apparently of doublets. The systems have been given the names parhelium and orthohelium, respectively.

Since the helium atom contains two electrons its spectrum would be expected to be similar to the alkaline-earth spectra, and to consist of singlet states and triplet states. The possibility that the apparent doublets of helium might be deformed triplets, and that the helium spectrum might be analogous to that of the alkaline-earths, was first proposed by Slater,[2] who suggested that two of the triplet levels come nearly into coincidence. This suggestion was quantitatively verified by Heisenberg.[3] The normal triplets result when only the interaction between the spin and the orbital motion of each electron is taken into account. This interaction energy of $\mathbf{l}_1$ on $\mathbf{s}_1$ and $\mathbf{l}_2$ on $\mathbf{s}_2$ is proportional to $(Z - S)^4$, while that arising from the action of the orbital motion or the spin of one electron on the spin of the other ($\mathbf{l}_2$ and $\mathbf{s}_1$, $\mathbf{l}_1$ and $\mathbf{s}_2$, and $\mathbf{s}_1$ and $\mathbf{s}_2$) is proportional to $(Z - S)^3$; accordingly normal triplets should occur when the nuclear charge is large. By taking into consideration all of the interactions with the use of the perturbation theory of the quan-

[1] One intercombination line was reported: T. LYMAN, *Nature*, **110**: 278, 1922; *Astrophys. Jour.*, **60**: 1, 1924; it has, however, since been shown to be a line in the neon spectrum: H. B. DORGELO, *Physica*, **6**: 150, 1926.

[2] J. C. SLATER, *Proc.*, Nat. Acad., **11**: 732, 1925.

[3] W. HEISENBERG, *Z. f. Phys.*, **39**: 499, 1926.

tum mechanics, Heisenberg obtained for the interaction energy of $1s \cdot 2p^3P$ of helium-like atoms the values

$$W^1 = a\{(Z - 3)[\tfrac{1}{2}, -\tfrac{1}{2}, -1] + [\tfrac{3}{8}, -\tfrac{3}{8}, \tfrac{3}{2}] - \tfrac{1}{4}\},$$

in which the numbers in the brackets refer to $j = 2$, 1, and 0, respectively. For Z very large this gives evidently the normal triplet with interval ratio 2:1. For small values of Z the intervals are anomalous. In particular they have the following values:

$$Z = 2, \text{He}: W^1 = a[-\tfrac{3}{8}, -\tfrac{1}{8}, \tfrac{9}{4}]$$
$$Z = 3, \text{Li}^+: W^1 = a[\tfrac{1}{8}, -\tfrac{5}{8}, \tfrac{5}{4}].$$

These results are shown in Figure 32, in which the levels $j = 2$, 1, and 0 are indicated by lines of lengths 5, 3, and 1, representing the relative intensities of transitions to the state $1s \cdot 2s^3S$. The structure shown for helium has been verified experimentally by Houston,[1] who found the intervals to be 0.992 cm.$^{-1}$ and 0.071 cm.$^{-1}$, in satisfactory agreement with Heisenberg's ratio 19:2. The fine structure of ionized lithium is also approximately in accordance with the theoretical result.

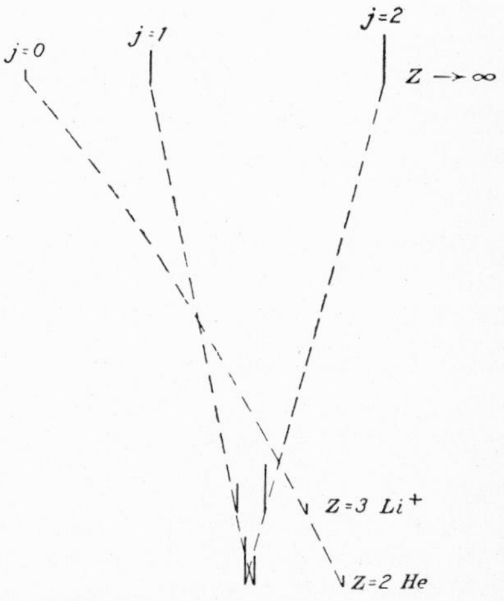

Fig. 32.—The fine structure of the state $1s2p^3P$ of helium-like atoms.

It is evident from these calculations that a similar deviation from the interval rules may be expected for other triplet states with small values of $Z - S$. Qualitatively the effect is such as to account for the interval ratio 3.5:1 of the similar state $2s \cdot 2p\ ^3P$ of beryllium (Table IX), for, as is evident from Figure 32, the change in interval ratio with increase in atomic number is the expected one. It is probable that the deviations in the opposite direction shown by $2p^2\ ^3P$ of beryllium-like atoms can be similarly accounted for.

The improbability of transitions from orthohelium to parhelium states and *vice versa* results from the small $\mathbf{l}_i\mathbf{s}_i$ interaction and the correspondingly small chance that s will change during a quantum jump (Chap. VIII).

[1] W. V. Houston, *Phys. Rev.*, **29**: 749, 1927.

24. OTHER COUPLING POSSIBILITIES

In the preceding discussion it was assumed that the apparent interaction between the two electron spins $\mathbf{s}_1$ and $\mathbf{s}_2$ was much greater than the interaction between the spin magnetism and the orbital motion of each electron; *i.e.*, between $\mathbf{s}_1$ and $\mathbf{l}_1$ and between $\mathbf{s}_2$ and $\mathbf{l}_2$. Now although the new quantum mechanics shows that the apparent interaction energy between $\mathbf{s}_1$ and $\mathbf{s}_2$ is, on account of the resonance phenomenon, much greater than that to be expected from our approximate model, it is not required that it be always greater than that between $\mathbf{s}_1$ and $\mathbf{l}_1$ or $\mathbf{s}_2$ and $\mathbf{l}_2$. In fact there are cases for which this is not true, and to which the above treatment is not applicable. We shall attempt to make this clear by means of a simple example.

Let us consider one electron in a *p* orbit and the other in an *s* orbit; and let the *p* electron be strongly bound, with a small principal quantum number *n*, and the *s* electron loosely bound, with *n* large, so that for much of the time it is far removed from the rest of the atom. In this case it is possible, but not necessary, that the interaction between the two spins be smaller than that between the spin of the first electron and its orbit. The magnitude of the interaction between the first electron and its orbit can be seen from the doublet separation obtained when only this electron is present. The apparent interaction between $\mathbf{s}_1$ and $\mathbf{s}_2$ evidences itself in the separation between singlets and triplets when both electrons are present. Now this separation decreases very rapidly as the principal quantum number *n* of either of the two electrons increases. In this way it can come about that the singlet-triplet separation can be smaller than the doublet separation for the first electron alone. There will then occur a different coupling of the quantum vectors.

If the inner electron were in an *s* orbit and the outer in a *p* orbit this would not occur; for with increasing *n* of the *p* electron the interaction energy between $\mathbf{s}_2$ and $\mathbf{l}_2$ as well as that between $\mathbf{s}_1$ and $\mathbf{s}_2$ would decrease, in both cases as a first approximation proportionally to $1/n^3$. This case occurs for the alkaline earths, for example, for in these excited atoms the inner of the two valence electrons usually remains in its normal *s* orbit. These spectra accordingly show nearly exclusively singlet and triplet structure.

The atoms of the fourth group of the periodic system, carbon, silicon, germanium, tin, and lead, have four valence electrons. In most states two of these are in *s* orbits, and together form a completed subgroup (Chap. IX), and hence, as will be shown later, need not be taken into consideration. For all of these states the atoms have effectively two external electrons, and are similar to the alkaline earths. Of these two electrons the inner one in excited states remains usually in the lowest *p* orbit; as a result of this there occur in addition to the ordinary singlet and triplet levels also others, whose structure will now be considered more closely.

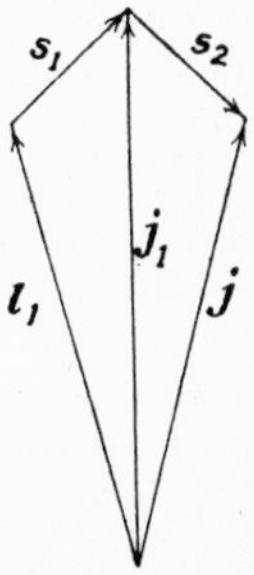

FIG. 33.—Coupling of one *s* electron and one other electron according to the scheme $\{(\mathbf{s}_1\mathbf{l}_1)\mathbf{s}_2\} = (\mathbf{j}_1\mathbf{s}_2) = \mathbf{j}$.

Whenever the energy of interaction between the second electron and the first is smaller than that between the first electron spin and its own orbit, the action exerted by the second electron on the first is similar to that of a weak external magnetic field. (It was mentioned in Section 21*b* that the preceding case was similar to that of a strong external magnetic field; that is, to the Paschen-Back effect.) The coupling between $\mathbf{s}_1$ and $\mathbf{l}_1$ will not be broken; instead they will form a resultant $\mathbf{j}_1$, as though the second electron were not present. Now if the second electron is in an *s* orbit, the total moment $\mathbf{j}$ of the atom will be a vector formed as the resultant of $\mathbf{j}_1$ and $\mathbf{s}_2$, as shown in Figure 33. Symbolically, this coupling may be written[1]

$$\{(\mathbf{s}_1\mathbf{l}_1)\mathbf{s}_2\} = (\mathbf{j}_1\mathbf{s}_2) = \mathbf{j}.$$

In these symbols brackets always include the vectors which form a resultant with each other. The other coupling described in Section 21*b* may be written

$$\{(\mathbf{s}_1\mathbf{s}_2)\mathbf{l}_1\} = (\mathbf{s}\mathbf{l}_1) = \mathbf{j}.$$

The vectors which form a resultant always carry out precessional motion about this resultant. The coupling scheme accordingly indicates that vectors in the innermost brackets undergo the most rapid precession about each other, since otherwise the coupling would be broken through the influence of the other precessions.

The relative positions of the energy levels can also be given for the coupling

$$\{(\mathbf{s}_1\mathbf{l}_1)\mathbf{s}_2\} = (\mathbf{j}_1\mathbf{s}_2) = \mathbf{j}.$$

If the second electron were not present, there would be only the doublet level of the first electron, with the state $j_1 = l_1 + s_1$

[1] S. GOUDSMIT and G. E. UHLENBECK, *Z. f. Phys.*, **35**: 618, 1925.

lying above, that with $j_1 = l_1 - s_1$ lying below. The spin vector of the second electron can assume two orientations with respect to the moment $\mathbf{j}_1$ of the first, corresponding to the values $j = j_1 + \frac{1}{2}$ and $j = j_1 - \frac{1}{2}$ for the total moment of the whole atom. Each of the two levels of the doublet due to the first electron is split by the addition of the second into two levels. Since we have assumed the effect of the second electron on the first to be smaller than that of the first on its own orbit the separations introduced will be smaller than the original doublet separation. We thus obtain four levels consisting not of a singlet and a triplet but of two double levels. (The name doublets

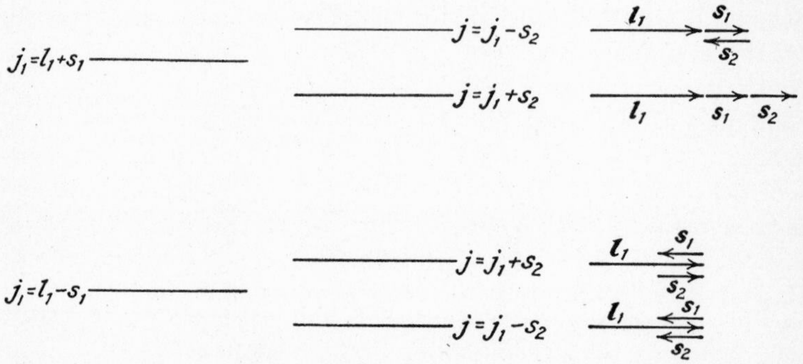

FIG. 34.—Energy level diagram for one s electron and one other electron according to scheme B. In the vector diagrams the vector magnitudes are taken to be l_1, s_1, s_2, etc. Figure 33 gives the vector diagram for the highest level with the alternative choice of vector magnitudes.

is not used for such double levels; it is reserved for the case with normal coupling when the resultant s is $\frac{1}{2}$.) It is possible to predict which of each of these doubled levels lies the higher. The interaction energy between the two electrons consists essentially of the energy of the resonance phenomenon described before, which is an apparent interaction of the two spins $\mathbf{s}_1$ and $\mathbf{s}_2$. For this apparent interaction it was stated that the energy is small when the angle between $\mathbf{s}_1$ and $\mathbf{s}_2$ is small. It is easily seen that, with $j_1 = l_1 + \frac{1}{2}$, $\mathbf{s}_1$ is parallel to $\mathbf{s}_2$ for $j = j_1 + s_2$, and opposed for $j = j_1 - s_2$; hence the former gives the lower level. For the other doublet state, with $j_1 = l_1 - \frac{1}{2}$, the reverse is true. These results are shown in Figure 34.

So far we have considered only a simple case, with the second electron in an s orbit. In the general case there are many possible couplings. That previously considered may be written symbolically as

A: $$\{(\mathbf{s}_1\mathbf{s}_2)(\mathbf{l}_1\mathbf{l}_2)\} = (\mathbf{sl}) = \mathbf{j}.$$

This coupling scheme *A* is called, after its discoverers, the scheme of Russell and Saunders.[1]

If the coupling between the spin and the orbital motion of the first electron is not broken by the addition of the second, the following coupling schemes can occur:

B: $$\{(\mathbf{s}_1\mathbf{l}_1)(\mathbf{s}_2\mathbf{l}_2)\} = (\mathbf{j}_1\mathbf{j}_2) = \mathbf{j}.$$
C: $$[\{(\mathbf{s}_1\mathbf{l}_1)s_2\}\mathbf{l}_2] = \{(\mathbf{j}_1\mathbf{s}_2)\mathbf{l}_2\} = \mathbf{j}.$$
D: $$[\{(\mathbf{s}_1\mathbf{l}_1)\mathbf{l}_2\}\mathbf{s}_2] = \{(\mathbf{j}_1\mathbf{l}_2)\mathbf{s}_2\} = \mathbf{j}.$$

Scheme *B* signifies that coupling between spin and orbit persists for the second electron also. In scheme *C* it is broken and there is a strong compling of $\mathbf{s}_2$ with j_1 to form a resultant which then combines with $\mathbf{l}_2$ to form the total moment $\mathbf{j}$. Scheme *D* is similar, with $\mathbf{l}_2$ and $\mathbf{s}_2$ interchanged. Whether all of these schemes actually occur has not been determined; there are some indications that only *A* and *B* occur, but in this respect nothing is known with certainty. For the case $l_2 = 0$ the schemes *B*, *C*, and *D* coincide to give the previously considered scheme

$$\{(\mathbf{s}_1\mathbf{l}_1)\mathbf{s}_2\} = (\mathbf{j}_1\mathbf{s}_2) = \mathbf{j}.$$

It is to be particularly emphasized that these schemes represent merely limiting cases. Just as in the Zeeman effect the theory for weak and for strong magnetic fields represents the limiting cases and in reality all intermediate stages occur, so here also it is to be expected that intermediate cases will arise for which none of these schemes is rigorously valid.

The relative positions of the levels in the general case can not be treated in complete detail. It is to be expected for schemes *B*, *C*, and *D* that the levels will form two groups with approximately the doublet separation of the first electron; for it is assumed in these cases that this doublet separation, which is a measure of the strength of the coupling $(\mathbf{l}_1\mathbf{s}_1)$, is greater than the other interaction energies, which cause the further splitting of each of the doublet levels.

We have already shown that for scheme *A* the terms are always singlets and triplets.

[1] H. N. Russell and F. A. Saunders, *Astrophys. Jour.*, **61**: 38, 1925.

CHAPTER VII

THE VECTOR MODEL FOR MANY-ELECTRON ATOMS

25. THE COUPLING SCHEME OF RUSSELL AND SAUNDERS. MULTIPLETS

An atom containing many electrons outside of completed groups or subgroups may be represented by means of an orbital moment vector $\mathbf{l}_i$ and a spin moment vector $\mathbf{s}_i$ for each electron and the resultant vectors formed from them. As in the case of two electrons, the coupling among these vectors may be of several kinds. The scheme used in the previous section can be easily extended; using the same nomenclature, scheme A may be written

$$A: \qquad \{(\mathbf{s}_1\mathbf{s}_2\mathbf{s}_3 \cdots)(\mathbf{l}_1\mathbf{l}_2\mathbf{l}_3 \cdots)\} = (\mathbf{sl}) = \mathbf{j}.$$

This signifies that the $\mathbf{s}_i$'s all combine to form a resultant $\mathbf{s}$ and independently the $\mathbf{l}_i$'s form a resultant $\mathbf{l}$. The vectors $\mathbf{s}$ and $\mathbf{l}$ then form the total moment $\mathbf{j}$.

In scheme B the spin moment of each electron is still coupled with its orbital motion and this coupling is not broken by interaction with the other electrons:

$$B: \qquad \{(\mathbf{s}_1\mathbf{l}_1)(\mathbf{s}_2\mathbf{l}_2)(\mathbf{s}_3\mathbf{l}_3) \cdots\} = (\mathbf{j}_1\mathbf{j}_2\mathbf{j}_3 \cdots) = \mathbf{j}.$$

Each electron thus has its own resultant $\mathbf{j}_i$ and all the $\mathbf{j}_i$'s combine to form the total resultant $\mathbf{j}$. Coupling according to this scheme is generally called "(jj) coupling."

Besides these two simple schemes a large number of other coupling possibilities among all these vectors can be imagined, analogous to schemes C and D for the case of two electrons, and to various other combinations.

If the value of l_i is given for each electron (s_i is one-half for each electron), then each of these schemes leads to precisely the same number of different energy levels. The values of j for these states are also always the same, independent of the coupling scheme. This can be easily shown in the not too complicated cases; but a general proof can not be simply given.[1] Hund[2]

[1] The theorem is proved by R. DE L. KRONIG, *Proc.*, Nat. Acad., **12**: 330, 1926, and K. KNOPP, *Z. f. Phys.*, **41**: 20, 1927.

[2] F. HUND, *Z. f. Phys.*, **34**: 296, 1925; **52**: 601, 1929.

especially has investigated the question of which state of one scheme a given state from another scheme is transformed into when the coupling is changed. This problem is analogous to that of the transition from strong to weak fields in the Zeeman effect.

Of these schemes that of Russell and Saunders, scheme A, occurs most often in spectra.[1] When it does not occur there is usually found an intermediate step between scheme A and another scheme; there are rather few cases known for which another scheme is rigorously valid.

In the case of alkali-like atoms, with a single valence electron, s was given a value $\frac{1}{2}$. The resultant s for two-electron atoms was either 1 or 0. In general s can have the values obtained by giving each spin vector either parallel on antiparallel orientation with respect to the resultant; that is, $s = \sum_i \pm s_i$. For three electrons, for example, $s = \frac{1}{2}$ or $\frac{3}{2}$, for four, $s = 0, 1$, or 2, etc. A state with $s = 2$ is called a quintet state, since if l is large enough ($l \geqq 2$) the total resultant j can assume five different values:

$$|l - s| \leq j \leq l + s.$$

The possible terms of an atom with $s = 2$ and with $l = 0, 1, 2, \cdots$, are given in Table I. If l is smaller than s the composition of the two vectors leads to less than five states, but the term is still called a quintet term. The names singlet, doublet, triplet, quartet, etc., give accordingly not always the actual complexity of the state, but rather the multiplicity, the value of the resultant s. The multiplicity is always taken equal to $2s + 1$. The possible terms for various multiplets are indicated in Table II.

TABLE I.—QUINTET TERMS

	$j = 0$	1	2	3	4	5	6
$l = 0$.	. . . . .	. . . .	$^5S_2$				
1.	. . . . .	$^5P_1$	$^5P_2$	$^5P_3$			
2.	$^5D_0$	$^5D_1$	$^5D_2$	$^5D_3$	$^5D_4$		
3.	. . . . .	$^5F_1$	$^5F_2$	$^5F_3$	$^5F_4$	$^5F_5$	
4.	. . . . .	. . . .	$^5G_2$	$^5G_3$	$^5G_4$	$^5G_5$	$^5G_6$

[1] Very probably this is only apparent, resulting from the fact that spectra for which this scheme is valid are most easily analyzed.

TABLE II.—MULTIPLET STATES

State	Values of j	Values of j
	Singlets $s = 0$	Doublets $s = 1/2$
$l = 0$ S	0	1/2
1 P	1	1/2 3/2
2 D	2	3/2 5/2
3 F	3	5/2 7/2
4 G	4	7/2 9/2
	Triplets $s = 1$	Quartets $s = 3/2$
$l = 0$ S	1	3/2
1 P	0 1 2	1/2 3/2 5/2
2 D	1 2 3	1/2 3/2 5/2 7/2
3 F	2 3 4	3/2 5/2 7/2 9/2
4 G	3 4 5	5/2 7/2 9/2 11/2
	Quintets $s = 2$	Sextets $s = 5/2$
$l = 0$ S	2	5/2
1 P	1 2 3	3/2 5/2 7/2
2 D	0 1 2 3 4	1/2 3/2 5/2 7/2 9/2
3 F	1 2 3 4 5	1/2 3/2 5/2 7/2 9/2 11/2
4 G	2 3 4 5 6	3/2 5/2 7/2 9/2 11/2 13/2
	Septets $s = 3$	Octets $s = 7/2$
$l = 0$ S	3	7/2
1 P	2 3 4	5/2 7/2 9/2
2 D	1 2 3 4 5	3/2 5/2 7/2 9/2 11/2
3 F	0 1 2 3 4 5 6	1/2 3/2 5/2 7/2 9/2 11/2 13/2
4 G	1 2 3 4 5 6 7	1/2 3/2 5/2 7/2 9/2 11/2 13/2 15/2

As a result of transitions from one multiplet state to another a line complex called a "multiplet" is produced.[1] The number of components in a multiplet is determined by the selection rules for j (Sec. 33), which state that j may change by 0 or ± 1, and that the jump from $j = 0$ to $j = 0$ is not allowed. It will be seen from Table II that the multiplet $^4P - {}^4D$, for example, will have eight components, and $^4D - {}^4F$ nine components.

For an atom or ion containing an even number of electrons the resultant s is always integral, and for one with an odd number

[1] Before 1922 only singlet, doublet, and triplet spectra were known. At this time M. A. CATALÁN discovered the existence of higher multiplicities (*Phil. Trans.*, A **223**: 127, 1922), and SOMMERFELD soon after (*Ann. d. Phys.*, **70**: 32, 1923) applied the vector model in the interpretation of CATALÁN's observations.

of electrons s is "half-integral." Accordingly, successive neutral atoms in the periodic system of the elements will show alternately even and odd multiplicities. This is illustrated in Table III, in which are shown the observed multiplicities of the atoms from potassium to manganese. Similarly, successive degrees

TABLE III.—ALTERNATION IN EVEN AND ODD MULTIPLICITIES

Atom. . . . . Atomic Number Z.	K 19	Ca 20	Sc 21	Ti 22	V 23	Cr 24	Mn 25
Multiplicities	Doublets	Singlets Triplets	Doublets Quartets	Singlets Triplets Quintets	Doublets Quartets Sextets	Triplets Quintets Septets	Quartets Sextets Octets

of ionization of an atom will lead to alternation between even and odd multiplicities. In Table IV are given the multiplicities observed for various ions of chlorine, in substantiation of this conclusion.

TABLE IV.—ALTERNATION IN EVEN AND ODD MULTIPLICITIES

Ion. . . . . Electron number. .	Cl^{+6}(Cl VII) 11	Cl^{+5}(Cl VI) 12	Cl^{+4}(Cl V) 13	Cl^{+3}(Cl IV) 14	Cl^{+2}(Cl III) 15	Cl^{+1}(Cl II) 16
Multiplicities	Doublets	Singlets Triplets	Doublets Quartets	Singlets Triplets	Doublets Quartets	Singlets Triplets

In calculating the possible multiplicities in any spectrum it is necessary to consider only the electrons not composing a completed subgroup, usually only the external or valence electrons. The reason for this will be given in Chap. IX, where this subject will be further treated.

26. COUPLING OF THE ATOM CORE AND THE EMITTING ELECTRON

Often the spectra of many-electron atoms can be discussed without treating the individual electrons in complete detail. If only one electron changes its quantum numbers during a quantum transition, it may suffice to consider interaction of the quantum vectors of this electron (the "emitting electron") and the resultant quantum vectors formed from all the other electrons in the atom (the "atom core"). Then the discussion given in the previous chapter for two electron atoms may be applied directly, the quantum vectors $\mathbf{l}_1$, $\mathbf{s}_1$, and $\mathbf{j}_1$ being interpreted not as the angular momentum vectors of a single electron but as the resultants for all the electrons in the atom core. The restriction of s_1 to the value $\frac{1}{2}$ is then no longer valid.

The same couplings are possible between the outermost electron and the atom core as between two electrons. Values of the Landé g-factor and multiplet separations can be calculated by the same methods.

It is evident that this picture cannot be used when the interaction between the atom core and the added electron is so great as to change the coupling scheme of the core.

27. THE ZEEMAN EFFECT FOR MANY-ELECTRON ATOMS. VALUES OF THE LANDÉ g-FACTOR

In the treatment of the different coupling schemes the usefulness of the vector model has been clearly seen. It would have been very difficult to have presented these considerations with the aid only of the orbital representation. In all of the vector schemes there was a total mechanical moment $\mathbf{j}$, composed of two or more vectors which precess about it. Each of these vectors was in general also the resultant of other vectors which similarly precess about it. The precession about $\mathbf{j}$ was slower than those about the component resultants.

The application of an external magnetic field has certain analogies with the introduction of a new quantum vector. If the external field is weak the whole vector system carries out a common Larmor precession about the field direction; that is, the total vector $\mathbf{j}$ no longer retains a fixed direction in space, but precesses about the field. The field is called weak if this precession is slower than that of the component vectors about $\mathbf{j}$, since, just as in the case of a single electron, the coupling between these vectors would be broken as soon as the precession about the field became of the same magnitude as that of the vectors about each other. The velocity and the energy of this Larmor precession are dependent on the ratio of the magnetic moment to the mechanical moment of the whole atom. We shall now give some general rules for the calculation of this ratio, which we shall designate here also (as for one-electron atoms) by the letter g or by $g(j)$.

Let us consider the total mechanical moment as built up of a number of moments $\mathbf{x}_i$, which arise in part from the orbital motion and in part from the spins of the electron (a moment $\mathbf{x}_i$ may itself arise as the resultant of orbital motion and spin). The magnetic moment of each of these vectors may be written $\mathbf{x}_i g_i$, in which g_i is the Landé factor giving the ratio of magnetic to mechanical moment when these are expressed in the customary units $h/2\pi \cdot e/2m_0c$ and $h/2\pi$, respectively. For the magnitude of the total magnetic moment of the atom we have then

$$jg(j) = \sum_i x_i g_i \overline{\cos(\mathbf{x}_i\mathbf{j})}$$

or

$$g(j) = \sum_i \frac{x_i}{j} g_i \overline{\cos(\mathbf{x}_i\mathbf{j})}. \tag{1}$$

The significance of this equation is evident; each vector $\mathbf{x}_i$ has an average component in the direction of $\mathbf{j}$ and so has each magnetic moment $\mathbf{x}_i g_i$. Only the component of magnetic moment along $\mathbf{j}$ is observed experimentally, since the component normal to $\mathbf{j}$ averages to zero during the precessional motion about $\mathbf{j}$. This is, of course, true only when the precession about $\mathbf{j}$ is to be considered fast; that is, not for a "strong" external magnetic field.

We can now express $g(j)$ in terms of the quantum numbers concerned with the use of this equation. We assume the $\mathbf{x}_i$'s to be the orbital moments $\mathbf{l}_i$ and the spin moments $\mathbf{s}_i$. For the former we know $g(l_i)$ to be 1, and for the spins we assumed $g(s_i) = 2$. Equation 1 then becomes

$$g(j) = \sum_i \frac{l_i}{j} \overline{\cos(\mathbf{l}_i\mathbf{j})} + 2\sum_i \frac{s_i}{j} \overline{\cos(\mathbf{s}_i\mathbf{j})}. \tag{2}$$

The total moment $\mathbf{j}$ is the sum of the projections of all the moments in the direction of $\mathbf{j}$:

$$j = \sum_i l_i \overline{\cos(\mathbf{l}_i\mathbf{j})} + \sum_i s_i \overline{\cos(\mathbf{s}_i\mathbf{j})}$$

or

$$1 = \sum_i \frac{l_i}{j} \overline{\cos(\mathbf{l}_i \mathbf{j})} + \sum_i \frac{s_i}{j} \overline{\cos(\mathbf{s}_i \mathbf{j})}. \qquad (3)$$

With the preceding equation this gives

$$g(j) = 1 + \sum_i \frac{s_i}{j} \overline{\cos(\mathbf{s}_i \mathbf{j})} = 2 - \sum_i \frac{l_i}{j} \overline{\cos(\mathbf{l}_i \mathbf{j})}. \qquad (4)$$

It is easily verified that for a single electron this reduces to Equation 2, Section 17.

If the coupling scheme of Russell and Saunders is strictly valid it is possible to calculate the values of $g(j)$ exactly. All the $\mathbf{s}_i$'s precess in this case about a resultant **s**, which itself precesses about **j**. It is easily seen[1] that then the average projection of $\mathbf{s}_i$ on **j** is equal to its average projection on **s** times the cosine of the angle between **s** and **j**. The same is true for $\mathbf{l}_i$ and **l**. Thus one obtains

$$g(j) = 1 + \sum_i \frac{s_i}{j} \overline{\cos(\mathbf{s}_i \mathbf{s})} \cos(\mathbf{sj}) = 2 - \sum_i \frac{l_i}{j} \overline{\cos(\mathbf{l}_i \mathbf{l})} \cos(\mathbf{lj}).$$

Now we have also

$$s = \sum_i s_i \overline{\cos(\mathbf{s}_i \mathbf{s})} \text{ and } l = \sum_i l_i \overline{\cos(\mathbf{l}_i \mathbf{l})}$$

so that

$$g(j) = 1 + \frac{s}{j} \cos(\mathbf{sj}) = 2 - \frac{l}{j} \cos(\mathbf{lj}). \qquad (5)$$

This equation is nearly the same as that for a single electron; it contains in place of s and l for the single electron the resultant s and l for *all* spins and *all* orbits. If l and s are known this equation can be used to calculate values of $g(j)$, or, conversely, observed values of $g(j)$ can be used to deduce those of l and s.

Using the quantum mechanics values of the cosines, Equation 5 may be rewritten (as in Sec. 17*a*)

$$g(j) = \frac{3j(j+1) + s(s+1) - l(l+1)}{2j(j+1)}. \qquad (6)$$

[1] The average value of the cosine between two vectors **a** and **c** such that **a** rotates uniformly about a vector **b** which in turn rotates uniformly about **c** is found on evaluation to be cos (**ab**) cos (**bc**).

TABLE V.—THE LANDÉ g-FACTOR FOR RUSSELL-SAUNDERS COUPLING

Singlets, $s = 0$

$j =$	0	1	2	3	4	5
^1S $l = 0$	0/0					
^1P 1	..	1				
^1D 2	..	..	1			
^1F 3	..	..	..	1		
^1G 4	..	..	..	..	1	
^1H 5	..	..	..	..	..	1

Doublets, $s = 1/2$

$j =$	1/2	3/2	5/2	7/2	9/2	11/2
^2S $l = 0$	2					
^2P 1	2/3	4/3				
^2D 2	..	4/5	6/5			
^2F 3	..	..	6/7	8/7		
^2G 4	..	..	..	8/9	10/9	
^2H 5	..	..	..	..	10/11	12/11

Triplets, $s = 1$

$j =$	0	1	2	3	4	5	6
^3S $l = 0$	..	2					
^3P 1	0/0	3/2	3/2				
^3D 2	..	1/2	7/6	4/3			
^3F 3	..	..	2/3	13/12	5/4		
^3G 4	..	..	..	3/4	21/20	6/5	
^3H 5	..	..	..	....	4/5	31/30	7/6

Quartets, $s = 3/2$

$j =$	1/2	3/2	5/2	7/2	9/2	11/2	13/2
^4S $l = 0$	..	2					
^4P 1	8/3	26/15	8/5				
^4D 2	0	6/5	48/35	10/7			
^4F 3	..	2/5	36/35	26/21	4/3		
^4G 4	..	....	4/7	62/63	116/99	14/11	
^4H 5	..	....	....	2/3	32/33	162/143	16/13

TABLE V.—(*Continued*)

Quintets, $s = 2$

$j =$	0	1	2	3	4	5	6	7
^5S $l = 0$	..	..	2					
^5P 1	..	5/2	11/6	5/3				
^5D 2	0/0	3/2	3/2	3/2	3/2			
^5F 3	..	0	1	5/4	27/20	7/5		
^5G 4	..	..	1/3	11/12	23/20	19/15	4/3	
^5H 5	..	..	...	1/2	9/10	11/10	17/14	9/7

Sextets, $s = 5/2$

$j =$	1/2	3/2	5/2	7/2	9/2	11/2	13/2	15/2
^6S $l = 0$	....	....	2					
^6P 1	....	12/5	66/35	12/7				
^6D 2	10/3	28/15	58/35	100/63	14/9			
^6F 3	−2/3	16/15	46/35	88/63	142/99	16/11		
^6G 4	....	0	6/7	8/7	14/11	192/143	18/13	
^6H 5	....	....	2/7	52/63	106/99	172/143	50/39	4/3

Septets, $s = 3$

$j =$	0	1	2	3	4	5	6	7	8
^7S $l = 0$	..	....	..	2					
^7P 1	..	....	7/3	23/12	7/4				
^7D 2	..	3	2	7/4	33/20	8/5			
^7F 3	0/0	3/2	3/2	3/2	3/2	3/2	3/2		
^7G 4	..	−1/2	5/6	7/6	13/10	41/30	59/42	10/7	
^7H 5	..	....	0	3/4	21/20	6/5	9/7	75/56	11/8

Octets, $s = 7/2$

$j =$	1/2	3/2	5/2	7/2	9/2	11/2	13/2	15/2	17/2
^8S $l = 0$	....	....	....	2					
^8P 1	....	....	16/7	122/63	16/9				
^8D 2	....	14/5	72/35	38/21	56/33	18/11			
^8F 3	4	2	12/7	34/21	52/33	222/143	20/13		
^8G 4	−4/3	14/15	44/35	86/63	140/99	206/143	284/195	22/15	
^8H 5	....	−2/5	24/35	22/21	40/33	186/143	88/65	118/85	24/17

Values of g calculated in this way for a number of multiplet levels are given in Table V[1].

As in the case of alkali-like atoms, discussed in Chap. V, the individual components of the Zeeman pattern of a level are indi-

[1] An extensive tabulation of the theoretical Zeeman effects for possible term combinations has been published by C. C. KIESS and W. F. MEGGERS, *Bureau of Standards Jour. of Res.*, **1**: 641, 1928.

cated by the magnetic quantum number m, which assumes the values $0, \pm 1, \pm 2, \cdots \pm j$ for j integral (multiplets of odd multiplicity), or $\pm 1/2, \pm 3/2, \cdots \pm j$ for j half-integral (multiplets of even multiplicity). The *a priori* probability or quantum weight of a state is hence in each case equal to $2j + 1$.

For the other coupling schemes it is not possible to derive a generally valid formula for g; usually it is not known what the values of the cosines are. The cosines are always known when only two vectors combine to form a resultant, as, for example, when there are only two electrons. Thus let us consider scheme B, the $(\mathbf{jj})$ coupling:

$$B: \qquad \{(\mathbf{s}_1\mathbf{l}_1)(\mathbf{s}_2\mathbf{l}_2)\} = (\mathbf{j}_1\mathbf{j}_2) = \mathbf{j}.$$

Here it is seen at once that the average projection of $\mathbf{s}_1$ on $\mathbf{j}$ is equal to its projection on $\mathbf{j}_1$ times the cosine of the angle between $\mathbf{j}_1$ and $\mathbf{j}$, so that the g-formula is

$$g(j) = 2\frac{s_1}{j}\cos(\mathbf{s}_1\mathbf{j}_1)\cos(\mathbf{j}_1\mathbf{j}) + 2\frac{s_2}{j}\cos(\mathbf{s}_2\mathbf{j}_2)\cos(\mathbf{j}_2\mathbf{j}) + \frac{l_1}{j}\cos(\mathbf{l}_1\mathbf{j}_1)\cos(\mathbf{j}_1\mathbf{j}) + \frac{l_2}{j}\cos(\mathbf{l}_2\mathbf{j}_2)\cos(\mathbf{j}_2\mathbf{j}).$$

These terms can be combined:

$$g(j) = \frac{j_1}{j}g(j_1)\cos(\mathbf{j}_1\mathbf{j}) + \frac{j_2}{j}g(j_2)\cos(\mathbf{j}_2\mathbf{j}) \qquad (7a)$$

or

$$g(j) = g(j_1)\frac{j(j+1) + j_1(j_1+1) - j_2(j_2+1)}{2j(j+1)} + g(j_2)\frac{j(j+1) + j_2(j_2+1) - j_1(j_1+1)}{2j(j+1)}, \qquad (7b)$$

in which $g(j_1)$ and $g(j_2)$, the g-values for the first and the second electron alone, respectively, can be calculated from the g-formula for a single electron.

Equation 7 is also applicable to a many-electron atom in which the coupling between the emitting electron and the atom core is that of scheme B. The g-values for the entire atom can be calculated if that of the core is known; conversely, that of the core can be obtained from experimental Zeeman-effect measurements giving the g values for the entire atom.

27a. The g-sum Rule.—The numbers g have a property which is of great usefulness in the interpretation of spectra. We have seen that, for a given set of l_i's, different coupling schemes lead to different sets of values of $g(j)$. However, the sum of the $g(j)$'s for all states with the same value of j is independent of the coupling scheme.[1] This *sum rule for g-values* holds even when none of the coupling schemes is strictly applicable. If one of the schemes holds, it is usually possible to deduce from the values of g and j found experimentally from Zeeman-effect measurements something about the quantum vectors. If no scheme holds rigorously, this is not so easy; but it is still possible to use the sum rule to help find how the observed states are related to the electron configurations and the quantum numbers.

Thus if there are two electrons, one in a p and one in a d orbit, then j can have a large number of values as the resultant of $l_1 = 1$, $l_2 = 2$, $s_1 = 1/2$, and $s_2 = 1/2$. The values of g for these states are given in Table VI both for Russell-Saunders and (jj) coupling.

TABLE VI.—LANDÉ g-VALUES FOR A pd CONFIGURATION

		$j = 4$	3	2	1	0	
^3F		5/4	13/12	2/3	....	..	Russell-Saunders Coupling
^3D		..	4/3	7/6	1/2	..	
^3P		..	......	3/2	3/2	0/0	
^1F		..	1	....	....	..	
^1D		..	......	1	....	..	
^1P		..	......	....	1	..	
Σg		5/4	41/12	13/3	3	0/0	
$j_1 = 3/2$	$j_2 = 5/2$	5/4	223/180	109/90	11/10	..	(jj) Coupling
$j_1 = 3/2$	$j_2 = 3/2$	..	16/15	16/15	16/15	0/0	
$j_1 = 1/2$	$j_2 = 5/2$	..	10/9	58/45	....	..	
$j_1 = 1/2$	$j_2 = 3/2$	..	......	23/30	5/6	..	

It follows from the sum rule that the j-values which occur only once (0 and 4) must retain their values of g for all couplings of the quantum vectors; the other predictions of the sum rule are also seen to be satisfied in this special case. The g-values for the ps configuration given in Table X, Section 29, provide an example of the application of the g-sum rule with an intermediate coupling.

28. THE PASCHEN-BACK EFFECT FOR MANY-ELECTRON ATOMS

In an external magnetic field so strong that the Larmor precession of **j** about the magnetic field **H** is faster than that of the component vectors about **j** itself the coupling will be

[1] W. PAULI, *Z. f. Phys.*, **16**: 155, 1923.

broken. Just as for a single electron (Sec. 26), **j** then looses all significance. The vectors which in the absence of the field united to form **j** now carry on independent Larmor precessions about **H**. With Russell-Saunders coupling in such a strong field m_s does not change during a transition, just as in the case of a single electron (Chap. VIII). The sole difference between many-electron atoms and a single electron is that m_s is not restricted to the values $+\frac{1}{2}$ and $-\frac{1}{2}$, but can assume the values $0, \pm 1, \pm 2 \ldots \pm s$ for s integral, or $\pm\frac{1}{2}, \pm\frac{3}{2}, \ldots \pm s$ for s half-integral.

28a. Transition from a Weak to a Strong Field.—Equations for calculating the energy levels for every field strength have been given by C. G. Darwin.[1] Formerly these were known only for doublets.[2] Darwin's derivation is based upon the quantum mechanics; only his results can be discussed here.

Consider the equation

$$
\begin{aligned}
-X_{m_l - 1,\, m_s + 1}\,\frac{A}{2}(l - m_l + 1)(s + m_s + 1) \\
+X_{m_l, m_s}\{E - Am_lm_s - (m_l + 2m_s)\omega\} \\
-X_{m_l + 1,\, m_s - 1,}\,\frac{A}{2}(l + m_l + 1)(s - m_s + 1) = 0. \quad (8)
\end{aligned}
$$

Here A is similar to the constant $a_1 + a_2$ in Equation 7, Chap. VI, and ω, the Lorentz unit $\frac{h}{2\pi}\frac{e}{2m_0c}\cdot H$, contains the field strength. $X_{m_l - 1,\, m_s + 1}$ and the other X's are variables. Now write for a given value of $m = m_s + m_l$ all the equations possible (a finite number, since $|m_s| \leqq s$ and $|m_l| \leqq l$). The determinant of this set of equations is to be equated to zero, and solved for E. The resultant values of E give the energy of the system; the largest value corresponds to the largest value of j, and so on in order (if A is negative, this is reversed).

In this way there is obtained for every value of m a set of equations, and it is possible to follow the energy levels completely from a weak to a strong field. It is not hard to show that when ω is much larger than A these equations lead simply to the equation of the Paschen-Back effect (Equation 11, Chap. V),

[1] C. G. Darwin, *Proc.*, Roy. Soc. A **115**: 1, 1927; see also W. Heisenberg and P. Jordan, *Z. f. Phys.*, **37**: 263, 1926.

[2] A. Sommerfeld, *Z. f. Phys.*, **8**: 257, 1922.

and when ω is much smaller than A to the equations for a weak field. The values of the X's obtained from these equations are needed for the calculation of intensities.

These calculations have been carried out numerically[1] for three cases, for $S - P$ doublets, $S - P$ triplets, and $P - D$ doublets.

The equations given by Darwin also show that in the general case of a many-electron atom the same rules for the transition of states from a weak to a strong field hold as were given in Section 19 for doublet spectra; for it is found that the different roots of Darwin's equation (Eq. 8), corresponding to a given value of $m = m_l + m_s$, do not cross as the parameter ω is changed.

It is also possible to think of a field so strong as to break not only the coupling between the component vectors which formed the resultant **j** but also that between the vectors which formed these component vectors themselves. Finally, the field could become strong enough to cause the spin and the orbital moment of each electron to carry out independent Larmor precession. This can be written symbolically

$$(\mathbf{s}_1\mathbf{H})(\mathbf{s}_2\mathbf{H}) \cdots (\mathbf{l}_1\mathbf{H})(\mathbf{l}_2\mathbf{H}) \cdots$$

28b. The *g*-permanence Rule and the *g*-sum Rule.—Pauli[2] has studied the relations which exist between the magnetic energies of a multiplet level in a weak and a very strong field. For this purpose it is desirable to introduce a new g-factor, g_{strong}, which is equal to the ratio of the total projection of the magnetic moments in the field direction to the total projection of the mechanical moments for an atom in a field strong enough to give a complete Paschen-Back effect.

The total projection of the magnetic moments in Bohr magnetons is $m_l + 2m_s$, while that of the mechanical moments in units $h/2\pi$ is $m = m_l + m_s$. Accordingly,

$$g_{\text{strong}} = \frac{m_l + 2m_s}{m_l + m_s} = 1 + \frac{m_s}{m_l} = 2 - \frac{m_l}{m_s}. \tag{9}$$

Now for a given multiplet level, characterized by its values of l and s, a definite value of m usually occurs several times; for j can in general have several values, each one leading to various values of m. Pauli pointed out that the sum of the values of

[1] K. Darwin, *Proc.*, Roy. Soc., A **118**: 264, 1928.
[2] W. Pauli, *Z. f. Phys.*, **16**: 155, 1923.

g_{strong} corresponding to a given m is equal to the sum of the values of the weak-field Landé g-factor for the same m; that is,

$$\Sigma g_{\text{strong}} = \Sigma g, \text{ for given } m,\ l, \text{ and } s. \tag{10}$$

In the strong field the sum is to be taken over the different sets of m_l and m_s with the same m, and in the weak field over the different j's which have the same projection m.

In Table VII there are given as an example values of g_{strong} and g for a ^3D level, with $l = 2$ and $s = 1$.

TABLE VII.—THE LANDÉ g-FACTOR AND THE STRONG FIELD g-FACTOR FOR A ^3D LEVEL

$m =$	+3	+2	+1	0	−1	−2	−3	
^3D $j = 3$......	4/3	4/3	4/3	4/3	4/3	4/3	4/3	
$j = 2$......	..	7/6	7/6	7/6	7/6	7/6	..	g
$j = 1$......	..	..	1/2	1/2	1/2			
Σg_{strong}	4/3	5/2	3	(3)	3	5/2	4/3	Σg
$m_s = +1$......	4/3	3/2	2	—	0	..	..	
$m_s = 0$......	..	1	1	—	1	1	..	g_{strong}
$m_s = -1$......	..	..	0	—	2	3/2	4/3	

The upper half of the table shows the Landé g-values ordered with respect to j and to m; the m-values in each row are limited by $+j$ and $-j$. The lower half shows the strong field g-values ordered with respect to m_s and m; here the rows are limited by m_l, which can assume only values from $-l$ to $+l$.

From Equation 10 it is possible to deduce several properties of the g-factors, mostly of minor importance. Of most significance is the fact that it permits the derivation of the Landé g-formula from the relatively simple rule determining the strong field g-factor (Equation 9). This treatment does not involve the use of the quantum mechanics corrections, which had to be used in the derivation of Section 17*a*. Thus the g-permanence rule (expressed in Equation 10) introduces these corrections automatically, and it must be connected with the fundamental principles underlying spectral phenomena as given by the quantum mechanics. It can be derived, as a matter of fact, from Darwin's equation of the preceding section; and this derivation shows that it is valid also for intermediate field strengths.

A somewhat similar treatment was later used by Pauli[1] in deriving further properties of the g-values of many-electron atoms. He considered the atom in an exceedingly strong magnetic field, such that all couplings within the atom are broken, and the spin and orbital moments of each electron are oriented relative

TABLE VIII.—VALUES OF $g_{\text{VERY STRONG}}$ FOR A *pd* CONFIGURATION

d: m_{s_2}	m_{l_2}	p: m_{s_1} = $+\frac{1}{2}$ m_{l_1} = $+1$	$+\frac{1}{2}$ 0	$+\frac{1}{2}$ -1	$-\frac{1}{2}$ $+1$	$-\frac{1}{2}$ 0	$-\frac{1}{2}$ -1
$+\frac{1}{2}$	$+2$	4 $\frac{5}{4}$	3 $\frac{4}{3}$	2 $\frac{3}{2}$	3 1	2 1	$1 = m$ $1 = g_{\text{very strong}}$
$+\frac{1}{2}$	$+1$	3 $\frac{4}{3}$	2 $\frac{3}{2}$	1 2	2 1	1 1	0
$+\frac{1}{2}$	0	2 $\frac{3}{2}$	1 2	0	1 1	0	-1 1
$+\frac{1}{2}$	-1	1 2	0	-1 0	0	-1 1	-2 1
$+\frac{1}{2}$	-2	0	-1 0	-2 $\frac{1}{2}$	-1 1	-2 1	-3 1
$-\frac{1}{2}$	$+2$	3 1	2 1	1 1	2 $\frac{1}{2}$	1 0	0 ...
$-\frac{1}{2}$	$+1$	2 1	1 1	0	1 0	0	-1 2
$-\frac{1}{2}$	0	1 1	0	-1 1	0	-1 2	-2 $\frac{3}{2}$
$-\frac{1}{2}$	-1	0	-1 1	-2 1	-1 2	-2 $\frac{3}{2}$	-3 $\frac{4}{3}$
$-\frac{1}{2}$	-2	-1 1	-2 1	-3 1	-2 $\frac{3}{2}$	-3 $\frac{4}{3}$	-4 $\frac{5}{4}$

$$m = m_{s_1} + m_{l_1} + m_{s_2} + m_{l_2}$$

$$g_{\text{very strong}} = \frac{2m_{s_1} + m_{l_1} + 2m_{s_2} + m_{l_2}}{m}$$

[1] W. PAULI, *Z. f. Phys.*, **31**: 765, 1925.

to the field. Pauli stated that even in this case the sum of the g-values for a given total m will retain its value. m is here, of course, equal to the sum of the individual m_{l_i}'s and m_{s_i}'s for all the electrons:

$$m = \sum_i (m_{s_i} + m_{l_i}).$$

The total projection of the magnetic moments is

$$\sum_i (2m_{s_i} + m_{l_i}).$$

TABLE IX.—VALUES OF g AND OF $g_{\text{very strong}}$ FOR A pd CONFIGURATION

$m =$	+4	+3	+2	+1	0	−1	−2	−3	−4	
	5/4	4/3	3/2	1	..	1	1	1	5/4	
		1	1	2	..	0	1/2	4/3		
		4/3	3/2	1	..	1	1	1		
		1	1	2	..	0	3/2	4/3		
			3/2	1	..	1	1			
			1	2	..	2	3/2			$g_{\text{very strong}}$
			1/2	1	..	1	1			
			1	0	..	2	3/2			
				1	..	1				
				0	..	2				
				1	..	1				
Σg	5/4	14/3	9	12	(12)	12	9	14/3	5/4	$\Sigma g_{\text{very strong}}$
$^3F_4$	5/4	5/4	5/4	5/4	5/4	5/4	5/4	5/4	5/4	
$^3F_3$	..	13/12	13/12	13/12	13/12	13/12	13/12	13/12		
$^3D_3$	..	4/3	4/3	4/3	4/3	4/3	4/3	4/3		
$^1F_3$	..	1	1	1	1	1	1	1		
$^3F_2$	..	....	2/3	2/3	2/3	2/3	2/3			
$^3D_2$	..	....	7/6	7/6	7/6	7/6	7/6			g
$^3P_2$	..	....	3/2	3/2	3/2	3/2	3/2			
$^1D_2$	..	....	1	1	1	1	1			
$^3D_1$	..	....	....	1/2	1/2	1/2				
$^3P_1$	..	....	....	3/2	3/2	3/2				
$^1P_1$	..	....	....	1	1	1				
$^3P_0$	..	....	....	....	0/0					

The ratio of these may be called $g_{\text{very strong}}$. In Table VIII its values are assembled for the case of a *pd* configuration.

In the upper half of Table IX the same values are arranged with respect to *m*, as in Table VII. The lower half of this table gives the *g*-values for this configuration in a weak field, with Russell-Saunders coupling, which leads to the levels ^3P, ^3D, ^3F, ^1P, ^1D, and ^1F. The rows in this part of the table have been arranged with respect to the *j*-values of these multiplet levels. Again it is seen that the sums in the *m* columns are the same for the two halves of the table.

It is in general not possible to deduce the *g*-values for a weak field from those for a very strong field with the use of a table of this type. Thus in this case the *g*-value for the $^3F_4$ level is given, but only the sum of the *g*-values for the $^3F_3$, $^3D_3$, and $^1F_3$ levels. Whenever a configuration gives rise to more than one level with the same *j*, only the sum of their weak field *g*-values can be obtained from the strong-field table. This sum is fixed, however; it is the same for all field strengths, and is independent of the coupling of the quantum vectors. This is the *g-sum rule*[1] as it was stated in Section 27.

29. THE ENERGY OF INTERACTION OF THE ORBITAL MAGNETIC MOMENTS AND THE SPIN MAGNETIC MOMENTS FOR MANY ELECTRONS. INTERVAL RULES

Of the various interaction energies among the many quantum vectors in an atom, it is possible to handle simply only that between $\mathbf{l}_i$ and the corresponding $\mathbf{s}_i$. As was discussed in Section 15, the interaction energy of the spin magnetic moment and the orbital motion of an electron is equal to (Equation 6)

$$a_i l_i s_i \overline{\cos (\mathbf{l}_i \mathbf{s}_i)}.$$

A calculation similar to that of Section 15 shows that the interaction energy between the spin magnetic moment of an electron and the spin or the orbital magnetic moment of another electron is as a first approximation proportional to the average third power of the effective nuclear charge, whereas a_i involves its average fourth power with the same proportionality constant.[2]

[1] The *g*-sum rule should not be confused with the *g*-permanence rule described above.

[2] See for example A. LANDÉ, *Z. f. Phys.*, **24**: 88, 1924; *cf.* Sec. 23 also.

In general, then, as a first approximation, these interactions can be neglected.

If energy states differing only in the orientation of the $\mathbf{s}_i$'s with respect to the $\mathbf{l}_i$'s are under discussion, everything is known regarding the energy differences. Considering only the interactions between each orbit and the corresponding spin, the interaction energy is

$$W_s{}^1 = \sum_i a_i s_i l_i \overline{\cos(\mathbf{l}_i \mathbf{s}_i)}. \tag{11}$$

With the coupling scheme of Russell and Saunders this averaged cosine is

$$\overline{\cos(\mathbf{l}_i \mathbf{s}_i)} = \overline{\cos(\mathbf{l}_i \mathbf{l})} \cos(\mathbf{ls}) \overline{\cos(\mathbf{s}_i \mathbf{s})}$$

and the energy is

$$W_s{}^1 = \cos(\mathbf{ls}) \sum_i a_i s_i l_i \overline{\cos(\mathbf{l}_i \mathbf{l})} \overline{\cos(\mathbf{s}_i \mathbf{s})},$$

which can be written, bearing the quantum mechanics value of $\cos(\mathbf{sl})$ in mind, as

$$W_s{}^1 = Asl \cos(\mathbf{sl}) = A \cdot \frac{j(j+1) - l(l+1) - s(s+1)}{2}. \tag{12}$$

This gives the interval rule of Landé: *With s and l given, the energy differences of states with different j are proportional to the differences of j(j + 1).* For example, a ^5D state, with $l = 2$ and $s = 2$, has $j = 4, 3, 2, 1, 0$, and the successive energy differences are proportional to

$$\{4(4 + 1) - 3(3 + 1)\} : \{3(3 + 1) - 2(2 + 1)\} : \{2(2 + 1) - 1(1 + 1)\} : \{1(1 + 1)\}$$

or

$$4 : 3 : 2 : 1.$$

The scheme of Russell and Saunders is differentiated from the other schemes by the fact that it shows great analogy with the case of a single electron. For example, if there are only two valence electrons in the atom and the scheme of Russell and Saunders is valid, the factor A can be calculated very easily, as was shown in Section 22. Thus in the alkali-earth spectrum it was found that when one of the two valence electrons is in an s orbit the total width of the triplet is given by the same equation as that leading to the separation of the alkali doublets. The evaluation of A and the discussion of the magnitudes of multiplet separations will be treated in Section 39.

29a. Fine Structure with Different Coupling Schemes.—As an example of the different coupling schemes there are shown in Figure 35 the lowest P states of silicon, germanium, tin, and lead. Here the first electron is in a p orbit and the second (the outer electron) in an s orbit. For silicon the scheme of Russell and Saunders holds pretty well, although the triplet does not strictly correspond to the interval rule. For lead (jj) coupling is valid. Equation 1 of Chap. VI shows that in the former case the total triplet separation must be equal to the doublet separation for the p electron alone. According to the discussion of Section 24 this is also true for the separation of the double levels for the other couplings. Hence the states with $j = 0$ and $j = 2$ for the different elements are drawn in the figures with the same ordinates.[1]

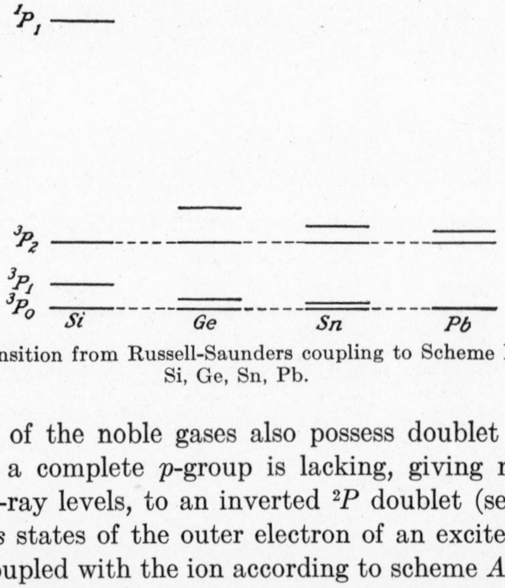

FIG. 35.—Transition from Russell-Saunders coupling to Scheme B in the series Si, Ge, Sn, Pb.

The ions of the noble gases also possess doublet states (one electron of a complete p-group is lacking, giving rise, just as with the X-ray levels, to an inverted ^2P doublet (see Sec. 39)). The lower s states of the outer electron of an excited noble gas atom are coupled with the ion according to scheme A, the higher according to scheme B. As a matter of fact, for neon and argon the triplet separation of the lower s states is nearly exactly equal to the separation of the double levels of the higher terms and hence to the doublet separation of the ion.

[1] S. GOUDSMIT and E. BACK, *Z. f. Phys.*, **40**: 530, 1926.

Following are the observed g-values for the lower s states of neon, tin, and lead, and those calculated from schemes A and B. The gradual transition is striking.

TABLE X.—g-VALUES FOR DIFFERENT COUPLINGS

j	Scheme A		Ne	Sn	Pb	Scheme B
2	$^3P_2$	1.50	1.50	1.500	1.501	1.50
1	$^3P_1$	1.50	1.46	1.375	1.350	1.33
1	$^1P_1$	1.00	1.03	1.125	1.150	1.17

The transition from scheme A to scheme B has been followed by Houston[1] with the aid of the quantum mechanics. His equations permit the expression of the fine-structure intervals, the g-factor, and the intensities of transitions in terms of a single constant. Houston evaluated this constant from the observed positions of the fine-structure levels and calculated the following values of g, which are in good agreement with the observed ones given above.

	Sn	Pb
$ps\ ^3P_2$	1.500	1.500
$^3P_1$	1.377	1.352
$^1P_1$	1.123	1.148

He also found similar agreement with experiment in other cases.

[1] W. V. HOUSTON, *Phys. Rev.*, **33**: 297, 1929.

CHAPTER VIII

THE INTENSITY AND POLARIZATION OF SPECTRAL LINES

30. THE EINSTEIN TRANSITION PROBABILITIES

The radiation emitted by an accelerated electrical charge according to the classical theory can be calculated by means of the electromagnetic equations. In the case of a one-dimensional harmonic oscillator with coordinate x defined by the equation

$$x = 2x_0 \cos 2\pi\tilde{\nu}_0 t,$$

the electric moment at a given instant is ex. This varying electric moment causes the emission of electromagnetic waves of frequency $\tilde{\nu}_0$ at a rate such that the energy radiated in unit time is

$$S = \frac{64\pi^4}{3c^3}\tilde{\nu}_0{}^4 e^2 x_0{}^2. \tag{1}$$

As a result of this emission of radiation the energy of the oscillator continuously becomes smaller.

Such a continuous change in the energy of a dynamical system is not in accord with the quantum theory. We have found that atoms may exist in successive stationary states, characterized by discrete energy levels; and that the emission or absorption of radiation is accompanied by the transition of the atom from one state to another. The intensity of a spectral line; that is, the rate of emission of radiant energy of the corresponding frequency, will be determined by the probability of the corresponding quantum transition.

Let us consider two quantum states m and n of a system, such that the energy level W_m lies above that W_n. Transition from one state to another will be accompanied by the emission or absorption of radiation of frequency

$$\tilde{\nu} = \frac{W_m - W_n}{h}.$$

If the system is in the lower state, the probability that it will absorb the energy $h\tilde{\nu}$ from the surrounding radiation field will be proportional to the density $\rho(\tilde{\nu})$ of this radiation; we may write it as

$$B_{n\to m}\rho(\tilde{\nu}).$$

$B_{n\to m}$ is called "Einstein's coefficient of absorption." The probability that the system will change from the upper to the lower state, with the emission of the energy $h\tilde{\nu}$, may be similarly written

$$A_{m\to n} + B_{m\to n}\,\rho(\tilde{\nu}).$$

Here $A_{m\to n}$ is "Einstein's coefficient of spontaneous emission" and $B_{m\to n}$ is "Einstein's coefficient of induced emission."

Now let us consider a large number of identical systems in equilibrium with black body radiation at the temperature T. Let the number in the states m and n be N_m and N_n. Then the number of systems going from state n to state m in unit time will be proportional to the number in the state n and to the probability of the transition:

$$\Delta N_{n\to m} = B_{n\to m}\rho(\tilde{\nu})N_n.$$

Similarly the number going from state m to state n in unit time will be

$$\Delta N_{m\to n} = \{A_{m\to n} + B_{m\to n}\rho(\tilde{\nu})\}N_m.$$

At equilibrium $\Delta N_{n\to m}$ must be just equal to $\Delta N_{m\to n}$, so that we may write

$$B_{n\to m}\rho(\tilde{\nu})\frac{N_n}{N_m} = A_{m\to n} + B_{m\to n}\rho(\tilde{\nu}).$$

The equations of statistical mechanics as applied to quantized systems lead to the result that at equilibrium at temperature T the ratio N_n/N_m is given by[1]

$$\frac{N_n}{N_m} = \frac{p_n}{p_m}e^{-\frac{W_n - W_m}{kT}} = \frac{p_n}{p_m}e^{\frac{h\tilde{\nu}}{kT}},$$

in which p_n and p_m are the *a priori* probabilities or quantum weights of the states n and m, and the exponent is the Boltzmann factor.

Introducing this in the above equation, we obtain

$$\rho(\tilde{\nu}) = \frac{A_{m\to n}}{B_{n\to m}\frac{p_n}{p_m}e^{h\tilde{\nu}/kT} - B_{m\to n}}. \tag{2}$$

[1] See, for example, R. C. Tolman, "Statistical Mechanics with Applications to Physics and Chemistry," Chemical Catalog Co., New York, 1927.

The relation between energy density and temperature for black body radiation is known, however, to be that given by Planck's radiation law:

$$\rho(\tilde{\nu}) = \frac{8\pi h\tilde{\nu}^3}{c^3} \frac{1}{e^{h\tilde{\nu}/kT} - 1}. \tag{3}$$

In order for Equation 2 to assume this form, the following relations among the Einstein coefficients must hold:

$$\begin{aligned} B_{m\to n} &= \frac{p_n}{p_m} B_{n\to m} \\ A_{m\to n} &= \frac{8\pi h\tilde{\nu}^3}{c^3} B_{m\to n}. \end{aligned} \tag{4}$$

These relations were first derived by Einstein[1]. Dirac[2] has obtained them in his study of the interaction of light quanta and atoms with the aid of the quantum mechanics.

The values of the Einstein coefficients are customarily expressed in terms of the amplitude constant a_{mn} of the equivalent classical harmonic oscillator[3] (the analogue of x_0 in Equation 1). From comparison with Equation 1, we may write the following expressions:

$$A_{m\to n} = \frac{64\pi^4 e^2}{3c^3 h} \tilde{\nu}^3{}_{mn}\, a^2{}_{mn} \tag{5}$$

$$B_{m\to n} = \frac{p_n}{p_m} B_{n\to m} = \frac{8\pi^3 e^2}{3h^2} a^2{}_{mn}.$$

The intensities of spectral lines, both in emission and absorption, depend on the constants a_{mn}. Methods of calculating these constants accurately are provided by the quantum mechanics. A discussion of the derivation of intensity and polarization formulas would be out of place here;[4] some of the formulas themselves will, however, be given in Sections 34 and 35.

Even before the development of the quantum mechanics considerable progress had been made in the prediction of spectral

[1] A. Einstein, *Verh. d. Deutschen Phys. Ges.*, **18**: 318, 1916; *Phys. Zeit.*, **18**: 121, 1917.

[2] P. A. M. Dirac, *Proc.*, Roy. Soc., A **114**: 243, 1927.

[3] By the equivalent harmonic oscillator is meant a harmonic oscillator of such frequency and amplitude that it would radiate energy classically at a rate corresponding to that given by the Einstein coefficient of spontaneous emission.

[4] Reference must be made to the original papers or to a treatise on quantum mechanics, such as Condon and Morse, Chap. III; and G. Birtwistle, "The New Quantum Mechanics," Cambridge, 1928, A. Sommerfeld, "Wellenmechanischer Ergänzungsband," 1928.

intensities, and especially in the derivation of selection and polarization rules, through the application of Bohr's correspondence principle, which will be the subject of the following sections.

31. THE CORRESPONDENCE PRINCIPLE

The classical motion of a dynamical system with one degree of freedom (an anharmonic oscillator, for example) can be expressed by a Fourier series

$$x = \sum_{\tau=0}^{\infty} 2a_\tau \cos(2\pi\tau\tilde{\nu}_0 t + \delta_\tau) \tag{6}$$

in which $\tilde{\nu}_0$ is the frequency of the periodic motion and δ_τ is the phase constant. For the harmonic oscillator only the term with $\tau = 1$ occurs, the fundamental term; but in general all the higher harmonics or overtones may be present, with frequencies which are integral multiples of the fundamental frequency $\tilde{\nu}_0$. The amplitude factors a_τ depend upon the system under consideration. During the motion of the system radiation of the various frequencies $\tau\tilde{\nu}_0$ will be emitted, the rate for each frequency being given by Equation 1 when $\tilde{\nu}_0$ is replaced by $\tau\tilde{\nu}_0$ and x_0 by a_τ. In other words, the Fourier analysis of the parameter x (or, better, of the electric moment ex) resolves the system into a set of equivalent harmonic oscillators of frequencies $\tilde{\nu}_0$, $2\tilde{\nu}_0$, . . . ; and the interaction of the system with radiation is just the interaction of this set of oscillators.

Both the amplitude constants a_τ and the fundamental frequency $\tilde{\nu}_0$ depend in general on the state of motion of the system, and hence will change as the energy of the system decreases through the emission of radiation. Now it can be shown[1] that there is a correspondence between the classical frequencies $\tau\tilde{\nu}_0$ and the quantum frequencies $\tilde{\nu}_{nm} = \dfrac{W_m - W_n}{h}$. The integer τ is to be identified with the change in the quantum number during the transition; that is, $\tau = m - n$. It is then found that in the *limiting case of large quantum numbers the quantum frequency* $\tilde{\nu}_{nm}$ *is equal to the classical frequency* $\tau\tilde{\nu}_0$. In the case of small quantum numbers the classical frequency $\tau\tilde{\nu}_0$ is different for the two states with energies W_n and W_m, and

[1] For a detailed discussion see J. H. Van Vleck, "Quantum Principles and Line Spectra," Chap. IX; M. Born, "Atommechanik," Secs. 11, 17.

the quantum frequency has an intermediate value, which can be found by a process of averaging. This is called the *correspondence theorem for frequencies.*

(The fundamental frequency of the motion of the electron in the hydrogen orbits is, according to Equation 21 of Section 5*a*:

$$\tilde{\nu}_0 = \frac{4\pi^2 m_0 e^4}{n^3 h^3} \text{ sec.}^{-1}$$

For large n and comparatively small Δn the emitted frequency in a transition from n to $(n - \Delta n)$ will be

$$\tilde{\nu} = Rc\left(\frac{1}{(n - \Delta n)^2} - \frac{1}{n^2}\right) \cong \frac{2Rc}{n^3}\Delta n = \frac{4\pi^2 m_0 e^4}{n^3 h^3}\Delta n \text{ sec.}^{-1}$$

This verifies the above statement about the relation between the orbital and the emitted frequencies in this simple case.)

These considerations suggest that the quantum amplitude a_{mn} may in the limit of large quantum numbers be equal to the classical factors a_τ, and for small quantum numbers be equal to some average value of these factors for the initial and final states. This postulate was made by Bohr, and expressed as his *correspondence principle for intensities.*

The components along the x, y, and z axes of the electric moment of systems with more than one degree of freedom may be similarly expressed as multiple Fourier series:

$$\left.\begin{aligned}
\mu_x = ex = e\sum_{\tau_1}\sum_{\tau_2} \cdots\ & 2x_{\tau_1\tau_2} \cdots \\
& \cos\,(2\pi\tilde{\nu}_{\tau_1\tau_2} \cdots t + \delta_{\tau_1\tau_2} \cdots) \\
\mu_y = ey = e\sum_{\tau_1}\sum_{\tau_2} \cdots\ & 2y_{\tau_1\tau_2} \cdots \\
& \cos\,(2\pi\tilde{\nu}_{\tau_1\tau_2} \cdots t + \delta_{\tau_1\tau_2} \cdots) \\
\mu_z = ez = e\sum_{\tau_1}\sum_{\tau_2} \cdots\ & 2z_{\tau_1\tau_2} \cdots \\
& \cos\,(2\pi\tilde{\nu}_{\tau_1\tau_2} \cdots t + \delta''_{\tau_1\tau_2} \cdots)
\end{aligned}\right\} \quad (7)$$

in which $\tilde{\nu}_{\tau_1\tau_2} \cdots = \tau_1\tilde{\nu}_1 + \tau_2\tilde{\nu}_2 + \cdots$ is composed of harmonics of the various fundamental frequencies $\tilde{\nu}_1, \tilde{\nu}_2, \ldots$ The quantum frequency will now depend on several quantum numbers. The correspondence theorem is valid in this case also, $\tau_1, \tau_2, \ldots$ being the changes made by the corresponding quantum numbers during a transition, and the correspondence principle for intensities may be similarly applied.

In general, only approximate values of the probabilities of quantum transitions in the region of small quantum numbers can be predicted with the aid of the correspondence principle, on account of lack of knowledge of how to average the classical amplitude factors between the initial and final states.

32. SELECTION RULES AND POLARIZATION RULES FOR ALKALI-LIKE ATOMS

The selection rules which we have used in the discussion of spectra can be simply derived with the correspondence principle. In the Fourier analysis of the electric moment it often occurs that some of the amplitude factors are identically zero for all states of motion of the system; it is then assumed that the corresponding quantum transitions do not take place at all.

For example, let us consider the motion of the valence electron in an alkali-like atom. The orbit described by the electron (Sec. 9) possesses two fundamental frequencies, the frequency $\tilde{\nu}_n$ of the radial motion, and the frequency $\tilde{\nu}_l$ of the precession of the orbit as a whole.[1] The Fourier analysis of the components $\mu_{x'}$ and $\mu_{y'}$ of the electric moment on the axes $x'y'$ (Figure 36) which precess with the orbit will contain not only the fundamental frequency $\tilde{\nu}_n$, but also all the overtones $2\tilde{\nu}_n$, $3\tilde{\nu}_n$, . . . and a constant term $0\tilde{\nu}_n$.[2] These axes precess uniformly with respect to stationary axes xy. Hence the expansion of the electric moment relative to x and y will be

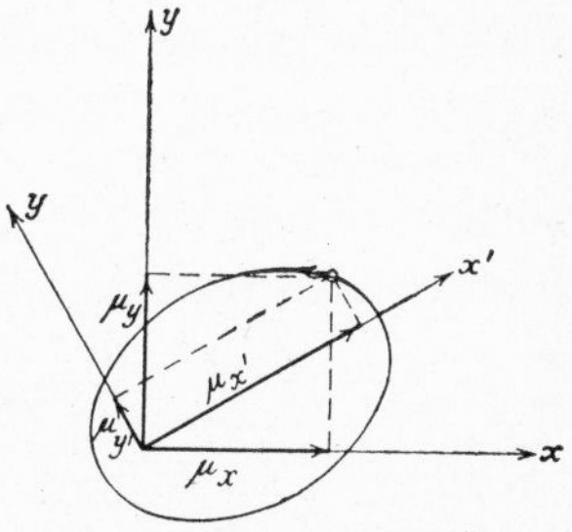

FIG. 36.—The components of electric moment of an orbit precessing in the orbital plane.

$$\left.\begin{aligned}\mu_x &= \mu_{x'} \cos 2\pi\tilde{\nu}_l t - \mu_{y'} \sin 2\pi\tilde{\nu}_l t\\ \mu_y &= \mu_{x'} \sin 2\pi\tilde{\nu}_l t + \mu_{y'} \cos 2\pi\tilde{\nu}_l t.\end{aligned}\right\} \qquad (8)$$

[1] The precessional motion may arise from penetration of inner electron shells or from the effect of polarization of the core, or (for hydrogen-like atoms) from the effect of the relativistic change of mass and interaction with the electron spin.

[2] The Fourier development of elliptical orbits is given by M. BORN, "Atommechanik," pp. 166–169.

In evaluating the products of sines and cosines, it is seen that the complete Fourier series representing the orbital motion and the superimposed precession will possess only terms with the frequencies

$$\tau\tilde{\nu}_n \pm \tilde{\nu}_l, \quad \tau = 0, \pm 1, \pm 2, \cdots \qquad (9)$$

If we now consider a transition in the region of large quantum numbers in which the principal quantum number n changes by τ and the azimuthal quantum number[1] l changes by σ, it can be shown that the corresponding energy change and the frequency of the emitted radiation are given by

$$\frac{\Delta W}{h} = \tilde{\nu} \cong \tau\tilde{\nu}_n + \sigma\tilde{\nu}_l. \qquad (10)$$

This holds with the same approximation with which $\tilde{\nu}_n$ and $\tilde{\nu}_l$ are equal in the initial and final states. The condition that the classical frequency (Equation 9) must become identical with the quantum theoretical frequency (Equation 10) in the case of large quantum numbers shows that n may undergo any change, including zero, but that l can change only by $+1$ or -1. This is the selection rule for l.

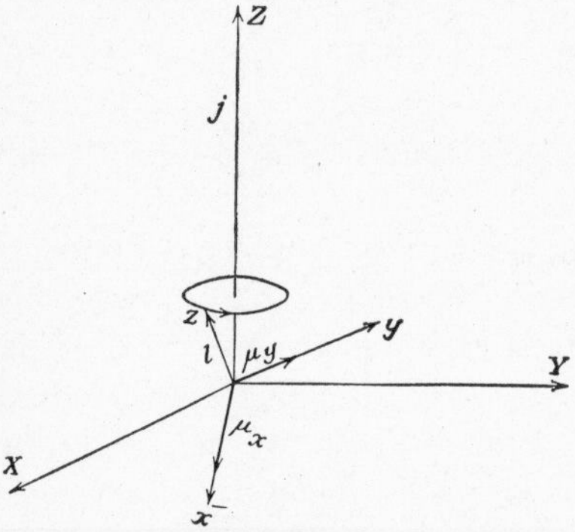

FIG. 37.—The precession of the orbital plane xy about j.

External electric fields have the effect of making the precession no longer uniform. In the Fourier expansion there then occur overtones of $\tilde{\nu}_l$. It is found experimentally that in this case the selection rules do not hold, and lines occur which are forbidden under normal conditions.

Similarly we can derive the selection rule for j, which represents the total angular momentum of the atom. The vector **l** was assumed to precess uniformly about **j**, which is fixed in space (Chap. IV), and the motion of the electron no longer takes place in a fixed plane. Three axes of reference are needed; one (the z-axis) may be taken along **j**, and the other two in the plane

[1] We have used k for the azimuthal quantum number, and placed $l = k - 1$. On account of this linear relation selection rules derived for k are valid for l also.

normal to it (Fig. 37). Since the precession of the orbital plane about **j** is uniform, the corresponding frequency occurs with the coefficients $+1$ and -1 in the Fourier expansions of the electric moments normal to **j**. On the other hand, this frequency does not occur at all in the Fourier expansion of the electric moment along **j**; that is, it occurs only with the coefficient 0. Hence the only jumps allowed for the quantum number j are 0, $+1$, and -1, completely in agreement with experiment. This selection rule for j cannot be rendered invalid by perturbing electric fields, as could that for l. It is, however, affected by strong external magnetic fields.

In the presence of a weak external magnetic field there is introduced a new uniform precession, that of **j** about the field direction **H**. The Fourier expansion of the electric moment in the plane normal to **H** contains the new frequency of the Larmor precession only with the coefficients $+1$ and -1, and that along **H** contains this frequency with the coefficient 0, just as in the case of the precession of **l** about **j**. The selection rule for the magnetic quantum number m accordingly allows jumps only of 0, $+1$ and -1.

Polarization rules are also easily derivable with the correspondence principle. Since the Larmor frequency occurs with the coefficient 0 only in the Fourier expansion of the electric moment of the atom along the field direction **H**, the transitions whereby m changes by 0 result in spectral lines which are linearly polarized with the electric vector parallel to **H**. When m changes by $+1$ or -1 the emitted line is circularly polarized in the plane normal to **H**.

Since such polarization rules hold for m, they must also hold for j. If j changes by zero, the emitted line must be polarized parallel to **j**. But the total moments **j** of different atoms have different directions, so that the observed light coming from many atoms is unpolarized. As soon as an external magnetic field is applied, however, all the atoms orient themselves with respect to this preferred direction, about which they all undergo Larmor precession, and the polarization due to **H** becomes experimentally observable.

In a sufficiently strong magnetic field the **ls** coupling is broken, and **l** and **s** undergo independent Larmor precessions about **H**. The Fourier analysis of the electric moment shows that in this case changes of 0, $+1$, and -1 are to be expected for m_l, and, since the electron spin does not greatly affect the orbital motion, no change is expected for m_s. This is observed experimentally in the Paschen-Back effect (Sec. 18).

33. SELECTION RULES FOR MANY-ELECTRON ATOMS

As a first approximation, the orbital motion of each electron in a many-electron atom is independent of that of the others. The Fourier expansion of the total electric moment will contain terms involving all multiples of the orbital frequency of each electron, so that all changes in the principal quantum number n_i of each electron are allowed.

A different selection rule holds for the resultant l than in the case of a single electron; for the electric moments arising from the individual electrons have components along **l** as well as in the plane normal to it. (In the case of one electron the orbital motion is in the plane normal to **l**.) The discussion of the frequencies is just that given for j in the preceding section; as a result of the nearly uniform precession of the $\mathbf{l}_i$'s about **l** there occur transitions for which the resultant l changes by ± 1 and by 0 and occasionally by ± 2 or more.

The interaction between **l** and **s** is shown by the multiplet separation. If this is small relative to the other interactions, the **ls** coupling will have little influence on the orbital motion of the electrons, and it is to be expected that s will not change during a transition. This is the explanation of the small intensities of intercombination lines, such as those corresponding to transitions from a triplet to a singlet state (from parhelium to orthohelium, for example). Only when the triplet separation is not much smaller than the distance between triplet and singlet states will transitions occur for which s changes. In helium the singlet-triplet distance is very large compared to the triplet separation itself. Going down in the periodic table from He to Be, Mg, Ca, Zn, Sr, Cd, Ba, Hg, the triplet separation increases very rapidly, while the distance between singlets and triplets of the same configuration decreases. As a result, intercombinations between singlet and triplet terms have not been found in the helium spectrum, whereas they give some of the strongest lines in the mercury spectrum.

The selection rule for j, $\Delta j = 0$ or ± 1, is strictly valid for many-electron atoms just as for alkali-like atoms, and it can be similarly derived with the aid of the correspondence principle.

In addition there now can occur the value $j = 0$, and special consideration must be given the possibility of a transition from a state with $j = 0$ to another with $j = 0$. Since s does not change during a transition, and since j can equal 0 only when $l = s$, l also does not change. In Figure 38 there are represented the vectors **l**, **s**, and **j** for the case when $l = s$ and j is very small (nearly zero). **l** and **s** precess uniformly about **j**; the component of the electric moment along **l**, which corresponds to $\Delta l = 0$, is nearly normal to j so that when this component is referred to stationary axes there occur terms containing the frequency of precession about **j** with the coefficients $+1$ and -1, but not (in the limit $j = 0$) with the coefficient 0. As a result, the transition from $j = 0$ to $j = 0$ must be excluded, in agreement with experience (Sec. 22).

FIG. 38.

The selection rules and polarization rules given in the preceding section for m, m_l, and m_s are also applicable to many-electron atoms.

The old selection rule $\Delta l_i = \pm 1$ holds for the electron which changes its state during a transition. It sometimes happens that two electrons jump at once; that is, the values of the quantum numbers associated with them change during the emission or absorption of a single spectral line. Heisenberg[1] has shown that in this case l_i for one electron may change by ± 1, and for the other by 0 or ± 2. This rule is also substantiated by experiment.[2]

These rules are valid in case the multiplet separation is not large; otherwise there occur larger changes of l_i, attributed to the perturbing effect of the $\mathbf{l}_i\mathbf{s}_i$ interactions.

34. THE SUMMATION RULES. INTENSITY FORMULAS FOR MULTIPLETS

A very simple method of deriving the relative intensities of the lines forming a multiplet was discovered by Burger, Dorgelo, and Ornstein.[3] Their rules, called the "summation rules," can be formulated in the following way.

Let us consider, for a multiplet resulting from transitions from one multiplet state to another, the sum of the intensities

[1] W. HEISENBERG, *Z. f. Phys.*, **32**: 841, 1925.

[2] It leads to the Laporte rule, given in Sec. 21d.

[3] H. C. BURGER and H. B. DORGELO, *Z. f. Phys.*, **23**: 258, 1924; L. S. ORNSTEIN and H. C. BURGER, *ibid*, **24**: 41, 1924.

of all lines common to a given level of the initial state. The summation rules state that for the different levels of the initial state these sums must be proportional to the quantum weights of the levels; that is, to the quantities $2l + 1$. Similarly, the intensity sums for the levels of the final state must be proportional to the quantum weights.

Some justification for these rules is provided by the correspondence principle. For, neglecting the small perturbing effect of the electron spins on the orbital motion, the Fourier analysis of the electric moment of the atom is the same for every transition from a level of the upper state to one of the lower state. We can accordingly assume that the probability that an atom in a given level of the upper state will jump to some level of the lower state is independent of the particular level which it occupies. The first rule then follows from the fact that at equilibrium the number of atoms occupying the various levels of the upper state are proportional to the quantum weights of the levels. Similarly, the probability that an atom in the lower state will absorb radiation and jump to the upper state is independent of the particular level occupied. Taking into account the relation between the Einstein coefficients of absorption and emission, this leads to the second summation rule.

As an example, let us consider the relative intensities of some multiplets in the doublet spectrum of the alkali-like atoms. The $^2D - {}^2P$ transition can be represented by the following scheme, in which the numbers near the term symbols represent the quantum weights $2j + 1$.

	$^2D_{5/2}$ 6	$^2D_{3/2}$ 4
$^2P_{3/2}$ 4	x	y
$^2P_{1/2}$ 2	—	z

x, y, and z represent the relative intensities of the corresponding lines; the transition $^2D_{5/2} - {}^2P_{1/2}$ is not allowed by the selection rule for j. The summation rules give the following equations, which suffice for the determination of the relative values of x, y, and z:

$$\frac{x + y}{z} = 2, \quad \frac{y + z}{x} = \frac{2}{3}; \text{ hence } x = 9y,\ z = 5y.$$

The intensity scheme may now be written

	$^2D_{5/2}$ 6	$^2D_{3/2}$ 4
$^2P_{3/2}$ 4	9	1
$^2P_{1/2}$ 2	—	5

Similar results are obtained for other multiplet lines; thus for $^2F - {}^2D$ the following:

	$^2F_{7/2}$ 8	$^2F_{5/2}$ 6
$^2D_{5/2}$ 6	20	1
$^2D_{3/2}$ 4	—	14

The lines $^2P_{3/2} - {}^2S_{1/2}$ and $^2P_{1/2} - {}^2S_{1/2}$ are seen from the summation rules to have the relative intensities 2:1. This is well verified by experiment on the sodium D-lines and the related lines of the other alkali metals.

Intensity formulas valid for multiplets in general are known. We shall not derive them here, but shall present some correspondence principle considerations to assist in their interpretation.

Let us consider the orbital motion of the electrons in an atom projected on an axis along the resultant **l** and in a plane normal to **l**. These projections are to be expanded in Fourier series. We shall then want to know the Fourier expansion along and normal to the total resultant **j**, about which **l** precesses uniformly. Let us now take one of the Fourier terms, for example along **l**, and discuss its components along and normal to **j**. The frequency of this harmonic wave projected along **j** is not changed, but its amplitude is, being now multiplied by cos (**lj**). The projection of this Fourier term on the plane normal to **j** gives a Lissajous figure resulting from the original wave and the uniform precession about **j**. This Lissajous figure can be thought of as composed of two uniform circular motions, one with the original frequency plus the precession frequency, the other minus the precession frequency. These motions are opposed in direction and have the same amplitude, $\frac{1}{2}\sqrt{2}$ sin (**lj**) times the original amplitude along **l**.

The significance of this in terms of quantum jumps is the following. We started with a Fourier term along **l**, which corresponds to a transition for which l does not change. The projection along **j** also accompanies a transition for which j does not change. For this case we found a wave polarized along **j** and with an intensity proportional to $\cos^2$ (**lj**). The projection normal to **j** led to two circularly polarized waves of intensity $\frac{1}{2}\sin^2(\mathbf{lj})$. One had the original frequency plus the precession frequency, and corresponds to a transition for which j increases by 1; the other corresponds to a transition for which j decreases by 1.

The treatment of the Fourier components normal to **l** is more complicated. Each of the Fourier terms along one of the axes normal to **l** is to be considered resolved into two oppositely directed circular motions around **l** of the same frequency and amplitude. One corresponds to a transition with l increasing by 1, the other with l decreasing by 1. Now if the projections of each of these circular motions along and normal to **j** are studied, there are found:

Along **j** a wave with unchanged frequency and amplitude $\sin(\mathbf{lj})$ times the original.

Normal to **j** a compound motion resolvable into two circular motions, one with the amplitude $\frac{1}{2}\sqrt{2}\{\cos(\mathbf{lj}) + 1\}$, the other with $\frac{1}{2}\sqrt{2}\{\cos(\mathbf{lj}) - 1\}$. In case we took the circular motion about **l** corresponding to an increase in l, the first of these amplitudes corresponds to an increase of j by 1, the second to a decrease of j by 1. The frequency of the first circular motion is the sum of the original frequency and the precession frequency, of the other the difference.

Now the question is, what values are to be introduced for these sines and cosines? These are in general from the model different for the initial and the final state, so that the model provides only approximate values of relative intensities. But the intensities must also satisfy the summation rules; and this suffices to determine them.[1] The formulas obtained in this way are the following:

Transition $l \rightarrow l,\ j \rightarrow j + 1 : I \sim \frac{1}{2}\sin^2(\mathbf{lj})$

$$I = -A\frac{(l + j + s + 2)(l + j - s + 1)(l - j + s)(l - j - s - 1)}{(j + 1)}$$

$$l \rightarrow l,\ j \rightarrow j : I \sim \cos^2(\mathbf{lj})$$

$$I = A\,\frac{\{l(l + 1) + j(j + 1) - s(s + 1)\}^2}{j(j + 1)}\,(2j + 1)$$

$$l \rightarrow l,\ j \rightarrow j - 1 : I \sim \tfrac{1}{2}\sin^2(\mathbf{lj})$$

$$I = -A\frac{(l + j + s + 1)(l + j - s)(l - j + s + 1)(l - j - s)}{j}$$

[1] R. de L. Kronig, *Z. f. Phys.*, **33**: 261, 1925; A. Sommerfeld and H. Hönl, *Sitzungsber. d. Preuss. Akad. d. Wiss.*, **9**: 141, 1925; H. N. Russell, *Nature*, **115**: 735, 1925.

Transition $l \to l+1, j \to j+1: I \sim \frac{1}{2}\{\cos(\mathbf{lj}) + 1\}^2$

$$I = B\frac{(l+j+s+3)(l+j+s+2)(l+j-s+2)(l+j-s+1)}{(j+1)}$$

$$l \to l+1, j \to j: I \sim \sin^2(\mathbf{lj})$$

$$I = B \frac{(l+j+s+2)(l+j-s+1)(l-j+s+1)(l-j-s)}{j(j+1)}(2j+1)$$

$$l \to l+1, j \to j-1: I \sim \tfrac{1}{2}\{\cos(\mathbf{lj}) - 1\}^2$$

$$I = B\frac{(l-j+s+2)(l-j+s+1)(l-j-s+1)(l-j-s)}{j}.$$

The intensities are expressed here in terms of the quantum numbers of the initial state. The intensities corresponding to the transitions during which l is decreased by 1 are given by the above expressions when the rôles of the initial and final states are interchanged.

In the limit of large quantum numbers, for which the angle between **l** and **j** no longer changes during a transition, these formulas approach those provided by the vector model and the correspondence principle.

These formulas have since been derived by Dirac[1] with the aid of the quantum mechanics.

The expressions given here are valid only for Russell-Saunders coupling. It is possible to derive similar formulas for other couplings.

For intermediate coupling one can only apply the summation rules of Burger, Dorgelo and Ornstein to all the states of the configuration under consideration. It is then only possible to find the sum of the intensities of all transitions to or from all levels of this configuration which have the same j. This sum will be proportional to $x \cdot (2j+1)$, if x denotes how often a level with this j value occurs in this configuration, $(2j+1)$ being the weight of each one of these levels. Table I gives the intensities[2] in the neon spectrum for all transitions from the configuration $2p^5 \cdot 3p$ to $2p^5 \cdot 3s$. The initial state deviates very much from Russell-Saunders coupling, so that the ordinary term symbols can not be used here and the terms have been denoted by numerals,[3] the subscript giving the j-value.

[1] P. A. M. Dirac, *Proc.*, Roy. Soc., A **111**: 281, 1926.

[2] H. B. Dorgelo, *Phys. Zeit.*, **26**: 756, 1925.

[3] The lowest term is denoted by 1, the next one by 2_3, etc.

TABLE I. INTENSITIES IN NEON

$2p^5 \cdot 3s$ \ $2p^5 \cdot 3p$	8_0	10_0	1_1	4_1	6_1	9_1	3_2	5_2	7_2	2_3	Sum obs.	Sum calc.
$^3P_2$			20	10	3	9	34	34	17.5	100	227.5	215
$^3P_1$	15	1	20	32.5	1.1	4	39.5	10	20.5			
											254.5	258
$^1P_1$	0.1	14	2	2	19.5	17	5	26	31.5			
$^3P_0$			1	15	16	10.5					42.5	43
Sum obs.	30		181.5				218			100		
calc.	29		171.5				214			(100)		

It must be born in mind that what were called intensities in this treatment are just quantities proportional to the square of the amplitude of the equivalent classical oscillator. According to Equation 1, Section 30, the actually observed intensity contains also the fourth power of the frequency of the spectral line as a factor. Only in comparing the intensities of lines which lie near together in the spectrum is it allowed to neglect this factor.

35. INTENSITY FORMULAS FOR THE ZEEMAN EFFECT

For the Zeeman effect the summation rules of Ornstein and Burger[1] are the following. The sum of the intensities for the transitions beginning from one of the levels into which the initial state is split by the external field is the same for all these levels. This is true also for the levels of the final state.

With their aid, the intensities in the case of the Zeeman effect can also be determined. The direction of the magnetic field then assumes the rôle previously played by **j** and **j** assumes that of **l**. The angle between **j** and **l** becomes now that between the field direction and **j**, and the formulas become simply:

Transition $j \rightarrow j$, $m \rightarrow m \pm 1$: $I \sim \frac{1}{2} \sin^2 (\mathbf{jm})$, polarization $\perp \mathbf{H}$,

$$I = A(j \pm m + 1)(j \mp m);$$

$j \rightarrow j$, $m \rightarrow m$: $I \sim \cos^2 (\mathbf{jm})$, polarization $\parallel \mathbf{H}$,

$$I = 4Am^2;$$

Transition $j \rightarrow j + 1$, $m \rightarrow m \pm 1$: $I \sim \frac{1}{2}\{\cos (\mathbf{jm}) \pm 1\}^2$, polarization $\perp \mathbf{H}$,

$$I = B(j \pm m + 1)(j \pm m + 2);$$

$j \rightarrow j + 1$, $m \rightarrow m$: $I \sim \sin^2 (\mathbf{jm})$, polarization $\parallel \mathbf{H}$,

$$I = 4B(j + m + 1)(j - m + 1).$$

These formulas hold for all coupling schemes

[1] L. S. ORNSTEIN and H. C. BURGER, *Z. f. Phys.*, **28**: 135; **29**: 241, 1924.

In applying the summation rules, it is to be remembered that when observations are made of the light emitted perpendicular to the field direction half the intensity of the light polarized circularly is seen and the total intensity of the linearly polarized light. By observations in the direction of the field the other half of the circularly polarized light is seen and none of that linearly polarized. The intensity formulas given above are for observation perpendicular to the field direction.

The total light emitted in every direction is non-polarized, as it is when the lines coincide (zero field).

In the case of the Paschen-Back effect the same rules are valid, except with **j** replaced by **l**; the Paschen-Back effect requires that the motion take place as if **s** were not present. There are, of course, relations between the intensities in a weak and in a strong field, but they cannot be discussed here.

CHAPTER IX

THE PAULI EXCLUSION PRINCIPLE AND THE PERIODIC SYSTEM OF THE ELEMENTS

36. THE PAULI EXCLUSION PRINCIPLE

A principle of extreme importance to spectroscopy as well as to other phases of physics and chemistry is the *exclusion principle* discovered by Pauli in 1925.[1] The applications of this principle made even before the development of the new quantum mechanics were of great significance; more recently the restatement of the principle in terms of the language of the quantum mechanics has led to a number of further important applications.[2] We shall consider the principle, which characterizes certain conceivable quantum states as being non-existent in nature, only in its connection with the structure of spectra and the periodic system of the elements. For these considerations the form in which it was originally stated by Pauli suffices.

Let us consider an atom in an external magnetic field so strong that the couplings among the various electrons are broken and the electrons orient themselves independently with respect to the field. It is of no importance whether or not the coupling of the spin and orbital moments of the individual electrons is broken. The state of each electron is then given by fixing the values of a set of quantum numbers, such as n_i, l_i, j_i, and m_i, in case the coupling between s_i and l_i has not been broken, or n_i, l_i, m_{l_i}, and m_{s_i}, in case it has been broken. The spin quantum number s_i could also be added to either set, but it need not be explicitely included since it has the value $\frac{1}{2}$ for every electron.

The Pauli exclusion principle in its original form can be expressed in the following way: *there cannot exist an atom in such a quantum state that two electrons within it have the same set of quantum numbers.*

[1] W. Pauli, *Z. f. Phys.*, **31**: 765, 1925.

[2] The extended exclusion principle of the quantum mechanics was formulated by P. A. M. Dirac, *Proc.* Roy. Soc., A. **112**: 661, 1926, and W. Heisenberg, *Z. f. Phys.*, **38**: 411, 1926.

37. THE NUMBERS OF ELECTRONS IN SUCCESSIVE ELECTRON SHELLS. ELECTRON CONFIGURATIONS OF THE ELEMENTS

The Pauli exclusion principle provides an immediate explanation of the salient features of the periodic system of the elements, and is fundamental to the variety and character displayed by the elements in their chemical and physical properties. If there were no exclusion principle the stable state of every atom would be that in which every electron had the principal quantum number 1. Any atomic property would then be a monotonic function of the atomic number; there would be no trace of the actual periodicity in physical and chemical properties shown by the elements when arranged in the order of increasing atomic number. The characteristic difference in the chemical properties of hydrogen, carbon, nitrogen, and oxygen, essential to life as we know it, would give way to a drab and sterile uniformity.

But Pauli's principle requires that there be not more than two electrons with $n_i = 1$ in a given atom; namely, one with $l_i = 0$, $m_{l_i} = 0$, and $m_{s_i} = \frac{1}{2}$, and one with $l_i = 0$, $m_{l_i} = 0$, and $m_{s_i} = -\frac{1}{2}$. An atom of lithium, with three electrons, will have in its normal state two electrons with $n_i = 1$, and one in the next most stable orbit, with $n_i = 2$. This outer electron could be either a $2s$ or a $2p$ electron, depending on which is the more stable. We have seen earlier that the $2s$ orbit, which penetrates more deeply into the inner electron shell, is more stable than $2p$, so that lithium in the normal state will have the configuration $1s^2 \cdot 2s$.

Let us calculate in general how many electrons with a given principal quantum number $n_i = n$ can exist in an atom. With $n_i = n$ given, l_i can have any one of the values $0, 1, 2, \cdots n - 1$. For each of these, m_{l_i} can go from $-l_i$ to $+l_i$, a total of $2l_i + 1$ possibilities. And for each of these, m_{s_i} can be either $+\frac{1}{2}$ or $-\frac{1}{2}$. Hence for given n there are

$$\sum_{l_i=0}^{n-1} (4l_i + 2) = 2n^2 \tag{1}$$

different sets of quantum numbers. This is the number of electrons with total quantum number n allowed in an atom by Pauli's principle. These $2n^2$ electrons are said to form a "completed shell" or "completed group." If both n_i and l_i are fixed there are $4l_i + 2$ different sets of quantum numbers, and the $4l_i + 2$ electrons with these quantum numbers are said to form a "completed subshell" or "completed subgroup."

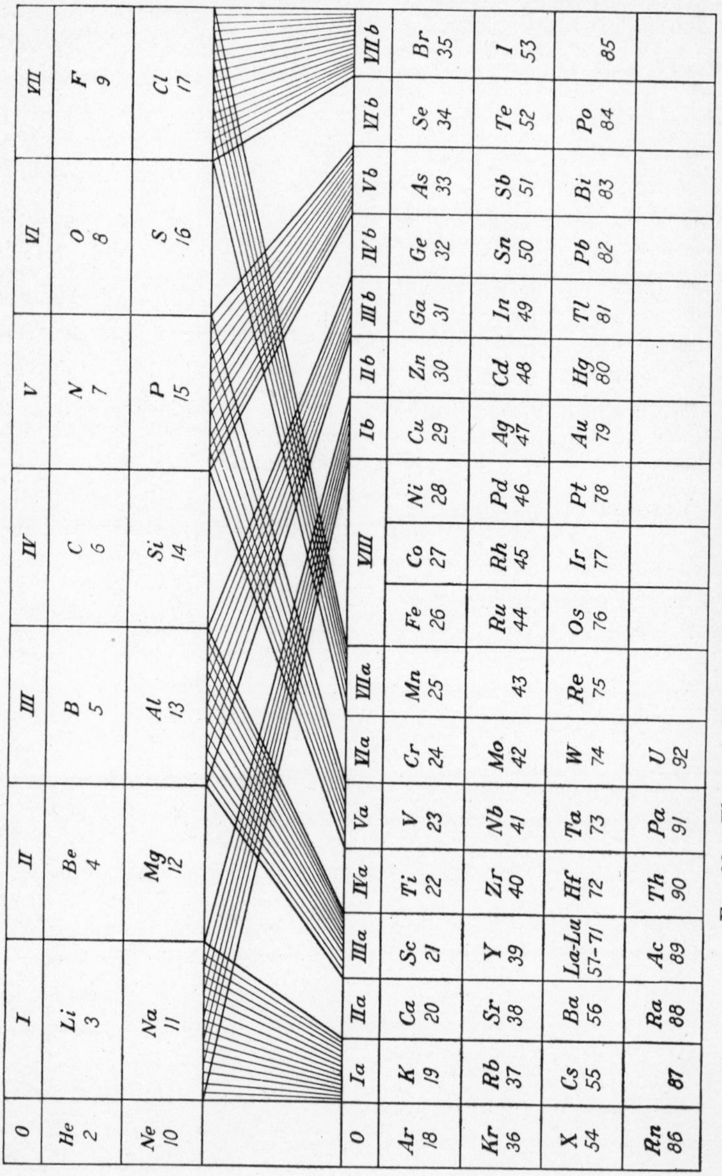
0 I II III IV V VI VII
He 2 Li 3 Be 4 B 5 C 6 N 7 O 8 F 9
Ne 10 Na 11 Mg 12 Al 13 Si 14 P 15 S 16 Cl 17
0 Ia IIa IIIa IVa Va VIa VIIa VIII Ib IIb IIIb IVb Vb VIb VIIb
Ar 18 K 19 Ca 20 Sc 21 Ti 22 V 23 Cr 24 Mn 25 Fe 26 Co 27 Ni 28 Cu 29 Zn 30 Ga 31 Ge 32 As 33 Se 34 Br 35
Kr 36 Rb 37 Sr 38 Y 39 Zr 40 Nb 41 Mo 42 43 Ru 44 Rh 45 Pd 46 Ag 47 Cd 48 In 49 Sn 50 Sb 51 Te 52 I 53
X 54 Cs 55 Ba 56 La-Lu 57-71 Hf 72 Ta 73 W 74 Re 75 Os 76 Ir 77 Pt 78 Au 79 Hg 80 Tl 81 Pb 82 Bi 83 Po 84 85
Rn 86 87 Ra 88 Ac 89 Th 90 Pa 91 U 92

FIG. 39.—The periodic system of the elements (after von Antropoff).

The formation of completed shells and subshells leads to the periodicity in properties indicated by the division of the elements into the successive groups of the periodic system (Figs. 39 and 40). The electron numbers of successive shells and of subshells are given in Table I.

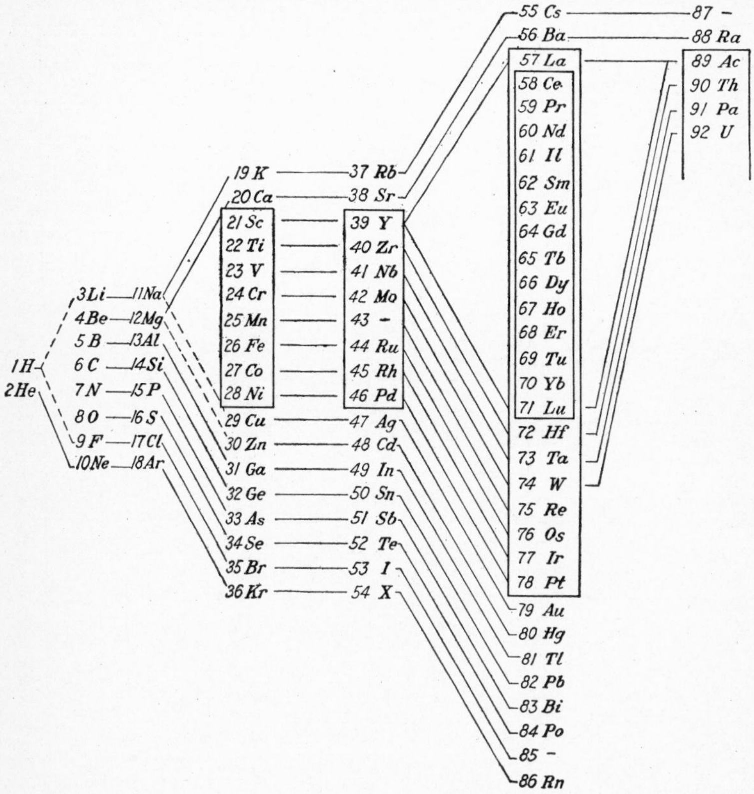

FIG. 40.—The periodic system of the elements (after Bohr).

TABLE I.—ELECTRON NUMBERS OF COMPLETED SHELLS

	Subshells					Completed shell
	$l_i = 0$	1	2	3	4	
K $n = 1$	2	..	..	..	..	2
L 2	2	6	..	..	..	8
M 3	2	6	10	..	..	18
N 4	2	6	10	14	..	32
O 5	2	6	10	14	18	50

The completion of the K shell (with $n_i = 1$) occurs at the noble gas helium. Further electrons in successive elements add on in the L shell, until at $Z = 10$, the noble gas neon, this, too, is completed. As additional electrons are added in the M shell

TABLE II.—ELECTRON CONFIGURATIONS OF THE ELEMENTS[1]

		K	L		M			N				O			P			Q	Lowest State
		1s	2s	2p	3s	3p	3d	4s	4p	4d	4f	5s	5p	5d	6s	6p	6d	7s	
H	1	1																	$^2S_{1/2}$
He	2	2																	$^1S_0$
Li	3	2	1																$^2S_{1/2}$
Be	4	2	2																$^1S_0$
B	5	2	2	1															$^2P_{1/2}$
C	6	2	2	2															$^3P_0$
N	7	2	2	3															$^4S_{3/2}$
O	8	2	2	4															$^3P_2$
F	9	2	2	5															$^2P_{3/2}$
Ne	10	2	2	6															$^1S_0$
Na	11	2	2	6	1														$^2S_{1/2}$
Mg	12				2														$^1S_0$
Al	13				2	1													$^2P_{1/2}$
Si	14	10			2	2													$^3P_0$
P	15	Neon core			2	3													$^4S_{3/2}$
S	16				2	4													$^3P_2$
Cl	17				2	5													$^2P_{3/2}$
A	18				2	6													$^1S_0$
K	19	2	2	6	2	6		1											$^2S_{1/2}$
Ca	20							2											$^1S_0$
Sc	21						1	2											$^2D_{3/2}$
Ti	22						2	2											$^3F_2$
V	23	18					3	2											$^4F_{3/2}$
Cr	24	Argon core					5	1											$^7S_3$
Mn	25						5	2											$^6S_{5/2}$
Fe	26						6	2											$^5D_4$
Co	27						7	2											$^4F_{9/2}$
Ni	28						8	2											$^3F_4$
Cu	29	2	2	6	2	6	10	1											$^2S_{1/2}$
Zn	30							2											$^1S_0$
Ga	31							2	1										$^2P_{1/2}$
Ge	32	28						2	2										$^3P_0$
As	33	Copper core						2	3										$^4S_{3/2}$
Se	34							2	4										$^3P_2$
Br	35							2	5										$^2P_{3/2}$
Kr	36							2	6										$^1S_0$
Rb	37	2	2	6	2	6	10	2	6			1							$^2S_{1/2}$
Sr	38											2							$^1S_0$
Y	39									1		2							$^2D_{3/2}$
Zr	40									2		2							$^3F_2$
Cb	41	36								4		1							$^6D_{1/2}$
Mo	42	Krypton core								5		1							$^7S_3$
Ma	43									6		1							$^6D_{9/2}$
Ru	44									7		1							$^5F_5$
Rh	45									8		1							$^4F_{9/2}$
Pd	46									10									$^1S_0$

TABLE II.—(*Continued*)

		K	L		M			N				O			P			Q	Lowest State
		1s	2s	2p	3s	3p	3d	4s	4p	4d	4f	5s	5p	5d	6s	6p	6d	7s	
Ag	47	2	2	6	2	6	10	2	6	10		1							$^2S_{1/2}$
Cd	48											2							$^1S_0$
In	49											2	1						$^2P_{1/2}$
Sn	50	46 Silver core										2	2						$^3P_0$
Sb	51											2	3						$^4S_{3/2}$
Te	52											2	4						$^3P_2$
I	53											2	5						$^2P_{3/2}$
Xe	54											2	6						$^1S_0$
Cs	55	2	2	6	2	6	10	2	6	10		2	6		1				$^2S_{1/2}$
Ba	56	54 Xenon core													2				$^1S_0$
La	57													1	2				$^2D_{3/2}$
Ce	58	2	2	6	2	6	10	2	6	10	1	2	6	1	2				$^3H_4$
Pr	59										2			1	2				$^4K_{11/2}$
Nd	60										3			1	2				$^5L_6$
Il	61										4			1	2				$^6L_{9/2}$
Sa	62										5			1	2				$^7K_4$
Eu	63										6	8		1	2				$^8H_{3/2}$
Gd	64										7	5s, 5p		1	2				$^9D_2$
Tb	65	46 1s to 4d									8			1	2				$^8H_{17/2}$
Ds	66										9			1	2				$^7K_{10}$
Ho	67										10			1	2				$^6L_{19/2}$
Er	68										11			1	2				$^5L_{10}$
Tu	69										12			1	2				$^4K_{17/2}$
Yb	70										13			1	2				$^3H_6$
Lu	71										14			1	2				$^2D_{3/2}$
Hf	72	2	2	6	2	6	10	2	6	10	14	2	6	2	2				$^3F_2$
Ta	73													3	2				$^4F_{3/2}$
W	74													4	2				$^5D_0$
Re	75													5	2				$^6S_{5/2}$
														6	1				$^6D_{9/2}$
Os	76	68 Hafnium core												6	2				$^5D_4$
														7	1				$^5F_5$
Ir	77													7	2				$^4F_{9/2}$
														8	1				$^4F_{9/2}$
Pt	78													9	1				$^3D_3$
														10					$^1S_0$
Au	79	2	2	6	2	6	10	2	6	10	14	2	6	10	1				$^2S_{1/2}$
Hg	80														2				$^1S_0$
Tl	81														2	1			$^2P_{1/2}$
Pb	82	78 Gold core													2	2			$^3P_0$
Bi	83														2	3			$^4S_{3/2}$
Po	84														2	4			$^3P_2$
—	85														2	5			$^2P_{3/2}$
Rn	86														2	6			$^1S_0$
—	87	2	2	6	2	6	10	2	6	10	14	2	6	10	2	6		1	$^2S_{1/2}$
Ra	88																	2	$^1S_0$
Ac	89	86 Radon core															1	2	$^2D_{3/2}$
Th	90																2	2	$^3F_2$
Pa	91																3	2	$^4F_{3/2}$
U	92																4	2	$^5D_0$

[1] This table is based upon those given by J. S. McLENNAN, A. B. McLAY, and H. G. SMITH, *Proc.*, Roy. Soc., A **112**: 76, 1926, and S. DUSHMAN, *Chem. Reviews*, **5**: 109, 1928.

the properties of the elements show similarities with those of the corresponding element in the L row of the periodic system (see Table II). Sodium, with one M electron, is similar to lithium, with one L electron; magnesium is similar to beryllium, and so on. The first two subgroups of the M shell are completed at the noble gas argon, whose properties are similar to those of neon and helium.

It might be expected that the ten elements following argon would have properties different from any of those before them; for the introduction of electrons with $l_i = 2$ could not take place in the previous shells. But it happens that the energy value of potassium in the state with an electron in the orbit $n_i = 3$, $l_i = 2$ is greater than that for the state with the orbit $n_i = 4$, $l_i = 0$ occupied. This arises from the greater penetration of the highly eccentric 4*s* orbit, which produces an energy change sufficient to overcome the effect of the principal quantum number. Potassium consequently has properties similar to those of sodium and lithium; the third row of the periodic system, like the second, contains only eight elements. In calcium in the normal state there are two 4*s* electrons. In scandium also there are two 4*s* electrons; the third electron has, however, dropped back into the M shell, for the 3*d* orbit is more stable than the 4*p* orbit. This continues until there are ten 3*d* electrons.[1]

Whereas in general the normal state of the ion is the same as that of the previous element, this is not so in scandium and similar elements. In the normal state of Sc^+ there is one electron in a 3*d* and one in a 4*s* orbit. In doubly ionized scandium the most stable state is with the outer electron in the 3*d* orbit. Comparing K, Ca^+, and Sc^{++} one finds that increase of the nuclear charge causes the 3*d* orbit to become more stable.

The state selected as normal state may not be differentiated to any pronounced degree by its energy value from others, and even the assignment of the outer electrons among the various shells sometimes depends on accidental circumstances. Different

[1] E. Fermi, (*Z. f. Phys.*, **48**: 73, 1928) has obtained the result with the aid of an approximate atomic model that the first *d* electron should occur at scandium, in agreement with experience. His equations require the first *f* electron at cesium ($Z = 55$), rather than the experimentally observed cerium ($Z = 58$). With the use of expressions for the central field in an atom obtained from observed term values, H. C. Urey and Y. Sugiura (*Danske Vid. Selsk.*, **7**: 13, 1927) were able to show that the rare earths should begin at $Z = 57$ and that scandium should have the first *d* electron.

configurations give rise to different sets of energy levels, which often overlap. The configuration entered in the table is that to which the very lowest energy level belongs. In the spectrum of vanadium, $Z = 23$, for example, the many multiplet levels arising from the configurations $3d^3 \cdot 4s^2$ and $3d^4 \cdot 4s$ are all mixed up together. The very lowest state, a ^4F term, happens to arise from $3d^3 \cdot 4s^2$; and the ^6D level of the other configuration lies only slightly higher.

Copper ($Z = 29$) has a completed M shell and one $4s$ electron (as the nuclear charge increases, the stability of $3d$ increases relative to that of $4s$). Although it has one outer electron, as the alkali metals have, the properties of copper differ from those of the alkali metals as a result of the influence of the completed shell of eighteen electrons, rather than only eight. In fact the configuration with nine electrons in $3d$ orbits and two in $4s$ orbits gives rise to an energy level which is only little higher than the normal state. As it is lower than the other excited states in copper it forms a metastable state of this atom. In successive atoms electrons are added in the N shell, until at the noble gas krypton ($Z = 36$) the first two subgroups of this shell are filled. This marks the end of the first long period in the periodic system. The number of elements in this period is eighteen, as a result of the completion of the $4s$, $4p$, and $3d$ subgroups.

As with potassium, the added electron in rubidium ($Z = 37$) does not go into the N shell, but rather the O shell, with the result that the properties of this element are those of an alkali metal. At yttrium ($Z = 39$) an electron drops into a $4d$ orbit; this continues until at palladium ($Z = 46$) the $4d$ subgroup is filled. Silver ($Z = 47$) has one $5s$ electron. The $5s$ and $5p$ subgroups are completed at the noble gas xenon ($Z = 54$), which marks the end of the second long period of eighteen.

Cesium ($Z = 55$), with a $6s$ electron, is an alkali metal. At cerium ($Z = 58$) an electron appears in the $4f$ subgroup, and at lutecium ($Z = 71$) this subgroup has its full complement of fourteen electrons. This succession of elements has no analogue in the earlier periods of the system, for no f electrons have occurred before. The properties of the rare earth metals also differ from those of the preceding elements. These facts find expression in the segregation of the rare earth metals in the periodic system reproduced in Figure 40. In filling up this $4f$

group the configurations of the outer electron shells remain completely unchanged, which explains why the rare earths are chemically so much alike.

From lutecium to platinum ($Z = 78$) electrons are introduced into the $5d$ subgroup, so that this succession is similar to the previous ones in which the $3d$ and $4d$ subgroups were filled. There is some doubt as to the electron distributions of some of these elements, since their spectra have not been sufficiently well analyzed to permit the confident recognition of the normal state.

Gold ($Z = 79$) has one s electron outside of an eighteen shell, and is accordingly similar to copper and silver. At the noble gas radon ($Z = 86$) the first two subgroups of the P shell are filled, and the third long period is ended. This long period consists of thirty-two elements, corresponding to the completion of the $6s$, $6p$, $5d$, and $4f$ subgroups.

Probable electron configurations for the succeeding elements are included in the table.

Each of the subgroups with given n_i and l_i can be further divided into two Stoner subgroups,[1] one with $j_i = l_i + \frac{1}{2}$ and one with $j_i = l_i - \frac{1}{2}$. There are $2j_i + 1$ orbits in each of these, so that the $4l_i + 2$ electrons are divided into Stoner subgroups of $2l_i + 2$ and $2l_i$ respectively.

The remark has been recently made by several people that this last subdivision is of no significance; it is said, for example, that when there are several electrons in a group it is not possible to assign values of j_i to the electrons. From our preceding discussion it is evident that this depends on the coupling scheme; if the scheme of Russell and Saunders is valid it is indeed meaningless to speak of the value of j_i for the individual electrons. The study of X-ray spectra, however, has shown that very probably not this scheme but rather (jj) coupling is valid for completed electron shells, especially those in the interior of the atom. Then each electron has its own total moment j_i, and we are justified in speaking of the Stoner subgroups.

[1] E. C. Stoner, *Phil. Mag.*, **48**: 719, 1924; also J. D. Main-Smith, "Chemistry and Atomic Structure," D. Van Nostrand Company, New York, 1924. The assignment of electron numbers to shells was first made by N. Bohr (*Z. f. Phys.*, **9**: 1, 1922), who also divided the shells into equal subgroups (4 and 4 in the L shell, etc.). The correct electron numbers of subgroups were given by Stoner and Main-Smith.

38. STATES WITH EQUIVALENT ELECTRONS. ALLOWED TERMS WITH RUSSELL-SAUNDERS COUPLING

As a result of the exclusion principle our vector diagram will give states actually occurring in spectra only in case equivalent electrons are not involved. Some of the states obtained by combining vectors in the usual way will be ruled out, as they correspond to an atom containing two or more electrons with the same values of n_i, l_i, m_{l_i}, and m_{s_i}. We shall now discuss how the allowed states are to be determined.

Let us consider an atom in a strong magnetic field by which the electrons are oriented independently. We first write down the quantum-number combinations allowed by the exclusion principle and assume that these all occur. Then we make use of the rule (discussed in Sec. 27) that during the transition from a strong to a weak field the projection of the total angular momentum of the atom in the field direction remains unchanged. This gives a number of values of m, from which, by grouping them properly, the possible values of j can be deduced.

With Russell-Saunders coupling the transition rule is valid for m_l and m_s individually, so that the allowed values of these quantum projections can be found and from them the values of s and l can be deduced. As an example, let us consider two p electrons with the same value of n. The following table shows

TABLE III.—ALLOWED STATES FOR TWO EQUIVALENT p ELECTRONS

m_{s_1}	m_{s_2}	m_{l_1}	m_{l_2}	$m_s = m_{s_1} + m_{s_2}$	$m_l = m_{l_1} + m_{l_2}$
$+\frac{1}{2}$	$+\frac{1}{2}$	+1	0	+1	+1
		+1	−1	...	0
		0	−1	...	−1
$+\frac{1}{2}$	$-\frac{1}{2}$	+1	+1	0	+2
		+1	0	...	+1
		+1	−1	...	0
		0	+1	...	+1
		0	0	...	0
		0	−1	...	−1
		−1	+1	...	0
		−1	0	...	−1
		−1	−1	...	−2
$-\frac{1}{2}$	$-\frac{1}{2}$	+1	0	−1	+1
		+1	−1	...	0
		0	−1	...	−1

the sets of quantum numbers remaining after the exclusion of those with m_{s_1} and m_{l_1} the same as m_{s_2} and m_{l_2}. There are also given the total projections of the two spin moments and of the two orbital moments.[1]

TABLE IV.—PASCHEN-BACK EFFECT FOR TWO EQUIVALENT p ELECTRONS

State	s	l	m_s	m_l
$^3P_2$, $^3P_1$, $^3P_0$....	1	1	+1	+1
	....			0
				−1
			0	+1
				0
				−1
			−1	+1
				0
				−1
$^1S_0$............	0	0	0	0
$^1D_2$............	0	2	0	+2
				+1
				0
				−1
				−2

It is next necessary to group these quantum numbers m_s and m_l so as to see what are the corresponding values of s and l in a weak field. In this example there is a term with $l = 1$ and $s = 1$, one with $l = 0$ and $s = 0$, and one with $l = 2$ and $s = 0$; that is, there is a ^3P, a ^1S, and a ^1D term. Hence, there are just five allowed levels, three for ^3P with $j = 2$, 1, and 0, one for ^1S with $j = 0$, and one for ^1D with $j = 2$.

The values of m_l and m_s which these levels give in the Paschen-Back effect are given in Table IV; it is seen that they are just those of Table III. The method of deriving the desired result by grouping together the quantum numbers can be best learned by actually carrying it out a couple of times.[2]

[1] It is not at all certain that on increasing the strength of the external magnetic field the projections of the resultants m_s and m_l conserve their values individually. The results derived in the text are not changed, for use is made only of the manifold of possible values of m_s and m_l; a state at the left in Table III, however, may not change when the field strength is slowly decreased into the state on the same line at the right.

[2] This derivation of the allowed states was first given by S. GOUDSMIT, *Z. f. Phys.*, **32**: 794, 1925. A similar treatment without the use of m_s was given by W. PAULI, *Z. f. Phys.*, **31**: 765, 1925.

Even though the scheme of Russell and Saunders be not valid, five terms with the same j values will always be found. They can then, of course, no longer be considered as a triplet and two singlets.

This method can also be used when the electrons do not have values of n_i and l_i in common. The table will then be larger, since Pauli's principle, which usually excludes a number of sets of quantum numbers, will not be of influence. The result obtained is precisely that found much more easily by the composition of vectors. For example, for two p electrons with different values of n_i there are found the states $s = 1$, $l = 0$, 1, and 2, and $s = 0$, $l = 0$, 1, and 2; that is, ^3S, ^3P, ^3D, ^1S, ^1P, and ^1D; ten states in all.

Assistance in grouping the quantum numbers to determine the allowed states is provided by a graphical scheme suggested by Breit.[1] If, for two equivalent p electrons, for example, the values of m_l be grouped in such a way that the corresponding values of m_{l_1} represent abscissæ and m_{l_2} ordinates, the adjacent scheme is obtained.

m_{l_i}	-1	0	$+1$	
m_{l_2}				
-1	-2	-1	0	(0)
0	-1	0	$+1$	(1)
$+1$	0	$+1$	$+2$	(2)

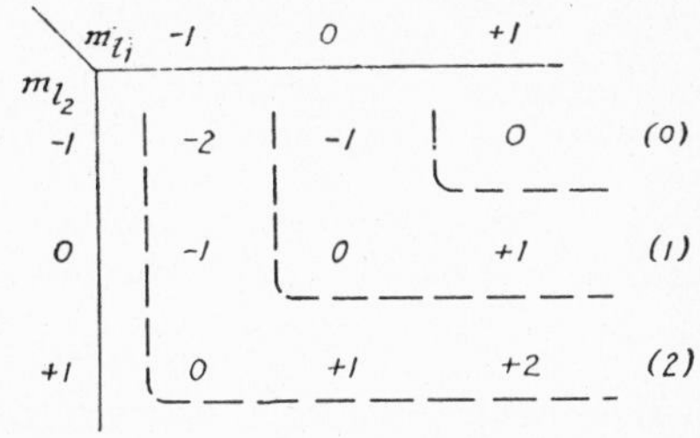

The values of m_l can then be grouped into runs as shown ((2) signifies the run $+2$, $+1$, 0, -1, -2) by outlining the L-shaped regions shown. These values of m_l are all valid in case $m_{s_1} = +\frac{1}{2}$, $m_{s_2} = -\frac{1}{2}$ or $m_{s_1} = -\frac{1}{2}$, $m_{s_2} = +\frac{1}{2}$. But if both m_{s_1} and m_{s_2} have the value $+\frac{1}{2}$ or $-\frac{1}{2}$ the diagonal terms in the m_l array are excluded, as shown in the scheme.

m_{l_i}	-1	0	$+1$	
m_{l_2}				
-1	$[-2]$	-1	0	(1)
0	-1	$[0]$	$+1$	
$+1$	0	$+1$	$[+2]$	
		(1)		

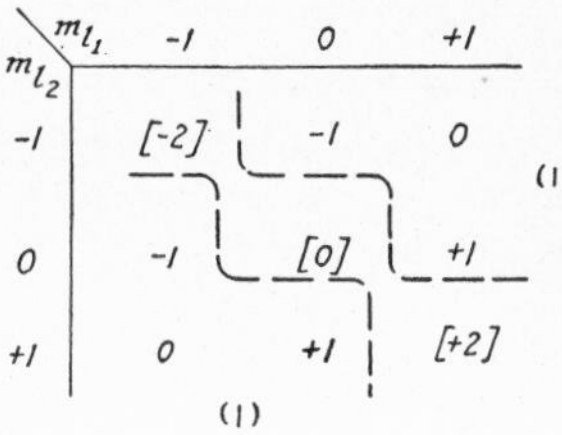

Only the runs (1) and (1) remain. The totality of runs can be tabulated as follows:

$m_s = 1$	$m_l =$		(1)		
0		(2)	(1)	(0)	
-1			(1)		
		^1D	^3P	^1S	

leading to the same allowed terms.

[1] G. BREIT, *Phys. Rev.*, **28**: 334, 1926; also H. N. RUSSELL, *ibid.*, **29**: 782, 1927.

The possible terms arising from a number of combinations are given in Tables V to IX.[1]

Table V.—Equivalent s Electrons

s —	^2S
s^2 —	^1S

Table VI.—Equivalent p Electrons

p^1 —		^2P		
p^2 —	^1S		^1D	^3P
p^3 —		^2P	^2D	^4S
p^4 —	^1S		^1D	^3P
p^5 —		^2P		
p^6 —	^1S			

Table VII.—Equivalent d Electrons

d^1	—		$^2(D)$						
d^2	—	$^1(SDG)$		$^3(PF)$					
d^3	—		$^2(D)$		$^2(PDFGH)$	$^4(PF)$			
d^4	—	$^1(SGD)$		$^3(PF)$	$^1(SDFGI)$	$^3(PDFGH)$		$^5(D)$	
d^5	—		$^2(D)$		$^2(PDFGH)$	$^4(PF)$	$^4(SDFGI)$	$^4(DG)$	$^6(S)$
d^6	—	$^1(SGD)$		$^3(PF)$	$^1(SDFGI)$	$^3(PDFGH)$		$^5(D)$	
d^7	—		$^2(D)$		$^2(PDFGH)$	$^4(PF)$			
d^8	—	$^1(SGD)$		$^3(PF)$					
d^9	—		$^2(D)$						
d^{10}	—	$^1(S)$							

Table VIII.—Equivalent f Electrons

f^1	$^2(F)$			
f^2	$^1(SDGI)$	$^3(PFH)$		
f^3	$^2(PDFGHIKL)$	$^4(SDFGI)$		
	2 2 2 2			
f^4	$^1(SDFGHIKLN)$	$^3(PDFGHIKLM)$	$^5(SDFGI)$	
	2 4 4 2 3 2	3 2 4 3 4 2 2		
f^5	$^2(PDFGHIKLMNO)$	$^4(SPDFGHIKLM)$	$^6(PFH)$	
	4 5 7 6 7 5 5 3 2	2 3 4 4 3 3 2		
f^6	$^1(SPDFGHIKLMNQ)$	$^3(PDFGHIKLMNO)$	$^5(SPDFGHIKL)$	$^7(F)$
	4 6 4 8 4 7 3 4 2 2	6 9 7 9 6 6 3 3	3 2 3 2 2	
f^7	$^2(SPDFGHIKLMNOQ)$	$^4(SPDFGHIKLMN)$	$^6(PDFGHI)$	$^8(S)$
	2 5 7 10 10 9 9 7 5 4 2	2 2 6 5 7 5 5 3 3		
f^8	$^1(SPDFGHIKLMNQ)$	$^3(PDFGHIKLMNO)$	$^5(SPDFGHIKL)$	$^7(F)$
	4 6 4 8 4 7 3 4 2 2	6 5 9 7 9 6 6 3 3	3 2 3 2 2	
f^9	$^2(PDFGHIKLMNO)$	$^4(SPDFGHIKLM)$	$^6(PFH)$	
	4 5 7 6 7 5 5 3 2	2 3 4 4 3 3 2		
f^{10}	$^1(SDFGHIKLN)$	$^3(PDFGHIKLM)$	$^5(SDFGI)$	
	2 4 4 2 3 2	3 2 4 3 4 2 2		
f^{11}	$^2(PDFGHIKL)$	$^4(SDFGI)$		
	2 2 2 2			
f^{12}	$^1(SDGI)$	$^3(PFH)$		
f^{13}	$^2(F)$			
f^{14}	$^1(S)$			

[1] From the tabulation of R. C. Gibbs, D. T. Wilber, and H. E. White, *Phys. Rev.*, **29**: 790, 1927. The sign ° to denote odd terms has been omitted in these tables. It is useful only when the electron configuration is not known or not given.

TABLE IX.—TWO ELECTRON SYSTEMS

$s \rightarrow {}^2S$	$s \cdot s \rightarrow$	${}^1S$	${}^3S$
$p \rightarrow {}^2P$	$ps \rightarrow$	${}^1P$	${}^3P$
	$p \cdot p \rightarrow$	${}^1(SPD)$	${}^3(SPD)$
$d \rightarrow {}^2D$	$ds \rightarrow$	${}^1(D)$	${}^3(D)$
	$dp \rightarrow$	${}^1(PDF)$	${}^3(PDF)$
	$d \cdot d \rightarrow$	${}^1(SPDFG)$	${}^3(SPDFG)$
$f \rightarrow {}^2F$	$fs \rightarrow$	${}^1(F)$	${}^3(F)$
	$fp \rightarrow$	${}^1(DFG)$	${}^3(DFG)$
	$fd \rightarrow$	${}^1(PDFGH)$	${}^3(PDFGH)$
	$f \cdot f \rightarrow$	${}^1(SPDFGHI)$	${}^3(SPDFGHI)$

In these tables the multiplicity of all terms included in parentheses is given by the common superscript to the left. Where several identical terms appear, their number is indicated by a small number placed directly below the term symbol.

One result of particular significance is easily derived. In a complete electron group or subgroup there is for every electron with given values m_{l_i} and m_{s_i} an electron with the values $-m_{l_i}$ and $-m_{s_i}$. Hence the sum of all m_{l_i}'s as well as of all m_{s_i}'s is zero, and there is only one allowed state, with $s = 0$ and $l = 0$. *The state of a completed group or subgroup is always* ${}^1S$. Furthermore, in determining the allowed states of an atom only the electrons not included in completed groups or subgroups need be considered.

39. THE MAGNITUDES OF MULTIPLET SEPARATIONS. INVERTED TERMS

It was shown by Pauli in his famous paper on the building up of electron groups that the same spectral terms arise from a configuration obtained by removing a given number of electrons from a completed subgroup as from the configuration composed of the given number of electrons alone. Thus in Table VI we see that the allowed terms for the configuration p^4 are the same as for p^2, for example. X-ray levels arise from the removal of one electron from a completed inner group, so that their observed doublet structure is to be expected. For a long time, however, there was no explanation as to why the X-ray doublets follow exactly the same doublet formula as optical doublets due to single electrons, but are inverted. The explanation of this fact and the derivation of formulas for multiplet separations were first given by Slater,[1] who gave an interesting treatment of a

[1] J. C. SLATER, *Phys. Rev.*, **28**: 291, 1926.

vector model of the atom with the methods of the old quantum theory. His treatment is not entirely trustworthy, however, and his results are in part valid only for large quantum numbers; in particular he assumed that cos $(\mathbf{s}_i\mathbf{s})$ is always either +1 or −1. An alternative and very simple treatment of the problem by methods similar to those used by Pauli for the g-values (Secs. 27 and 28b) has been given by Goudsmit.[1]

It was shown in Section 29 that the interaction energy of the spin moments and the orbital motion of the electrons in an atom is

$$W^1_s = \Gamma = \sum_i a_i l_i s_i \overline{\cos(\mathbf{l}_i\mathbf{s}_i)} \tag{2}$$

in which

$$a_i = \frac{R\alpha^2 Z^4_{\mathrm{eff}\cdot i}}{n_i^3 l_i(l_i + \frac{1}{2})(l_i + 1)}. \tag{3}$$

This may be rewritten as

$$\Gamma = Als\cos(\mathbf{ls}) = A\,\frac{j(j+1) - l(l+1) - s(s+1)}{2}, \tag{4}$$

with

$$A = \sum_i a_i \frac{s_i}{s}\overline{\cos(\mathbf{s}_i\mathbf{s})}\,\frac{l_i}{l}\overline{\cos(\mathbf{l}_i\mathbf{l})}, \tag{5}$$

in case that the coupling is Russell-Saunders. Our problem is the evaluation of the A's for the different multiplet levels.

39a. The Γ-permanence Rule and the Γ-sum Rule.—In a weak magnetic field an atom is spatially quantized so that the vector $\mathbf{j}$ has the component $\mathbf{m}$ along the field. If the field strength is increased to such an extent that the $\mathbf{sl}$ coupling is broken, each of these vectors is quantized relative to the field, their components along the field being $\mathbf{m}_s$ and $\mathbf{m}_l$ respectively. In this case the interaction energy of spin and orbital motion of the electrons is changed, so that, since

$$\overline{\cos(\mathbf{sl})} = \cos(\mathbf{sH})\cos(\mathbf{lH}) = \frac{m_s m_l}{sl},$$

the Γ values become

$$\Gamma = Als\cos(\mathbf{ls}) = Am_l m_s. \tag{6}$$

In Table X there are given Γ-values for a ^3D term in a weak and a strong magnetic field, calculated by Equations 4 and 6. They

[1] S. Goudsmit, *Phys. Rev.*, **31**: 946, 1928.

are arranged according to values of the total projection m, which for the strong field is taken equal to $m_s + m_l$.

TABLE X.—Γ-VALUES FOR ^3D

	m =	−3	−2	−1	0	+1	+2	+3	
j = 3		+2A	+2A	+2A	+2A	+2A	+2A	+2A	Weak field
2		.....	− A	− A	− A	− A	− A		
1		.....	.....	−3A	−3A	−3A	.....		
ΣΓ		+2A	+A	−2A	−2A	−2A	+A	+2A	
m_s = −1		+2A	+A	0	−A	−2A	.....	.....	Strong field
0		.....	0	0	0	0	0	.....	
+1		.....	.....	−2A	−A	0	+A	+2A	

It is seen that the sum of the Γ-values corresponding to a given value of m is the same for a strong field as for a weak field. This result was given by Landé;[1] it is analogous to the g-permanence rule of Section 28b, and may be called the "Γ-permanence rule."

In Section 28b we also considered the behavior of the resultant magnetic moment of the atom in a very strong field, such that the spins and orbital moments of the individual electrons are quantized relative to the field, their projections being $\mathbf{m}_{s_i}$ and $\mathbf{m}_{l_i}$; in this case, too, it was found that the g-sums for a given value of m (which in a very strong field equals $\sum_i (m_{s_i} + m_{l_i})$) are conserved. In this very strong field Γ is given by the equation

$$\Gamma = \sum_i \gamma_i = \sum_i a_i \, m_{s_i} \, m_{l_i}, \tag{7}$$

in which γ_i is used to represent Γ for a single electron. In analogy with the g-sum rule, Goudsmit formulated the following Γ-*sum rule: For a given electronic configuration the sum of all* Γ-*values corresponding to a given value of m is independent of the field strength.* With the help of this rule and the Γ-permanence rule it is possible to evaluate Γ in many important cases.

39b. Γ-values for Configurations of Equivalent Electrons.—As an example, we shall treat the case of two equivalent p electrons.

[1] A. LANDÉ, *Z. f. Phys.*, **19**: 112, 1923.

The factor a_i is the same for the two electrons, and can be set equal to a. In Table XI there are given values of γ_1 and γ_2 and of their sum Γ for the various states of the atom in a very strong field. The columns on the left contain the sets of values of the quantum numbers compatible with Pauli's principle, the next contain values of γ_1 and γ_2, then values of m_s and m_l, of m, and of Γ.

TABLE XI.—VERY STRONG FIELD Γ-VALUES FOR A p^2 CONFIGURATION

m_{s_1}	m_{l_1}	m_{s_2}	m_{l_2}	γ_1	γ_2	m_s	m_l	m	Γ
$+\frac{1}{2}$	$+1$	$+\frac{1}{2}$	0	$+\frac{1}{2}a$	0	$+1$	$+1$	$+2$	$+\frac{1}{2}a$
....	$+1$	....	-1	$+\frac{1}{2}a$	$-\frac{1}{2}a$	$+1$	0	$+1$	0
....	0	....	-1	0	$-\frac{1}{2}a$	$+1$	-1	0	$-\frac{1}{2}a$
$+\frac{1}{2}$	$+1$	$-\frac{1}{2}$	$+1$	$+\frac{1}{2}a$	$-\frac{1}{2}a$	0	$+2$	$+2$	0
....	$+1$	....	0	$+\frac{1}{2}a$	0	0	$+1$	$+1$	$+\frac{1}{2}a$
....	$+1$	....	-1	$+\frac{1}{2}a$	$+\frac{1}{2}a$	0	0	0	$+a$
....	0	....	$+1$	0	$-\frac{1}{2}a$	0	$+1$	$+1$	$-\frac{1}{2}a$
....	0	....	0	0	0	0	0	0	0
....	0	....	-1	0	$+\frac{1}{2}a$	0	-1	-1	$+\frac{1}{2}a$
....	-1	....	$+1$	$-\frac{1}{2}a$	$-\frac{1}{2}a$	0	0	0	$-a$
....	-1	....	0	$-\frac{1}{2}a$	0	0	-1	-1	$-\frac{1}{2}a$
....	-1	....	-1	$-\frac{1}{2}a$	$+\frac{1}{2}a$	0	-2	-2	0
$-\frac{1}{2}$	$+1$	$-\frac{1}{2}$	0	$-\frac{1}{2}a$	0	-1	$+1$	0	$-\frac{1}{2}a$
....	$+1$	....	-1	$-\frac{1}{2}a$	$+\frac{1}{2}a$	-1	0	-1	0
....	0	....	-1	0	$+\frac{1}{2}a$	-1	-1	-2	$+\frac{1}{2}a$

In the upper half of Table XII these Γ-values are shown arranged according to the total projection m, and the sums are calculated. In the lower half of the table symbols representing the weak-field Γ-values are similarly arranged according to m. A configuration of two equivalent p electrons leads to five states, two with $j = 2$, one with $j = 1$, and two with $j = 0$. Their Γ-values, which are, of course, independent of m, are called Γ_2', Γ_2'', Γ_1, Γ_0', and Γ_0'', respectively. A comparison of Γ-sums for different values of m yields the equations

$$\Gamma_2' + \Gamma_2'' = a/2, \qquad \Gamma_1 = -a/2, \qquad \Gamma_0' + \Gamma_0'' = -a.$$

Thus we are able to calculate the sums of Γ-values for levels with the same j resulting from a given electron configuration; and these Γ-sums are the same for all couplings. The individual values can be determined only when the type of coupling is known. This treatment exactly parallels that for the g-sums described in Section 18*b*.

TABLE XII.—STRONG FIELD AND WEAK FIELD Γ-VALUES FOR A p^2 CONFIGURATION

$m =$	-2	-1	0	$+1$	$+2$	
$m_s = +1$	.....	.....	$-\frac{1}{2}a$	0	$+\frac{1}{2}a$	
$m_s = 0$	0	$+\frac{1}{2}a$	$+\ a$	$+\frac{1}{2}a$	0	Strong field
	.....	$-\frac{1}{2}a$	0	$-\frac{1}{2}a$	.....	$m_l = m - m_s$
	.....	.....	$-\ a$	.....	.....	
$m_s = -1$	$+\frac{1}{2}a$	0	$-\frac{1}{2}a$	.....	.....	
$\Sigma\Gamma =$	$+\frac{1}{2}a$	0	$-a$	0	$+\frac{1}{2}a$	
$j = 2$	Γ_2'	Γ_2'	Γ_2'	Γ_2'	Γ_2'	
$j = 2$	Γ_2''	Γ_2''	Γ_2''	Γ_2''	Γ_2''	
$j = 1$	....	Γ_1	Γ_1	Γ_1	.....	Weak field
$j = 0$	....	....	Γ_0'	....	.....	
$j = 0$	....	....	Γ_0''	....	.....	

The most important application of the Γ-sum rule is to X-ray doublets. These arise from the configuration obtained by removing one electron from a completed group or subgroup. If the azimuthal quantum number for the removed electron is l, the values of j for the two levels resulting from its removal are $l + \frac{1}{2}$ and $l - \frac{1}{2}$; and it can be shown by the construction of tables similar to Tables XI and XII that the corresponding values of Γ are $-la/2$ and $+(l + 1)a/2$, respectively, as for one electron, but inverted. In this case the individual Γ-values are determined, and are independent of the coupling; the usual doublet formula holds for X-ray doublets despite the fact that for light atoms the coupling is Russell-Saunders, while (jj) coupling holds in inner shells of heavy atoms.

The individual Γ-values can be calculated for the various types of coupling. With (jj) coupling of two equivalent p electrons, $\mathbf{j}$ is composed of two vectors $\mathbf{j}_1$ and $\mathbf{j}_2$. j_1 and j_2 can have either of the values $\frac{3}{2}$ or $\frac{1}{2}$, for which γ_i is $\frac{1}{2}a$ and $-a$, respectively. The Γ-values for the entire atom are $\Sigma\gamma_i$; they are listed in the following table. It is evident that with this coupling Γ-values can be easily calculated for any state.

p^2: $j_1 = \frac{3}{2}$	$j_2 = \frac{3}{2}$	$j = 0$	$\Gamma = a$
		$j = 2$	a
$j_1 = \frac{3}{2}$	$j_2 = \frac{1}{2}$	$j = 2$	$-a/2$
		$j = 1$	$-a/2$
$j_1 = \frac{1}{2}$	$j_2 = \frac{1}{2}$	$j = 0$	$-2a$

For Russell-Saunders coupling of two electrons Γ can be calculated, as was done in Section 22, for the angles between the quantum vectors are known. But with more than two electrons this method cannot be used; it is found instead that the Γ-permanence rule, which requires that the Γ-sums for a given m do not change during the Paschen-Back orientation of **l** and **s**, provides just enough further information to permit the evaluation of the individual Γ's. This can be illustrated by our p^2 configuration. The allowed states with Russell-Saunders coupling are $^1S_0$, $^1D_2$, $^3P_2$, $^3P_1$, $^3P_0$. Of these $^1D_2$ is the only one which leads to the projection $m_l = 2$; reference to Table XI shows that the only Γ-value for $m_l = 2$ is 0, so that we may put

TABLE XIII.—MULTIPLET SEPARATIONS FOR EQUIVALENT p AND d ELECTRONS

Configuration	Multiplet	Total separation	A	Configuration
p	^2P	$\frac{3}{2}a$	a	$-p^5$
p^2	^3P	$\frac{3}{2}a$	$\frac{1}{2}a$	$-p^4$
p^3	^2D	0	0	$-p^3$
	^2P	0	0	
d	^2D	$\frac{5}{2}a$	a	$-d^9$
d^2	^3F	$\frac{7}{2}a$	$\frac{1}{2}a$	$-d^8$
	^3P	$\frac{3}{2}a$	$\frac{1}{2}a$	
d^3	^4F	$\frac{7}{2}a$	$\frac{1}{3}a$	$-d^7$
	^4P	$\frac{4}{3}a$	$\frac{1}{3}a$	
	^2H	$\frac{11}{10}a$	$\frac{1}{5}a$	
	^2G	$\frac{27}{20}a$	$\frac{3}{10}a$	
	^2F	$-\frac{7}{12}a$	$-\frac{1}{6}a$	
	^2D, ^2D [1]	$\frac{5}{6}a$	$\frac{1}{3}a$	
	^2P	a	$\frac{2}{3}a$	
d^4	^5D	$\frac{5}{2}a$	$\frac{1}{4}a$	$-d^6$
	^3H	$\frac{11}{10}a$	$\frac{1}{10}a$	
	^3G	$\frac{27}{20}a$	$\frac{3}{20}a$	
	^3F, ^3F	$\frac{7}{12}a$	$\frac{1}{12}a$	
	^3D	$-\frac{5}{12}a$	$-\frac{1}{12}a$	
	^3P, ^3P	$\frac{3}{2}a$	$\frac{1}{2}a$	
d^5	all	0	0	$-d^5$

[1] The values given are the sums for the two states.

$\Gamma_2' = 0$, and $\Gamma_2'' = a/2$. Since for ${}^1S_0$ $\Gamma_0' = 0$, we also have $\Gamma_0'' = -a$; so that the resultant values are

$$\begin{array}{llll} {}^1S_0 & \Gamma = 0 & {}^3P_2 & \Gamma = a/2 \\ {}^1D_2 & \quad 0 & {}^3P_1 & \quad -a/2 \\ & & {}^3P_0 & \quad -a. \end{array}$$

The total separation of ${}^3P$ is seen to be $\frac{3}{2}a$. The value of A in Equation 4 must hence be equal to $a/2$ for this p^2 ${}^3P$ state.

By methods such as this, values of A have been calculated for various configurations of equivalent electrons; they are listed in Table XIII.

Several features of this table are noteworthy. The most striking is that with Russell-Saunders coupling the absence of a given number of electrons leads to a multiplet which is identical with that arising from the presence of these electrons but is inverted. It is also seen that in general A is positive for configurations with less than half of the electrons in a subgroup

TABLE XIV.—OBSERVED AND CALCULATED MULTIPLET SEPARATIONS IN Ti II

Term notation (Russell)	Ti II, d^3 configuration Multiplet separations				
b^4F	observed	128.37	103.41	75.84	
	calculated	*133.2*	*103.6*	*74.1*	
a^4P	......	......	......	122.29	32.05
	......	......	......	*74.1*	*44.4*
a^2H	97.82				
	(*97.8*)				
a^2G	......	120.46			
	......	*120.0*			
b^2F	......	......	−59.89		
	......	......	*−51.8*		
b^2D	......	......	......	129.38	
$-{}^2D$	......	......	......	—[1]	
	......	......	......	$\Sigma = 74.1$	
a^2P	......	......	......	......	125.02
	......	......	......	......	*88.9*
$j = 11/2$	$9/2$	$7/2$	$5/2$	$3/2$	$1/2$

[1] This state has not been identified.

present, so that the lowest level of a multiplet is that with the smallest j. Only two of the states listed in the table are exceptions. For configurations composed of more than half the electrons in a subgroup, the lowest level usually has the largest j. When just half the electrons in a subgroup are present the multiplet separation is very small.

To illustrate the application of this table, we may consider the terms arising from a d^3 configuration in the spark spectrum of titanium[1]. Observed and calculated multiplet separations are given in Table XIV. The constant a was obtained from the ^2H separation. The agreement is very good in most cases; thus the expected anomalous inversion of the ^2F term is observed. It is probable that the poor agreement in the case of levels with small values of j is due to large deviations from the interval rule; that is, to departure from Russell-Saunders coupling.

39c. Multiplet Separations for More General Configurations.—Goudsmit and Humphreys[2] have shown that the factors A can be calculated for configurations obtained by adding an electron to a configuration of known A, in particular one of equivalent electrons, in case that the coupling of the original configuration is not changed. This is done by the method indicated in Section 26. If A' and a_2 are the A values for the original configuration; that is, the atom core and the added electron, respectively, and l_1, s_1 and l_2, s_2 are their quantum numbers, then

$$A = A'\frac{l(l+1)+l_1(l_1+1)-l_2(l_2+1)}{2l(l+1)}\cdot\frac{s(s+1)+s_1(s_1+1)-s_2(s_2+1)}{2s(s+1)} + a_2\frac{l(l+1)+l_2(l_2+1)-l_1(l_1+1)}{2l(l+1)}\cdot\frac{s(s+1)+s_2(s_2+1)-s_1(s_1+1)}{2s(s+1)}. \quad (8)$$

This equation is found to agree well with observed separations in complicated spectra. A simple example is provided by the spark spectrum of oxygen. In Table XV there are included data for terms of O_{II} arising from the addition of an s or p electron to O_{III} with the configurations s^2p^2 and p^4. Since six p electrons make a completed subgroup, the value of A' for p^4 should be just equal to that for s^2p^2, except that it should have the opposite sign (a small change in absolute value might occur as a result of the different screening action of two s and

[1] H. N. Russell, *Astrophys. J.*, **66**: 283, 1927.
[2] S. Goudsmit and C. J. Humphreys, *Phys. Rev.*, **31**: 960, 1928.

two p electrons). This is actually observed; the A' values for the two configurations are 95 ± 5 and -89 ± 3, respectively.

TABLE XV.—MULTIPLET SEPARATIONS FOR O_{II}

Electron configuration	Separation from Equation 8	Separation factor from		A'
		Adjacent levels	Total separation	
$s^2p^2 \cdot s$				$A'(p^2)$
$^3P + 3s$	$^4P\ A = \frac{2}{3}A'$	$A = 64, 70$	66	99
$4s$	....	65, 70	67	100
$3s$	$^2P\ A = \frac{4}{3}A'$	120	120	90
$4s$	....	125	125	94
$3s$	$^2D\ A = 0$	−0.4	−0.4	
$4s$	....	−0.3	−0.3	
$p^4 \cdot s$	....	....	....	$A'(p^4)$
$^3P + s$	$^4P\ A = \frac{2}{3}A'$	$A = -65, -55$	− 61	−91
	$^2P\ A = \frac{4}{3}A'$	−115	−115	−86
$^1D + s$	$^2D\ A = 0$	− 4	− 4	
$s^2p^2 \cdot p$	....	....	....	$A'(p^2)$
$^3P + p$	$^4P\ A = \frac{1}{3}A' + \frac{1}{6}a_2$	$A = 37, 31$	34	
	$^4D\ A = \frac{1}{3}A' + \frac{1}{6}a_2$	36, 37, 37	36	
	$^2P\ A = \frac{2}{3}A' - \frac{1}{6}a_2$	40	40	
	$^2D\ A = \frac{2}{3}A' - \frac{1}{6}a_2$	76	76	
	$\Sigma = 2A'$	$\Sigma = 186$	.....	93
$^1D + p$	$^2P\ A = -\frac{1}{2}a_2$	$A = 31$	31	
	$^2D\ A = +\frac{1}{6}a_2$	−8	− 8	
	$^2F\ A = +\frac{1}{3}a_2$	7	7	

40. THE RELATIVE POSITIONS OF SPECTRAL TERMS

The sequence of terms arising from a given electron configuration can be predicted with the aid of the following rules, which are applicable to a great number of spectra. We shall assume that of the interactions among the quantum vectors the apparent **ss** interaction (actually arising from the resonance phenomenon) is the greatest. This splits the terms into several groups with different values of s. Within each group, terms are again subdivided as a result of the **ll** interaction. And finally, each term with given values of s and l is split into the levels forming a multiplet by the **ls** interaction. It has been found, at first empirically, that

1. *Of the terms arising from a given configuration those with the largest value of s lie lowest, those with the next largest next, and so on.*

2. *Of the group of terms with a given value of s, that with the largest value of l lies lowest.*

3. *Multiplets arising from a configuration consisting of less than half the electrons in a completed subgroup are usually normal (smallest j lowest), and those from a configuration consisting of more than half are usually inverted (largest j lowest).*

The justification for these rules has been provided by the quantum mechanics and the spinning electron. Before then they were discussed theoretically by Slater,[1] who treated an idealized vector model with the methods of the old quantum theory. The third rule, regarding normal and inverted multiplets, has been discussed in the preceding section.

With the aid of these rules, Hund[2] predicted the sequences of multiplets to be expected in the spectra of various elements, and was extraordinarily successful in using them in correlating and interpreting the experimental term values in a great number of spectra.

Their application needs to be shown by only a simple example. The lowest configuration for the elements carbon and silicon is a p^2 configuration, which gives rise to the states ^1S, ^1D, and ^3P. According to the above rules, the expected order of terms is $^3P_0$, $^3P_1$, $^3P_2$, $^1D_2$, $^1S_0$; these terms are actually observed to be the low terms, and in this order, with $^3P_0$ as the ground term. For oxygen, on the other hand, with a p^4 configuration, $^3P_2$ is the ground state.

It has been found that although these rules are well fulfilled by the lower states of an atom, the higher states generally show large deviations.

41. THE NORMAL STATES OF ATOMS AND IONS

The application of these rules leads to the prediction of the term which lies lowest for every atom or ion. The terms which have been attributed in this way to the various elements are included in Table II. In the case of most of the light elements these normal states have been verified experimentally. With

[1] J. C. Slater, *Phys. Rev.*, **28**: 291, 1926; see also his quantum mechanical discussion, *Phys. Rev.*, **34**: 1293, 1929.

[2] F. Hund, *Z. f. Phys.*, **33**: 345, 1925.

the very heavy elements, however, there is considerable uncertainty in attributing to them any such term symbol, for the coupling of the quantum vectors is not Russell-Saunders, so that it is not possible to determine a resultant s and a resultant l for them.

42. IONIZATION POTENTIALS OF THE ELEMENTS

The difference in energy of an atom in its normal state and of its ion (obtained on removing one electron) in its normal state is eV, in which V is the first *ionization potential* of the atom. Thus the first ionization potential multiplied by the electronic charge is the work which must be done to remove one electron from the neutral atom. The second and succeeding ionization potentials measure the work which must be done to remove further electrons.

Ionization potentials can be obtained with great accuracy from spectroscopic data. It was in this way that most of those in the table on the following page, taken from Noyes and Beckman,[1] were obtained.

42a. Chemical Valence and Ion Formation.—The ionization potentials of an element determine the charges of the positive ions which it can form in solution or in crystals.[2] Thus it will be seen in the table that the first electron can be easily removed from an alkali atom, the energy required being about 5 v.e. or 120,000 cal/mole; but the second electron is held very strongly, around six or eight times as much energy being required to remove it. Two electrons can be easily removed from the alkaline earth metals, and the third is again held tightly. These facts make clear at once why the alkali metals form only univalent cations, and why the alkaline earth metals form bivalent cations; for the energy quantities available in a chemical reaction, such as crystal energy or hydration energy and the electron affinity of electronegative elements, are of such magnitude as to accomplish the removal of loosely held electrons only. In general there is a discontinuity in the trend of successive ionization potentials when the ion reaches a rare gas structure; and for this reason ions with such a structure are formed almost to the exclusion of others.

[1] A. A. Noyes and A. O. Beckman, *Chemical Reviews*, **5**: 85, 1928.

[2] See H. G. Grimm and K. F. Herzfeld, *Z. f. Phys.*, 19: 141, 1923, as well as Noyes and Beckman, *loc. cit.*

TABLE XVI.—IONIZATION POTENTIALS[1]

Z.	Element	1	2	3	4	5	6	7
1	H	1.000						
2	He	1.803	4.000					
3	Li	0.397	(5.6)[2]	9.000				
4	Be	0.702	1.340	(11.4)	16.000			
5	B	0.616	1.787	2.791	(19.3)			
6	C	0.835	1.794	3.360	4.744	(29.2)		
7	N	1.070	2.183	3.486	(5.43)	7.193		
8	O	1.002	2.585	4.047	5.687	(8.07)	10.144	
9	F	1.248	2.386	(4.62)	(6.40)	(7.56)		
10	Ne	1.587	3.025					
11	Na	0.378	3.47					
12	Mg	0.562	1.106	5.98				
13	Al	0.440	1.342	2.092	9.00			
14	Si	0.761	1.202	2.338	3.320	12.47		
15	P	0.982	1.462	2.216	(3.53)	4.778		
16	S	0.761	(1.74)	(2.37)	3.479	(4.93)	6.473	
17	Cl	0.96	1.66	2.93	3.50	5.00	(6.55)	8.400
18	A	1.159	2.00					
19	K	0.319	2.34					
20	Ca	0.450	0.873	3.76				
21	Sc	0.49	0.948	1.817	(5.33)			
22	Ti	0.503	1.003	2.038	3.301	(7.07)		
23	V	0.524	1.041	....	....	5.072	(9.0)	
24	Cr	0.496	1.23					
25	Mn	0.547	1.161					
26	Fe	0.578	1.22					
27	Co	0.577	1.27					
28	Ni	0.564	1.34					
29	Cu	0.567	1.503					
30	Zn	0.690	1.320					
31	Ga	0.440						
32	Ge	(0.70)						
33	As	0.86						
34	Se	(0.70)						
35	Br	(0.86)						
36	Kr	0.98						

[1] These are given in units Rhc = 13.53 volts.
[2] Values enclosed in parentheses are estimated.

Spectral terms are also of importance in the formation of molecules involving shared electron bonds. It has been shown by Heitler[1] and London[2] that the maximum number of shared electron bonds which an atom in a given spectral state can form with other atoms without a change in the electronic quantum state is related to the multiplicity of the state, being equal to $2s$; that is, bonds can be formed to a number one less than the multiplicity of the state.

[1] W. Heitler, *Z. f. Phys.*, **46**: 47 , 1927; **47**: 835, 1928; **51**: 805, 1928.
[2] F. London, *ibid*, **46**: 455, 1928; **50**: 24, 1928.

CHAPTER X

X-RAY SPECTRA

43. So far we have considered only spectra arising from transitions in the outermost electrons of the atom. Under normal circumstances no transitions involving electrons in inner shells can occur, for the inner shells are completed. It is possible, however, to remove one of the electrons from an inner shell either by the absorption of radiation of sufficiently high frequency or by the bombardment of the atom with high-velocity electrons. An electron from one of the outer shells in the atom can then jump into the vacant orbit, emitting a spectral line of frequency corresponding to the energy difference of the two states of the atom. Another electron in a shell still further out can jump into the newly vacated orbit, with the emission of still another line; and so on. Finally, the singly charged positive ion can combine with a free electron to form an atom identical with the original one. Such processes as these take place in the familiar X-ray tube;[1] spectra arising from electronic changes in the inner shells of atoms are called "X-ray spectra" or "Röntgen spectra."[2]

The energy changes during such transitions are usually so large that the corresponding spectral lines are of very short wave-length: the hard X-ray region extends from about 0.01 Å

[1] In addition to the line spectrum characteristic of the material of the anticathode, a continuous background of X-radiation is emitted as a result of the sudden stopping of the electrons. The highest frequency of this radiation corresponds to the emission in one quantum of all the energy of the electron, according to the relation

$$h\tilde{\nu}_{\text{max.}} = \tfrac{1}{2}mv^2 = eV,$$

in which V is the maximum potential difference of the cathode and anticathode.

[2] W. Kossel (*Verh. d. deutsch. physik. Ges.*, **16**: 898, 953, 1914; **18**: 339, 1916) was the first to recognize that X-ray spectra are due to the removal of inner electrons from the atom.

to 1 Å, the soft X-ray region from 1 to 10 Å, and the very soft region from 10 to 100 Å.

Wave-lengths of X-rays are often reported in X-units, such that 1X.U. = 1×10^{-3} Å.

43a. X-ray Spectroscopy.—The wave-lengths of X-rays are usually measured by the use of a crystal as a three-dimensional diffraction grating. The angle of reflection θ of a beam of X-rays diffracted by atom layers parallel to the crystallographic plane (hkl) of a crystal is given by the Bragg equation

$$n\lambda = 2d_{hkl} \sin \theta, \qquad (1)$$

in which n is the order of reflection and d_{hkl} is the interplanar distance for the plane (hkl) in the crystal.[1] Very precise measurements have been made by Siegbahn,[2] who has achieved nearly the same percentage accuracy in the X-rays region as is possible in the visible optical region.

In recent years considerable progress has been made in the determination of the wave-length of X-rays by diffraction with ruled line-gratings.[3] This method may be of particular value in the investigation of very soft X-rays.

43b. X-ray Absorption Spectra.—Under normal conditions none of the X-ray emission lines will appear in absorption, as the lines originate in ionized atoms with one or more inner electrons missing. Instead, absorption within a continuous region bounded by one or more sharp edges on the long wavelength side is observed. Radiation of frequency such that the energy $h\tilde{\nu}_{\text{abs.}}$ is just sufficient to remove an electron from one of the inner shells of the atom will be absorbed by the atom, as will radiation of higher frequencies, the extra energy then being converted into kinetic energy of the emitted photoelectron. Radiation of lower frequencies will not be absorbed, however. It is seen that the frequency $\tilde{\nu}_{\text{abs.}}$ of the absorption edge gives exactly the energy of removal of an electron from an inner shell of the atom, so that it is possible to obtain directly from absorp-

[1] For a discussion of this equation and its application see W. H. and W. L. Bragg, "X-Rays and Crystal Structure;" P. P. Ewald, "Kristalle und Röntgenstrahlen;" etc.

[2] M. Siegbahn, "The Spectroscopy of X-Rays," Oxford University Press, 1925.

[3] A. H. Compton and R. L. Doan, *Proc.*, Nat. Acad., **11**: 598, 1925; F. L. Hunt, *Phys. Rev.*, **30**: 227, 1927; A. P. R. Wadlund, *Phys. Rev.*, **32**: 841, 1928; J. Thibaud, *Rev. d'Opt.*, **5**: 105, 1926; *Phys. Z.*, **29**: 241, 1928.

tion experiments the energy-level diagram for the different X-ray quantum states.

Figure 41 is a reproduction of the X-radiation from a tube with molybdenum anticathode resolved into a spectrum by a crystal of gypsum, $BaSO_4.2H_2O$. The characteristic *K*-radiation of molybdenum is shown superimposed on a general background of minimum wave-length 0.25 Å corresponding to a peak voltage of 50,000 volts. The distinct change in blackening of the plate at about 0.33 Å arises from the large absorption of radiation of wave-length less than this value by the barium atoms in the crystal, with the removal of an electron from the K shell ($K_{abs.}$ of barium = 0.3308 Å). The *K* edges of the silver (0.4852 Å) and bromine (0.9182 Å) in the photographic plate are also

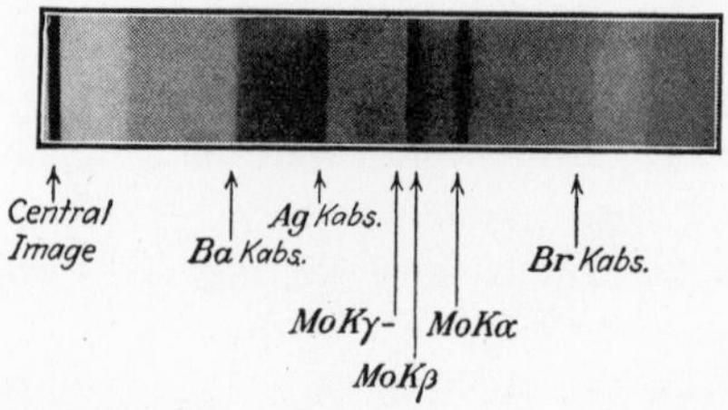

FIG. 41.—A photograph of the X-radiation from a molybdenum anticathode reflected from a barite crystal, showing the *K* absorption edges of Ba, Ag, and Br as well as the *K* emission lines of Mo.

shown; they show increased blackening on the short wave-length side because of the greater action of strongly absorbed radiation on the grains in the photographic emulsion.

It is found experimentally that there are three absorption edges corresponding to the removal of an electron from the L shell. These edges, called the L_I, L_{II}, and L_{III} edges,[1] lie close together; their interpretation is given in the following section. Similarly there are five *M* edges, seven *N* edges, etc.

The energy level diagram for uranium is shown in Figure 42.

43c. X-ray Levels.[2]—There are two 1*s* electrons in a completed K shell. When one has been removed the state of the atom can be represented by the symbol $1s\ ^2S_{1/2}$, using the notation of optical

[1] These three edges are called L_{11}, L_{21}, and L_{22} by Sommerfeld. In some respects this nomenclature is preferable, as it indicates the difference in the origin of the L_IL_{II} separation and the $L_{II}L_{III}$ separation.

[2] The first papers dealing with the systematization of X-ray levels are the following: A. SMEKAL, *Z. f. Phys.*, **5**: 91, 1921; G. WENTZEL, *Z. f. Phys.*, **6**: 84, 1921; D. COSTER, *Phil. Mag.*, **43**: 1070, 1922; **44**: 546, 1922.

spectroscopy. In X-ray spectroscopy this level is customarily designated as the K level.

The $2s$ electrons are the most tightly bound of those outside of the K shell. The removal of one $2s$ electron from the atom will again give rise to a $^2S_{1/2}$ state; namely, $2s\ ^2S_{1/2}$. This corresponds to the L_I level, which lies below and next to the K level. There is, indeed, this important difference between

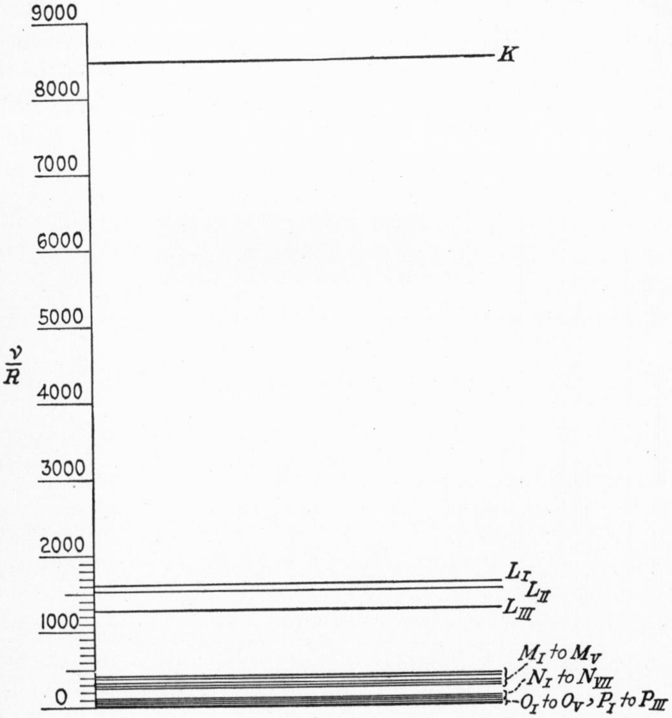

FIG. 42.—X-ray term values of uranium, $Z = 92$, in units of the Rydberg constant, plotted to scale.

X-ray and optical spectra, that the terms of the former are generally inverted. In optical spectra the term $1s$, for example, is always lower than $2s$, while in X-ray spectra it is higher. This arises from the fact that the X-ray levels result from the removal of an electron from a given orbit, while the optical levels correspond to the presence of an electron in that orbit.

Next come the $2p$ electrons, composing a completed group of six; removal of one leaves the configuration $2p^5$. It was shown in Chap. IX that the removal of one electron from a completed group gives rise to the same states as the presence of a single electron in the group. We thus expect two levels in this case, one with $j = 3/2$ and one with $j = 1/2$. In case Russell-Saunders coupling were valid for the electrons, the levels would be $2p^5\ ^2P_{1/2}$ and $2p^5\ ^2P_{3/2}$. The doublet would be inverted, so that L_{II} would correspond to $j = 1/2$ and L_{III} to $j = 3/2$.

But the high nuclear charge effective for the L shell in atoms with large atomic number tends to break down the Russell-Saunders coupling and replace it by the (**jj**) coupling, according to which the spin and orbital moments of the individual electrons are combined to form individual resultant moments $\mathbf{j}_i$, which then combine to a resultant $\mathbf{j}$. This coupling is to be expected for all X-ray levels except those of very light atoms or possibly those arising in outer electron shells. The individual p electrons can hence be divided into two subgroups, one composed of the two electrons with $j_i = 1/2$, the L_{II} subgroup, and the other of the four electrons with $j_i = 3/2$, the L_{III} subgroup. These electron numbers two and four of the subgroups are obtained with the Pauli exclusion principle (Sec. 36). If the values of n_i, l_i and j_i are given, there are still $2j_i + 1$ possible values for the quantum number m_{j_i} in a strong magnetic field and there can thus be a maximum of $2j_i + 1$ electrons in this subgroup. From the alkali spectra and the considerations of Chap. VI, we know that the electrons with $j_i = 1/2$ are more strongly bound than those with $j_i = 3/2$, in agreement with our assignment of the levels L_{II} and L_{III}.

The corresponding values of the resultant j are also $1/2$ and $3/2$, since the completed group has $j = 0$. This coupling scheme thus leads to the same qualitative results as Russell-Saunders coupling—two states, one with $j = 1/2$ and one with $j = 3/2$, the former lying higher in the level scheme.

The existence of the j_i subgroups was assumed by Stoner[1] on empirical evidence from X-ray spectra at a time when it was not yet possible to account for these subgroups. Main-Smith[2] independently suggested the same division into subgroups. After the discovery of Russell-Saunders coupling and its wide applicability to optical spectra it was generally thought that

[1] E. C. Stoner, *Phil. Mag.*, **48**: 719, 1924.

[2] J. D. Main-Smith, "Chemistry and Atomic Structure," D. Van Nostrand Co., New York, 1924.

this division into subgroups was meaningless, and that only the resultant s and l for all electrons, and not the individual j_i's, could be assigned values. We now know that this is merely a question of the coupling type, and that very probably the division of inner electron groups into subgroups is permitted and is of significance.[1]

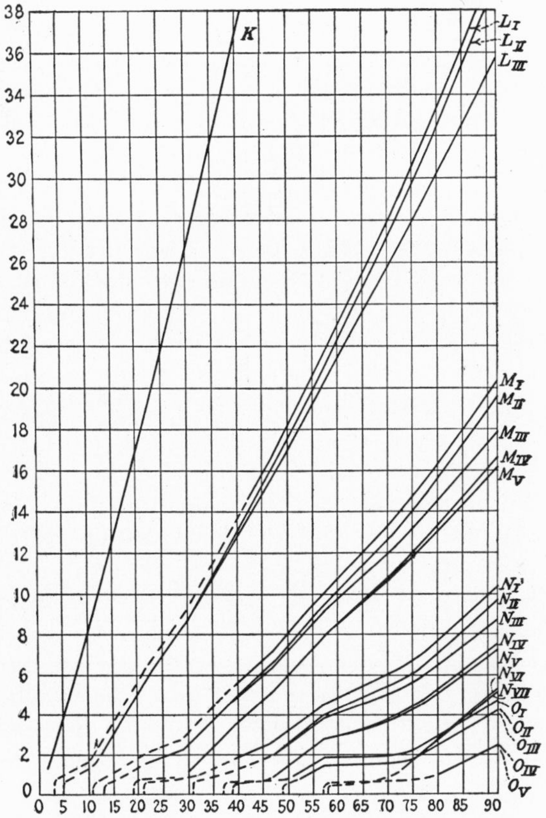

FIG. 43.—Moseley diagram of term values. (*From Bohr and Coster.*)

The removal of a $3s$ or a $3p$ electron leads to three M levels, M_{I}, M_{II}, and M_{III}, analogous in their origin and relative positions to the three L levels. In atoms with atomic number higher

[1] It is seen that in the Sommerfeld nomenclature (L_{11}, L_{21}, L_{22}, etc.) the first subscript represents the state of the removed electron (1 for an s electron, 2 for a p electron, etc.) and the second subscript the value of $j + \frac{1}{2}$.

than 29 there are ten $3d$ electrons. They can be considered as inner electrons only for the heavier atoms, and probably only for these is the coupling of the (jj) type discussed above. Independent of the coupling, however, we expect the removal of one $3d$ electron from the completed group to lead to two possible $3d^9$ states, the upper one with $j = 3/2$ and the lower one with $j = 5/2$. These are the levels M_{IV} and M_V.

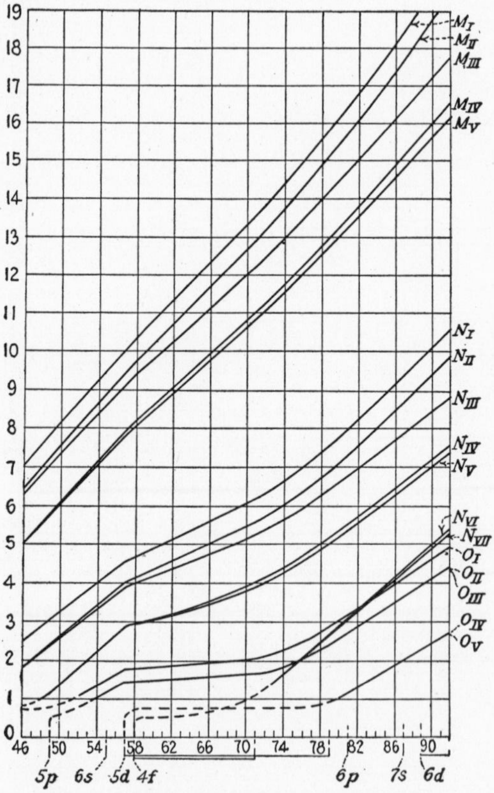

FIG. 44.—An enlarged portion of Fig. 43.

A similar treatment can be given the succeeding levels.

43d. Term Values.—It is found that the dependency of term values on atomic number for the various X-ray levels is such that there is an approximately linear relation between the square roots of the term values for a given level and the atomic numbers of successive elements. This relation is shown graphically by the Moseley diagrams in Figures 43 and 44, taken from Bohr and Coster's paper.[1] It will be shown in the following pages that not only the salient features, but many of the detailed peculiarities of these diagrams can be satisfactorily explained. It will be observed in particular that the separations of the square roots of term values for successive levels are of two kinds; the

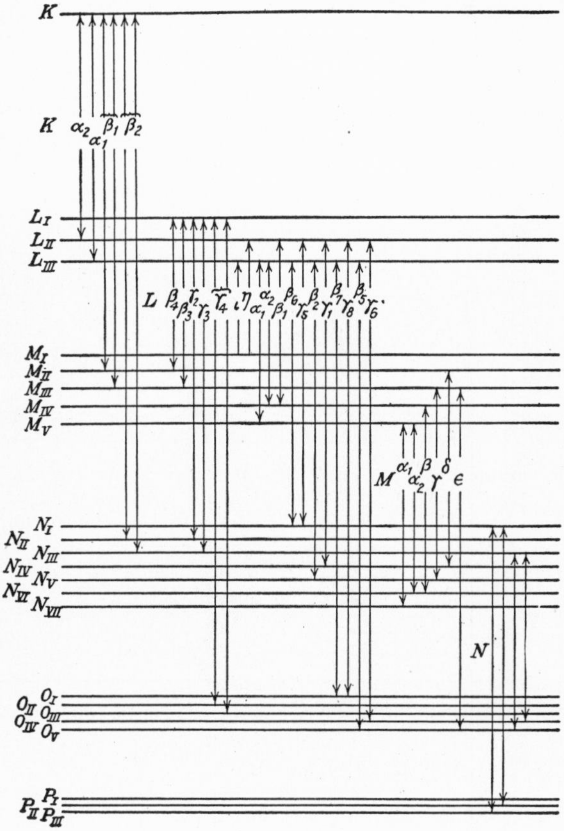

FIG. 45.—Diagram showing X-ray levels and lines.

separations $L_{\mathrm{I}} - L_{\mathrm{II}}$, $M_{\mathrm{I}} - M_{\mathrm{II}}$, $M_{\mathrm{III}} - M_{\mathrm{IV}}$, etc., are independent of Z, while those $L_{\mathrm{II}} - L_{\mathrm{III}}$, $M_{\mathrm{II}} - M_{\mathrm{III}}$, $M_{\mathrm{IV}} - M_{\mathrm{V}}$, etc., increase very rapidly as Z increases. This distinction is, of course, related to the removal of a $2p$ rather than a $2s$ electron in going from L_{I} to L_{II}, and a $2p$ electron with $j_i = 3/2$ rather than $j_i = 1/2$ in going from L_{II} to L_{III}. The doublets with

[1] N. BOHR and D. COSTER, *Z. f. Phys.*, **12**: 342, 1923.

constant square root separation, called *screening doublets*, in general differ in the values of l_i of the removed electron; those with increasing separation, now called *spin doublets*,[1] differ in the values of j_i of the removed electron.

The sharp bends in some of the curves are also of interest. These changes in slope are seen to occur at atomic numbers at which electrons begin to go into previously unoccupied sub-shells, and it is, in fact, possible to account for this correlation.

43e. X-ray Line Spectra.—A transition from one X-ray level to a lower one is accompanied by the emission of an X-ray line. Observed transitions are represented in Table I and Figure 45, together with the symbols used to designate the lines. Lines with K as the initial state are said to form the K series. Four lines are generally resolved in the K series; for molybdenum these can be seen in Figure 41.

The notation used for the lines, while convenient for practical X-ray spectroscopy, differs from that used for optical spectra. It would be simpler to designate the X-ray lines by the symbols of the initial and final states; some effort to introduce this system has recently been made.

From Table I it can be seen that the selection rules for optical spectra,

$$\begin{aligned} &\Delta n \text{ arbitrary}, \\ &\Delta j = +1, 0, -1, \\ &\Delta l = +1, -1, \end{aligned}$$

are valid also for X-ray spectra. Not all the possible transitions have been observed, however, perhaps on account of the low intensity of some of the lines. For example, transitions for which Δn is zero are allowed, provided the selection rules for l and j are obeyed; in the alkali spectra the strongest lines arise from such transitions. Nevertheless, lines corresponding to these transitions have never been found in X-ray spectra, although they have been looked for, and in some cases should lie in a spectral region favorable to observation.[2] The explanation of the failure to find these lines probably is that the intensity formulas for spectral lines contain a factor ν^4, which for these

[1] Formerly the spin doublets were called regular doublets or relativistic doublets; the screening doublets were sometimes called irregular doublets.

[2] D. Coster, *Phil. Mag.*, **43**: 1070; **44**: 546, 1922.

TABLE I.—X-RAY NOMENCLATURE[1]

Final state		Initial state: K-series	L-series			M-series				
	j	$1s$, $j = \frac{1}{2}$, K	$2s$, $\frac{1}{2}$, L_{I}	$2p$, $\frac{1}{2}$, L_{II}	$2p$, $\frac{3}{2}$, L_{III}	$3s$, $\frac{1}{2}$, M_{I}	$3p$, $\frac{1}{2}$, M_{II}	$3p$, $\frac{3}{2}$, M_{III}	$3d$, $\frac{3}{2}$, M_{IV}	$3d$, $\frac{5}{2}$, M_{V}
$1s$	$\frac{1}{2}$ K									
$2s$	$\frac{1}{2}$ L_{I}	—								
$2p$	$\frac{1}{2}$ L_{II}	α_2								
	$\frac{3}{2}$ L_{III}	α_1								
$3s$	$\frac{1}{2}$ M_{I}	—	—	η	ι					
$3p$	$\frac{1}{2}$ M_{II}	β_1	β_4	—	—					
	$\frac{3}{2}$ M_{III}		β_3	—	—					
$3d$	$\frac{3}{2}$ M_{IV}	—	—[2]	β_1	α_2					
	$\frac{5}{2}$ M_{V}	—	—[2]	—	α_1					
$4s$	$\frac{1}{2}$ N_{I}	—	—	γ_5	β_6	—			—	—
$4p$	$\frac{1}{2}$ N_{II}	β_2	γ_2	—	—		—	—		
	$\frac{3}{2}$ N_{III}		γ_3	—	—		—	—		
$4d$	$\frac{3}{2}$ N_{IV}	—	—	γ_1		—	δ	γ_2	—	—
	$\frac{5}{2}$ N_{V}	—	—	—	β_2	—	—	γ_1	—	—
$4f$	$\frac{5}{2}$ N_{VI}	—	—	—	—	—	—	—	β_1	α_2
	$\frac{7}{2}$ N_{VII}	—	—	—	—	—	—	—	—	α_1
$5s$	$\frac{1}{2}$ O_{I}	—	—	γ_8	β_7	—			—	—
$5p$	$\frac{1}{2}$ O_{II}		γ_4	—	—		—	—		
	$\frac{3}{2}$ O_{III}			—	—		—	—		
$5d$	$\frac{3}{2}$ O_{IV}	—	—	γ_6		—			—	—
	$\frac{5}{2}$ O_{V}	—	—	—	β_5	—		ϵ	—	—

[1] Forbidden transitions are indicated by dashes.

[2] The forbidden transitions $L_I - M_{IV} = L\beta_{10}$ and $L_I - M_V = L\beta_9$ were observed by COSTER, *Phil. Mag.*, **43**: 1070, 1922.

lines is very small compared with lines corresponding to other transitions from the same initial state.[1]

[1] This is not true for the outer electron groups. The energy difference of the N and O levels is of the same order of magnitude as for the different N levels themselves, so that for the N levels one would expect transitions with $\Delta n = 0$ to be of the same order of intensity as the transitions from N to O. Very recently certain lines in the X-ray spectra of Ta, W, Pt and Au have been interpreted by Sakae Idei (*Nature*, **123**: 643, 1929) and Jean Thibaud (*C.r.*, **188**: 1394, 1929) as transitions from N_{IV} to N_{VI} and N_V to $N_{VI,VII}$; that is, from $4d$ to $4f$.

44. THE INTERPRETATION OF TERM VALUES

44a. The Main Energy Term.—It is possible to derive more accurate expressions for the energy values of X-ray levels than of optical levels in many-electron atoms (except the hydrogen-like levels), inasmuch as the changes in effective nuclear charge along an electron orbit in the interior of an atom are rather small compared with the effective nuclear charge itself. A $3p$ electron in sodium moves in a field of an effective nuclear charge varying from e to about $9e$ in the inner part of its orbit; but for a $3p$ electron in mercury, for example, the effective nuclear charge varies only within the relatively narrow limits of about $70e$ and $78e$. In this case, then, the orbit can be considered as approximating a hydrogen-like orbit with an average effective nuclear charge somewhere within these limits. The energy of removal of this electron from the field of the nucleus and the inner electrons can be represented by the hydrogen-like equation

$$W_0' = \frac{Rhc(Z - \sigma_0)^2}{n^2} \tag{2}$$

in which σ_0 is a measure of the screening action of other inner electrons in effectively reducing the nuclear charge.

44b. External Screening.—Outer electrons, however, also influence the energy of an inner orbit. If, as a first approximation, in accordance with the discussion of Chap. IV, outer electron shells are replaced by a uniform distribution of negative charges on the surfaces of spheres of suitable radii, it is easily seen that the energy of removal of an inner electron is reduced. The potential energy of an electron within a spherical shell of electricity of total charge ze and radius ρa_0 is given by $ze^2/\rho a_0$. These energy terms, summed over all the outer shells, are to be subtracted from the main energy term of Equation 2:

$$W_0 = \frac{Rhc(Z - \sigma_0)^2}{n^2} - \sum_i \frac{z_i e^2}{\rho_i a_0}.$$

It is difficult to distinguish the energy change due to this external screening from that due to screening by the inner electrons; and, moreover, no sharp distinction is even theoretically possible, since the various orbits interpenetrate. For these reasons and for simplicity it is customary to include the two effects in a single screening constant σ_1, given by the following equation:[1]

[1] Obtained with the use of the value $e^2/2\,Rhc$ for a_0 (Sec. 5).

$$W_0 = \frac{Rhc(Z - \sigma_1)^2}{n^2}, \text{ with } (Z - \sigma_1)^2 = (Z - \sigma_0)^2 - 2n^2\sum_i \frac{z_i}{\rho_i}. \quad (3)$$

44c. Fine Structure.—To represent the fine structure of X-ray levels the relativity correction and the interaction energy between the electron spin and orbital motion must be taken into account. As a first approximation these lead to the equation

$$W = \frac{Rhc(Z - \sigma_1)^2}{n^2} - \frac{Rhc\alpha^2(Z - \sigma_2)^4}{n^3}\left\{\frac{3}{4n} - \frac{1}{l + \frac{1}{2}} + \frac{j(j + 1) - l(l + 1) - s(s + 1)}{2l(l + \frac{1}{2})(l + 1)}\right\}, \quad (4)$$

in close analogy with Equation 14 of Chap. IV for the hydrogen levels. In this equation, as before, α is the Sommerfeld fine-structure constant.

44d. The Spin Doublets.—We have interpreted the two states of an atom corresponding to a spin doublet, $L_{\text{II}} - L_{\text{III}}$, for example, as differing only in the direction of the spin of the removed electron. The value of the screening constant σ_1 in the main energy term is expected to depend only on the nature of the electron orbits, so that for these two states the main energy term will be the same. The doublet separation is found from Equation 4 by placing $j = l + \frac{1}{2}$ and $j = l - \frac{1}{2}$ to be

$$\Delta W = \frac{Rhc\alpha^2(Z - \sigma_2)^4}{n^3} \frac{2l + 1}{2l(l + \frac{1}{2})(l + 1)} = \frac{Rhc\alpha^2(Z - \sigma_2)^4}{n^3 l(l + 1)}. \quad (5)$$

This equation, first derived by Sommerfeld with the old quantum theory from considerations involving only the relativistic change of mass of the electron, was found to lead to difficulties when applied to the experimental data. It is expected that σ_2 should be a constant, independent of Z, for it depends mainly on the positions of the inner electrons relative to the removed electron, and these relative positions are not affected by change in Z[1]. But the experimental values of σ_2 found from Equation 5 vary

[1] It is found experimentally that σ_2 and σ_1 do not have the same value for a given level, nor do σ_2 and σ_0. Both $Z - \sigma_0$ and $Z - \sigma_2$ are averages of the effective nuclear charge, but different averages; $(Z - \sigma_0)^2$ is approximately equal to the average value of the square of the effective nuclear charge along the orbit, and $(Z - \sigma_2)^4$ to the average value of its fourth power. This leads us to expect σ_0 to be larger than σ_2 for a given state. σ_2 and σ_0 should be nearly independent of Z; since the external screening varies with the number of outer electrons and with their varying configuration, however, σ_1 is expected to be a function of Z, in agreement with observation.

markedly with Z, and in the case of the $L_{II} - L_{III}$ doublet become negative for values of Z greater than 75. This discrepancy is, however, only apparent, and results from the use of the approximate equation with only the term in α^2. Sommerfeld, using only the relativity correction of the old quantum theory, derived the complete expression involving terms in $\frac{\alpha^4}{n^6}(Z - \sigma_3)^6$, $\frac{\alpha^6}{n^8}(Z - \sigma_4)^8$, etc.; these terms, while negligible for the lighter elements, especially hydrogen and ionized helium, are of importance for the X-ray levels of the heavier elements. For the $L_{II} - L_{III}$ doublet the separation in wave-numbers is given by the equation

$$\Delta\nu = \frac{R\alpha^2(Z - \sigma_2)^4}{2^4}\left\{1 + \frac{5\alpha^2}{2^3}(Z - \sigma_2)^2 + \frac{53\alpha^4}{2^7}(Z - \sigma_2)^4 + \cdots\right\}. \quad (6)$$

in which $\sigma_3, \sigma_4, \ldots$ have been given the approximately correct value σ_2. Similar expressions hold for the other spin doublets.[1]

The introduction of the observed values of $\Delta\nu$ in Equation 6 leads to values of σ_2 for the successive elements which are remarkably constant. The average value for thirty-eight elements, from niobium, $Z = 41$, with $\sigma_2 = 3.50$, to uranium, $Z = 92$, with $\sigma_2 = 3.49$, is $\sigma_2 = 3.50$, and deviations from this average rarely exceed 0.05. Similarly constant values of σ_2 for the other spin doublets are found; these are given in Table II. In agreement with expectation they increase with n; that is, with the size of the orbit of the removed electron, and, moreover, for a given value of n they increase with increase in l, for the less eccentric orbits penetrate less deeply into the region of large effective nuclear charge.

The s states, K, L_I, M_I, etc., are single, so that values of σ_2 cannot be derived for them from doublet separations. Approximate values have been obtained by an indirect method to be described shortly, and these are included in the table.

These considerations, in particular the necessity for the higher order terms and the resultant constancy of the values of σ_2 as well as their reasonable magnitudes, provided one of the most

[1] See A. Sommerfeld, "Atombau und Spektrallinien," 4th ed., Chap. 6., for these expressions and for details concerning the evaluation of the screening constants from the experimental data.

convincing arguments substantiating the wide-spread belief, from 1916 to 1925, that the Sommerfeld relativistic mechanism as well as the Sommerfeld equation for the doublet separation was correct, and that these doublets arose from the relativistic change in mass alone. Soon after the introduction of the spinning electron, however, it was shown by Heisenberg and Jordan that the approximate equation 4 can be derived from the treatment of the spinning electron atomic model with the methods of the quantum mechanics; and recently it has been shown[1] that Dirac's theory of the electron leads not only to the approximate equation, but also to Sommerfeld's exact equation, including all higher terms. The equation, as well as the values of screening constants derived with it, are accordingly still valid, but the mechanism giving rise to the doublets is now believed to lie in the magnetic interaction of the spin moment of the removed electron and its orbital motion. For this reason the doublets are no longer called relativistic doublets, but rather magnetic or, better, spin doublets.[2]

A first-order perturbation treatment of the problem[3] of the theoretical calculation of the screening constant σ_2 leads to the values included in Table

TABLE II.—THE SCREENING CONSTANT σ_2

	1s K	2s L_I	2p $L_{II}L_{III}$	3s M_I	3p $M_{II}M_{III}$	3d $M_{IV}M_V$	4s N_I	4p $N_{II}N_{III}$	4d $N_{IV}N_V$	4f $N_{VI}N_{VII}$
σ_2 observed.	. . . . .	2.0 ± 0.2	3.50 ± 0.02	6.8 ± 0.5	8.4 ± 0.2	13.0 ± 0.3	14 ± 2	17.0 ± 0.8	24 ± 2.5	34 ± 4
σ_2 calculated.	0.167	2.11	2.85	7.04	7.94	10.37	15.55	17.20	20.43	26.27

[1] W. GORDON, *Z. f. Phys.*, **48**: 11, 1928; C. G. DARWIN, *Proc.*, Roy. Soc., A **118**: 654, 1928.

[2] The correction term includes both spin and relativity corrections, the latter, however, being the same for the two levels comprising a spin doublet.

[3] LINUS PAULING, *Z. f. Phys.*, **40**: 344, 1926.

II, which are in general agreement with the experimental ones. The method used was such as to give more accurate results with the more eccentric or bits, so that the excellent agreement found for the most eccentric orbits, corresponding to L_{I}, M_{I}, N_{I} and $N_{\text{II}}N_{\text{III}}$, as well as the somewhat less eccentric $M_{\text{II}}M_{\text{III}}$, is particularly satisfactory.

It is a remarkable coincidence that two such different mechanisms as the relativistic change in mass of the electron and the interaction of its spin moment and orbital motion should lead to the same equation; Sommerfeld's no longer acceptible derivation of his still valid highly complicated formula is without parallel in the history of physics. The coincidence becomes less remarkable through Dirac's derivation of the spin from relativistic equations, for the electron spin may now be considered a relativistic phenomenon, and it is not out of place to speak, as Sommerfeld did, of relativistic doublets.

44e. Moseley Diagrams for Term Values.—Bohr and Coster plotted $(W/Rhc)^{1/2}$ or $(\nu/R)^{1/2}$ against the nuclear charge, as shown in Figures 43 and 44, for the purpose of studying the properties of the first-order screening constant σ_1. Such graphs are called "Moseley diagrams."[1] From Equation 4, neglecting the fine-structure term, it is seen that the ordinates in these diagrams roughly represent values of $\frac{Z - \sigma_1}{n}$; or, more accurately, values of the quantity

$$\sqrt{\frac{\nu}{R}} = \frac{Z - \sigma_1}{n} - \frac{\alpha^2(Z - \sigma_2)^4}{2n^2(Z - \sigma_1)}\left\{\frac{3}{4n} - \frac{1}{l + \frac{1}{2}} + \frac{j(j+1) - l(l+1) - s(s+1)}{2l(l + \frac{1}{2})(l+1)}\right\}. \quad (7)$$

[1] In his first papers Moseley plotted $\sqrt{\nu}$ against Z, with ν the wave-numbers of the X-ray lines themselves. He found it necessary to assign particular values to Z in order that his curves should be smooth; this was the way in which the correct values of the atomic numbers of the heavy elements were first found. Two significant improvements in the construction of Moseley diagrams were introduced by Sommerfeld, who was the first to use for ν X-ray term values instead of line frequencies, and who divided them by R to obtain a dimensionless quantity (*Ann. d. Phys.*, **51**: 125, 1916). Bohr and Coster (*Z. f. Phys.*, **12**: 342, 1923), using Coster's careful measurements, made accurate Moseley diagrams and discussed them in terms of the electronic configurations of the atoms, making especial use of their mechanism of external screening.

The curves consist, for the most part, of nearly straight lines with a slight upward curvature due to the spin and relativity term. It is seen that the slope of the lines is indeed roughly inversely proportional to n. The sudden changes in slope which occur at certain places are of extreme interest. These arise from the external screening term in σ_1, which has the form given by Equation 3, or, roughly,

$$\sigma_1 = \sigma_0 + \frac{n^2}{Z - \sigma_0} \sum_i \frac{z_i}{\rho_i}.$$

In going from one element to the following one the change of one unit in Z will not be of great direct significance. The addition of an extra outer electron, however, brings with it an increase of $\frac{n^2}{(Z - \sigma_0)\rho_i}$ in σ_1. If the added electron goes into an outer orbit, with a large radius $\rho_i a_0$, this increase will not be large; moreover, if for a series of elements the added electrons go into the same shell, their contribution to σ_1 will be uniform and will give a linear contribution to the Moseley curve. But when the successively added electrons begin to be introduced into an inner shell there will be a change in the magnitude of this increase, and $Z - \sigma_1$ will show a sudden decrease in slope. From Table II, Chap. IX, we expect such a bending at scandium, $Z = 21$, where the $3d$ subshell begins to be occupied. At copper, $Z = 29$, this subshell is filled, and here the curves resume approximately their original slopes. The same effect of the occupation of the $4d$ subshell, from yttrium, $Z = 39$, to palladium, $Z = 46$, and of the $4f$ subshell, from cerium, $Z = 58$, to lutecium, $Z = 71$, is also clearly evident in the diagrams.

44f. Screening Doublets.—With σ_2 known for states forming spin doublets, the relativity and spin correction can be calculated and subtracted from the observed term values, to give the *reduced term values* ν'. It is then possible to solve for σ_1. This has been done by Sommerfeld,[1] from whose book Figure 46 is taken. The curves show very clearly the steady increase of σ_1 with increase in Z. It is of interest to note that the curves for $M_{II}M_{III}$ and $M_{IV}M_{V}$ are parallel, as are those for the various L and N levels. This shows that the external screening for orbits with the same total quantum number, as $3p$ and $3d$, is the same, while the screening of inner electrons is different on account of a difference

[1] A. Sommerfeld, "Atombau und Spektrallinien," 4th ed. p. 460.

in penetration. This is in agreement with expectation; we expect, moreover, that the external screening will also be the same for 3*s*, and that its σ_1 curve will parallel the others.

A spin doublet is formed by two states with the same value of l and different values of j; namely, $l + \frac{1}{2}$ and $l - \frac{1}{2}$. The doublet formed by two states with the same j and different

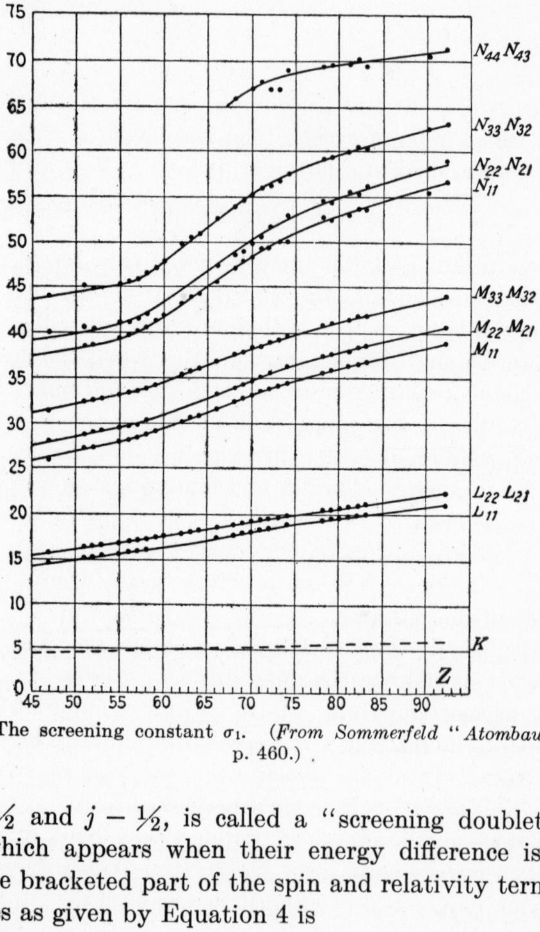

FIG. 46.—The screening constant σ_1. (*From Sommerfeld "Atombau,"* 4th ed. p. 460.)

l's, $j + \frac{1}{2}$ and $j - \frac{1}{2}$, is called a "screening doublet," for a reason which appears when their energy difference is written out. The bracketed part of the spin and relativity term for the two states as given by Equation 4 is

$$\left\{\frac{3}{4n} - \frac{1}{l + \frac{1}{2}} + \frac{j(j+1) - l(l+1) - s(s+1)}{2l(l + \frac{1}{2})(l+1)}\right\} = \left\{\frac{3}{4n} - \frac{1}{j + \frac{1}{2}}\right\},$$

leading to a difference in $\sqrt{\frac{\nu}{R}}$ of

$$\sqrt{\frac{\nu(l')}{R}} - \sqrt{\frac{\nu(l'')}{R}} = \frac{\sigma_1(l') - \sigma_1(l'')}{n} + \frac{\alpha^2}{2n^2}\left\{\frac{3}{4n} - \frac{1}{j + \frac{1}{2}}\right\}\Delta\frac{(Z - \sigma_2)^4}{(Z - \sigma_1)}. \quad (8)$$

As a first approximation the term in α^2 may be neglected, so that we may write

$$\Delta\sqrt{\frac{\nu}{R}} \cong \frac{\Delta\sigma_1}{n}, \quad (9)$$

where $\Delta\sigma_1$ is a constant. This equation expresses the *screening doublet law*, discovered by Hertz.[1] It explains immediately why some of the curves in the Moseley diagram are nearly parallel; namely, those with the same n and j but different l.

Equation 9 should hold accurately for reduced term values. That it does is shown by the constancy of $\Delta\sigma_1$ for $3p - 3d$, etc., Figure 46. It is possible to make use of this fact to obtain approximate values of σ_2 and σ_1 for the states which form no spin doublets, such as $2s$, $3s$, etc. If an arbitrary value of σ_2 is chosen for $2s$ and the reduced term values for L_{I} are calculated from the observed term values with its use, it is found in general that the reduced Moseley curve does not parallel that for L_{II} and L_{III}; that is, that $\Delta\sigma_1$ is not independent of Z. Only by choosing a certain value for σ_2, about 2.0, is this constancy obtained. Similarly, values of σ_2 for other s levels can be calculated; this was done by Wentzel,[2] whose results are incorporated in Table II. Knowing σ_2 for these states, σ_1 can also be found. The results of this treatment for L_{I}, M_{I}, and N_{I} are shown in Figure 46; it obviously cannot be applied to the K level. Average values of $\Delta\sigma_1$ as given by Sommerfeld are to be found in Table III. It is of particular interest that the values of $\Delta\sigma_1$ are integral multiples of the constant 0.57.

44g. External Screening: a Quantitative Discussion.—The qualitative discussion given the question of external screening by Bohr and Coster could evidently be replaced by a quantitative treatment in case values of the effective radii $\rho_i a_0$ of the outer electron shells were known. The calculation of these radii for various atoms can be made with the use of a general method

[1] G. Hertz, *Z. f. Phys.*, **3**: 19, 1920.
[2] G. Wentzel, *Z. f. Phys*, **16**: 14, 1923.

TABLE III.—DIFFERENCES IN THE ENERGY SCREENING CONSTANT σ_1

	$2s$ L_{I}	$2p$ $L_{\mathrm{II}}L_{\mathrm{III}}$	$3s$ M_{I}	$3p$ $M_{\mathrm{II}}M_{\mathrm{III}}$	$3d$ $M_{\mathrm{IV}}M_{\mathrm{V}}$	$4s$ N_{I}	$4p$ $N_{\mathrm{II}}N_{\mathrm{III}}$	$4d$ $N_{\mathrm{IV}}N_{\mathrm{V}}$	$4f$ $N_{\mathrm{VI}}N_{\mathrm{VII}}$
$\Delta\sigma_1$		1.15 2×0.57		1.70 3×0.57	3.49 $2 \times 3 \times 0.58$		2.2 4×0.55	4.9 $2 \times 4 \times 0.6$	10 $4 \times 4 \times 0.6$

of discussing the properties of many-electron atoms by considering each orbit to be a hydrogen-like orbit in the field of an effective nuclear charge. For properties involving the size

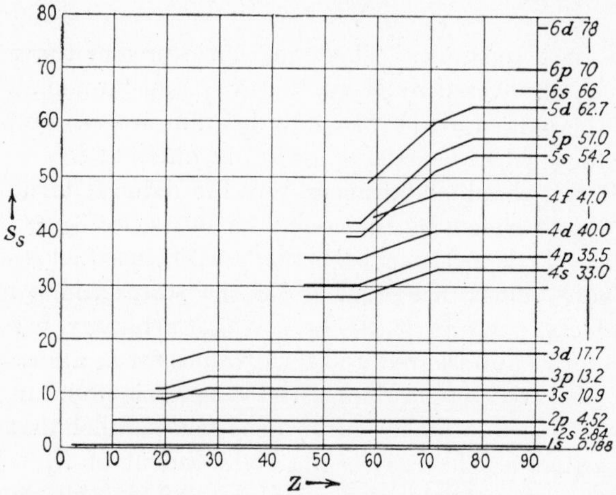

FIG. 47.—The size screening constant S_s for various electrons as a function of Z.

of the orbits the values of the screening constant S_s to be used for the various orbits are shown in Figure 47.[1] $\rho_i a_0$ should be

[1] Values of S_s for certain values of Z are given by LINUS PAULING, *Proc., Roy. Soc.*, A **114**: 181, 1927. In the construction of Figure 47, S_s was assumed to be independent of Z for a given orbit except when an inner shell is being completed. For this reason there is probably some inaccuracy in the curves for Z large.

To assist in preventing confusion, there are listed below the various screening constants used in this chapter, with the section in which each first occurs.

σ_0: energy screening constant due to inner electrons; Sec. 44a.

σ_1: energy screening constant due to both inner and outer electrons; Sec. 44b.

σ_2: spin doublet screening constant; Sec. 44c.

σ_3, σ_4: spin doublet screening constants for terms of higher order in the Sommerfeld equation; Sec. 44d.

S_s: size screening constant, giving the average distance of the electron from the nucleus; Sec. 44g.

chosen in such a way as to give the right average value to $1/r_i$; that is,

$$\frac{1}{\rho_i a_0} = \overline{\left(\frac{1}{r_i}\right)}$$

From the quantum mechanics expression for $\overline{\left(\frac{1}{r}\right)}$ of Section 7 it is seen that we must place

$$\rho_i = \frac{n_i^2}{Z - S_{s_i}}. \tag{10}$$

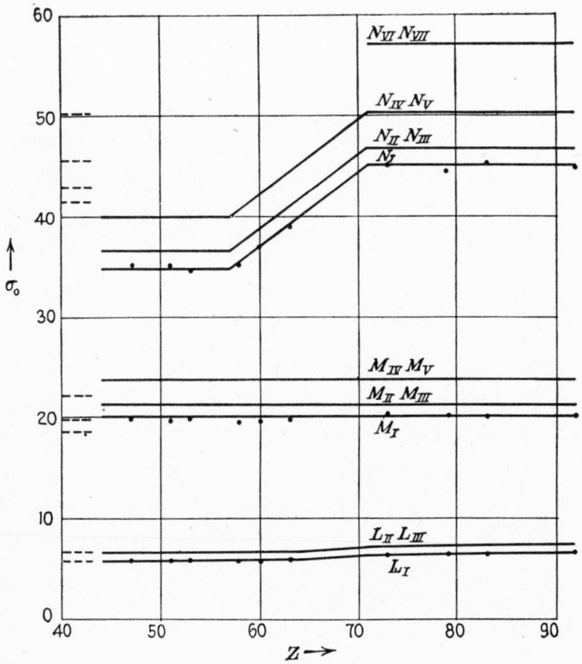

FIG. 48.—Values of σ_0 obtained from σ_1 by correction for external screening.

Substituting this in Equation 3, it is found that σ_0 and σ_1 are related by the equation

$$(Z - \sigma_0)^2 = (Z - \sigma_1)^2 + 2n^2\sum_i z_i \frac{Z - S_{s_i}}{n_i^2}, \tag{11}$$

with the aid of which σ_0 can be evaluated.

The results of the application of this equation are shown in Figure 48. The dots represent values of σ_0 for the levels L_{I}, M_{I}, and N_{I} calculated for representative elements. It is seen that σ_0 is sensibly constant for succeeding elements; the increase in σ_1 for M_{I} from 26.0 for silver, $Z = 47$, to 38.9 for uranium, $Z = 92$, is due entirely to the external screening term. Moreover, the characteristic shapes of the σ_1 curves are seen to arise from external screening. Quantitative verification is given the suggestion that the changes in slope of σ_1 at $Z = 57$ and $Z = 71$ are due to the change in external screening accompanying the insertion of electrons in the $4f$ subshell.

For elements with $Z < 65$, σ_0 for L_{I} varies between 5.90 and 6.00. Above $Z = 65$ it shows a trend, increasing to 6.7 at $Z = 92$. It is probable that this trend is not real, but is due to error in the S_s curves in this region.

The increase in σ_0 for the level N_{I} in the region from $Z = 57$ to $Z = 71$ is the expected result of the completion of the $4f$ subshell.

The σ_0 curves for $L_{\text{II}}L_{\text{III}}$, $M_{\text{II}}M_{\text{III}}$, etc., are easily obtained from the corresponding σ_1 curves and the L_{I}, M_{I}, etc., curves in the following way. If $\Delta\sigma_0$ and $\Delta\sigma_1$ represent the differences in the values of σ_0 and σ_1 for two levels in the same shell, such as L_{I} and $L_{\text{II}}L_{\text{III}}$, then there hold the relations

$$(Z - \sigma_0)^2 = (Z - \sigma_1)^2 + C,$$
$$(Z - \sigma_0 - \Delta\sigma_0)^2 = (Z - \sigma_1 - \Delta\sigma_1)^2 + C,$$

in which C, arising from external screening, has the same value for the two levels. Eliminating C, we obtain the relation

$$\Delta\sigma_0 = \Delta\sigma_1\left\{1 - \frac{1}{Z}\left(\sigma_1 - \sigma_0 + \frac{\Delta\sigma_1 - \Delta\sigma_0}{2}\right)\right\}.$$

It is found on substitution of numerical values that $\Delta\sigma_0$ is equal to about 78 per cent of $\Delta\sigma_1$ for all values of Z and for all levels. As a result the values of $\Delta\sigma_0$ show the same integral relation as do those of $\Delta\sigma_1$ (Table III), with the fundamental separation equal to about 0.44.

It is possible to calculate theoretical values for σ_0 in a way similar to that used for σ_2.[1] The results of this calculation are represented in Figure 48 by the dashed lines at the left, and are included in Table IV, together with the averages obtained from the experimental term values. The agreement is in general satisfactory; so that we are justified in saying that Sommerfeld's

[1] The calculation consists in the application of a treatment exactly paralleling that used for σ_2, and described by Linus Pauling, *Z. f. Phys.*, **40**: 344, 1926.

prediction[1] of the early development of a rational theory of X-ray term values has been realized; the theory has not the simplicity he anticipated, however.[2]

TABLE IV.—THE SCREENING CONSTANT σ_0

	L_I	$L_{II}L_{III}$	M_I	$M_{II}M_{III}$	$M_{IV}M_V$	N_I	$N_{II}N_{III}$	$N_{IV}N_V$	$N_{VI}N_{VII}$
σ_0 observed.	5.95	6.85	20.0	21.3	23.8	45	46.8	50.2	57
σ_0 calculated. . . .	5.94	6.79	18.6	19.8	22.0	41.4	42.8	45.6	50.2

45. COMPARISON WITH ALKALI-LIKE AND HYDROGEN-LIKE SPECTRA

The foregoing description shows that there exists a great similarity in structure between the X-ray level diagram and that for the alkali atoms, the difference being mainly a difference

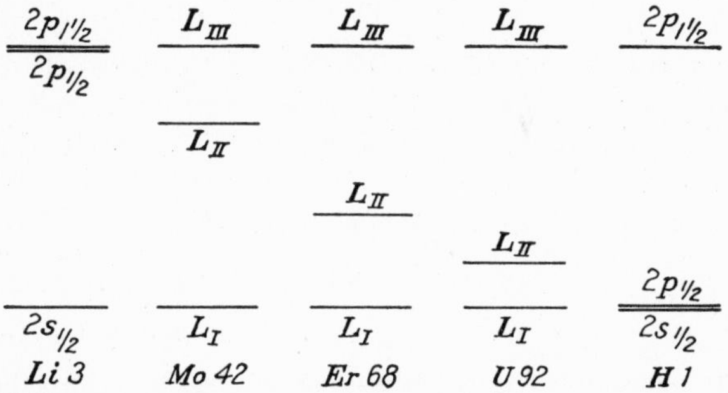

FIG. 49.—Relative positions of the L levels for various elements, showing the transition from lithium, with a very wide screening doublet, to hydrogen, with a very wide spin doublet.

in sign. If one turns an X-ray level diagram upside down, the similarity becomes evident; it is only necessary to leave out the X-ray levels which have n smaller than the n of the valence electron (in the normal state) of the alkali atom under consideration. Thus an X-ray level diagram from the M levels on is similar to the sodium diagram, and from the L levels on to the lithium diagram; the complete level scheme is related to that of hydrogen.

Figure 49 gives as an example the L levels, turned upside down, for the elements molybdenum, $Z = 42$, erbium, $Z = 68$, and

[1] A. SOMMERFELD, "Atombau," p. 461.

[2] An approximate calculation of term values for the level $M_{IV}M_V$ with the use of the Thomas-Fermi atomic model has been given by F. RASETTI, *Z. f. Phys.*, **49**: 546, 1928. Accurate X-ray term values are also provided by Hartree's method of treating many-electron atoms, mentioned in Sec. 8.

uranium, $Z = 92$, compared with the $2s$ and $2p$ levels of lithium on one side and hydrogen on the other. The scales are different for each element and arbitrarily chosen so as to make the outer levels coincide. In lithium the spin doublet is very small compared with the $2s - 2p$ separation; that is, with the screening doublet separation. In molybdenum the spin doublet is already of the same order of magnitude as the screening doublet and in uranium the spin doublet is by far the larger. In hydrogen there is no screening effect at all, so that the levels $^2S_{1/2}$ and $^2P_{1/2}$ fall exactly together. The hydrogen fine structure can be considered as a limiting case of the X-ray fine structure for very large Z. For if Z becomes very large the screening effect will have relatively little influence, whereas the spin doublet will be very wide. The levels in lithium can be likewise considered as a limiting case of the X-ray fine structure when the screening effect is large and the spin correction negligibly small.

46. MULTIPLET STRUCTURE IN X-RAY SPECTRA

In our treatment of X-ray spectra we have made extensive use of the fact that the removal of one electron from a completed group gives rise to a doublet state of the atom, without paying attention to the possibility that there may be other incompleted groups present in the atom at the same time. In fact, the deductions of the foregoing paragraphs concerning the structure of X-ray levels are only strictly true when all electron groups in the normal atom are completed. This is the case only for atoms which have $^1S_0$ as normal state, such as the rare gases or the alkaline earths. For atoms with any other normal state the removal of an electron from an inner completed group will not lead to exactly the doublet levels described above. It is instead necessary to consider the result of combining the quantum vectors of the inner incompleted group with those of the outer one. Almost always the interaction between the inner group and the outer electrons will be very weak, so that the influence of the outer electrons will consist merely in a small splitting of the original doublet levels. Each doublet level will be transformed into as many sublevels as there are possible resultants between the **j**'s of the inner and the outer incompleted group. This is an extreme example of the (**jj**) coupling, similar, however, to that found in the higher series members of the neon spectrum. The splitting of the levels is usually so small that it can not be detected with the present resolving power of X-ray spectroscopic apparatus.

In atoms with a partially completed inner electron group a large interaction between this group and neighboring electron groups is to be expected. Thus the fact that the 4*f* orbits are not all occupied in the elements from cerium, $Z = 58$, to lutecium, $Z = 71$, must give rise to rather large disturbances of the doublet structure of the outer X-ray levels of these atoms. Investigations made by Coster, Druyvesteyn, and Van der Tuuk[1] have proved the existence of such disturbances in these elements. The levels N_{VI} and N_{VII}, arising from the incompleted 4*f* group itself, were found to have a very complicated structure in the rare earths, somewhat similar to the structure found in optical spectra. The resolving power of the existent apparatus is, however, not sufficient to allow more detailed conclusions to be reached.

46a. The Structure of Absorption Edges.—X-ray absorption edges often show a complicated structure; multiple edges very close together, fine lines, and other structural peculiarities have been observed. No doubt different processes are responsible for this structure in different cases.

It was suggested early in the development of X-ray theory[2] that the ejected electron may sometimes not be removed completely from the atom by the absorbed quantum of radiation, but only to an unoccupied outer orbit. The softest X-radiation absorbed would then have a frequency corresponding to the energy required to lift an electron from an inner orbit to the most stable of the unoccupied outer orbits. Such processes would lead to an absorption edge showing absorption lines on the long wave-length side. Absorption lines have actually been observed[3] in argon gas, and their positions have been correlated with the expected energy levels. Conditions are less favorable for the production of these lines in solids, on account of the perturbing influence of surrounding atoms on the outer orbits. They might be expected, however, to be shown by atoms with an incompleted inner electron group, in which case their distance

[1] D. Coster and M. J. Druyvesteyn, *Z. f. Phys.*, **40**: 765, 1927; J. H. van der Tuuk, *Z. f. Phys.*, **44**: 737, 1927.

[2] W. Kossel, *Z. f. Phys.*, **1**: 124, 1920.

[3] D. Coster and J. H. van der Tuuk, *Nature*, **117**: 586, 1926; *Z. f. Phys.*, **37**: 367, 1926.

from the edge of the region of continuous absorption would be rather large. As a matter of fact, more or less sharp absorption lines in the neighborhood of an absorption edge are shown by many elements.

It is also possible for the absorbed quantum of radiation to remove two electrons from the atom; this would give rise to a number of subsidiary edges in the neighborhood of the principal one.[1]

A further effect influencing the position and structure of absorption edges arises from the state of chemical combination of the atom; that is, from the action of the atoms with which it is combined.[2] This effect usually leads to a shift of the edge by an amount depending mainly on the valence state of the atom. A generally applicable quantitative theory of this shift has not yet been developed.[3]

47. X-RAY SPECTRA OF HIGHER RANK

So far we have considered the X-ray levels resulting from the removal of only one electron from the atom. Certain X-ray lines which appear as satellites on the high frequency side of the ordinary lines can be explained as resulting from the removal of two or more inner electrons at the same time. The resulting spectra are called X-ray spectra of the second, third, etc., rank.

Wentzel[4] was the first who called attention to this possible explanation of these satellites. The most recent theoretical treatment has been given by Coster and Druyvesteyn,[5] who improved Wentzel's method by using the newer developments of the theory of spectral structure. That these satellites are

[1] For details concerning the not yet satisfactorily solved problem of this fine structure, reference may be made to K. Chamberlain, *Phys. Rev.*, **26**: 525, 1926; J. M. Nuttall, *ibid.*, **31**: 742, 1928; G. A. Lindsay and H. R. Voorhees, *Phil. Mag.*, **6**: 910, 1928; B. B. Ray, *Z. f. Phys.*, **55**: 119, 1929; etc.

[2] J. Bergengren, *Z. f. Phys.*, **3**: 247, 1920; A. E. Lindh, *ibid.*, **6**: 303 1921; **31**: 210, 1925; O. Stelling, *Z. f. anorg. Chem.*, **131**: 48, 1923; *Z.f. phys. Chem.*, **117**: 161, 175, 194, 1925; *Z. f. Phys.*, **50**: 506, 626, 1928; S. Aoyama, K. Kimura, and Y. Nishina, *Z. f. Phys.*, **44**: 810, 1927; etc.

[3] See, however, Linus Pauling, *Phys. Rev.*, **34**: 954, 1929, for the theory of the shift in crystals of simple structure.

[4] G. Wentzel, *Ann. d. Phys.*, **66**: 437, 1921.

[5] D. Coster and M. J. Druyvesteyn, *Z. f. Phys.*, **40**: 765, 1927; M. J. Druyvesteyn, *Z. f. Phys.*, **43**: 707, 1927.

actually due to multiple inner ionization has also been proved by various experiments on the energy required to excite the atom sufficiently to cause their emission.

The energy to remove a K and an L electron from the same atom will be approximately equal to the energy to remove the K electron plus the energy to remove an L electron from the element with atomic number one unit greater, for the effect of the removal of the K electron in changing the energy of the L electrons will be approximately given by increasing the nuclear charge by one unit. This may be written symbolically

$$K(Z) + L(Z) < KL(Z) = K(Z) + L(Z) + \delta \cong K(Z) + L(Z + 1),$$

in which $KL(Z)$ signifies the energy required to remove a K and an L electron simultaneously from an atom of atomic number Z, and $K(Z)$ and $L(Z)$ signify the energies to remove the K or L electron alone. If the open space in the K shell is now filled by an L electron there will result an atom with two L electrons missing. The energy of this state cannot be predicted with certainty. One reason for this is that there is some question as to whether the (jj) coupling or Russell-Saunders coupling will hold; in the latter case the coupling energy would have to be calculated, and this cannot be easily done. For not too small nuclear charge, however, the (jj) coupling may be expected to hold, even for two electrons in the same group. The energy $L^2(Z)$ required to remove two L electrons from the atom will then be given by

$$2L(Z) < L^2(Z) = 2L(Z) + \epsilon < L(Z) + L(Z + 1).$$

The position of the spectral line corresponding to the transition from the L^2 state to the KL state is found in the usual way by subtracting the energy of the final state from that of the initial state:

$$KL(Z) - L^2(Z) = K(Z) - L(Z) + \delta - \epsilon.$$

Since $K(Z) - L(Z)$ represents the ordinary X-ray line, $\delta - \epsilon$ gives the displacement of the satellite relative to this line, and since δ is larger than ϵ the satellite will occur on the high frequency or short wave-length side. This conclusion is substantiated by experiment. Furthermore, the displacement is expected not to exceed a maximum value found by equating $L^2(Z)$ to its minimum value $2L(Z)$; that is

$$\delta - \epsilon \leqq L(Z + 1) - L(Z).$$

That the observed satellites of the $K\alpha$ lines actually lie in this predicted region provides support for the theory of Coster and Druyvesteyn.

This treatment can be easily extended to other cases. We have not yet taken into account that there are three kinds of L electrons, corresponding to the levels L_{I}, L_{II}, and L_{III}. If the validity of the (jj) coupling can be accepted, any one of these L levels can be used in the reasoning given above. $L^2(Z)$ will mean, for instance, either $L_{\mathrm{I}}L_{\mathrm{II}}$, or $L_{\mathrm{II}}L_{\mathrm{III}}$, or L^2_{II}, etc. But in the case of the Russell-Saunders coupling, which might occur in light elements for electrons of the same group, it is necessary to be more careful. It will then be meaningless to speak of $L_{\mathrm{II}}\ L_{\mathrm{III}}$, for instance; the atom must instead be considered, as in optical spectra, as having a $2p^4$ configuration, giving rise to an inverted ^3P, a ^1D, and a ^1S term. It has not yet been possible, however, to go into such details in attempting to account for the exact position of the X-ray lines of higher rank.

48. THE APPLICATION OF X-RAY LAWS TO OPTICAL SPECTRA

The laws governing the multiplet separations in optical spectra have been discussed in detail in Sections 15, 22, and 29. As these multiplets have the same origin as the X-ray spin doublets a comparison of the two suggests itself. The optical spectra of a sequence of isoelectronic atoms and ions (having the same number of extranuclear electrons) are completely analogous to ordinary X-ray spectra in case the atoms have only one valence electron. Such a sequence has been discussed in Section 15*b*, where the $3p$ doublet separations of the sodium-like atoms $\mathrm{Na_I}$ to $\mathrm{Cl_{VI}}$ were shown to be given by an equation similar to that given in Section 44d for X-ray spin doublets. The applicability of the X-ray doublet equation to optical spectra was recognized by Millikan and Bowen[1] and by Landé[2] long before the reason for it was discovered.

These investigators emphasized further the analogy between X-ray and optical spectra, such as the law of screening doublets. Millikan and Bowen even made use of deductions from Moseley

[1] R. A. Millikan and I. S. Bowen, *Phys. Rev.*, **23**: 764, 1924; **24**: 209, 1924. Sommerfeld, in fact, had pointed out very early (*Ann. d. Phys.*, **51**: 1, 1916) that the doublet separation for lithium is given by the equation derived by him for hydrogen and applied also to the X-ray doublets.

[2] A. Landé, *Z. f. Phys.*, **25**: 46, 1924.

X-ray diagrams. In Figure 50 there is shown, as an example, the optical Moseley diagram for the $3s$, $3p$, and $3d$ levels of sodium-like ions. (In most optical spectra the spin doublet separation is so small that it can be neglected, as is done in this figure.) It is seen that the Moseley curves are actually nearly straight lines, with slopes of nearly ⅓, which is the expected $1/n$ in this case. This suggests that the main energy expression can be represented by Equation 3, which gives for term values

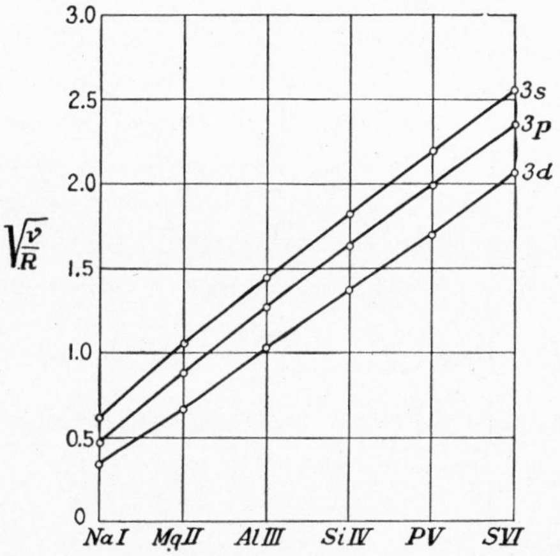

FIG. 50.—Moseley diagram for optical levels of sodium-like atoms. This figure is based on one given by I. S. Bowen and R. A. Millikan. (*Phys. Rev.*, **25**, 295, 1925.)

$$-\frac{W}{hc} = \frac{R(Z - \sigma_1)^2}{n^2}, \tag{12}$$

instead of the usual Rydberg formula for penetrating orbits

$$-\frac{W}{hc} = \frac{Rz^2}{(n - \Delta)^2}, \tag{13}$$

in which z denotes the effective nuclear charge in the outer region of the atom.

The applicability of Equation 3 to X-ray levels was supported by the argument that in the inner shells the effective nuclear charge varies only within relatively narrow limits along an electron orbit. It is accordingly an unexpected and surprising result that this equation can be used also for the penetrating orbits of the alkali-like atoms.

The validity of the screening doublet law for optical spectra is also shown by Figure 50. The curves for $3s$, $3p$, and $3d$ are nearly parallel, showing that there is a nearly constant difference in the values of σ_1 for these levels throughout the isoelectronic sequence. Instead of studying the square roots of the term values, we may consider the differences of the term values themselves. From Equation 12 we obtain

$$3s - 3p = \frac{R(Z - \sigma_1)^2}{n^2} - \frac{R(Z - \sigma_1 - \Delta\sigma_1)^2}{n^2} = \frac{R}{n^2}\{2\Delta\sigma_1(Z - \sigma_1) - \Delta\sigma_1^2\}. \quad (14)$$

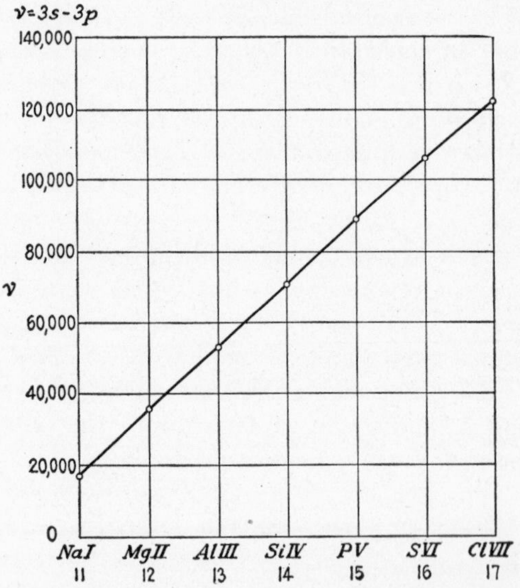

FIG. 51.—Plot of the separation $3s - 3p$ for sodium-like atoms as a function of Z.

Since $\Delta\sigma_1$ is a constant and σ_1 is a linear function of Z, this equation shows that the separation $3s - 3p$ is also a linear function of the atomic number. The accuracy of this relation is shown by Figure 51, in which are plotted the $3s - 3p$ separations as a function of Z for the sodium-like isoelectronic sequence. It was mentioned in Section 43*e* that transitions between two levels with the same value of n are not observed in X-ray spectra. In optical spectra, however, these transitions often produce the strongest lines observed, as in the example we are discussing. For this reason Equation 14 is of extreme importance, showing as it does a linear relation between atomic number and the wave-numbers of the strongest lines in the spectra of isoelectronic ions. With the aid of diagrams such as Figure 51 it is possible to predict with great accuracy the positions of a spectral line for many atoms if the corresponding line has been observed for two atoms in the sequence. The graphical extrapolation also takes into account small deviations from the screening doublet law. It is clear that this extrapolation becomes more and more accurate for higher degrees of ionization, for then the effective nuclear charge varies less along the orbit, which becomes more and more similar to an X-ray orbit.

It is possible to give a still more detailed account of the change of σ_1 with Z in the isoelectronic sequence. It was pointed out by Laporte[1] that in the optical region σ_1 decreases gradually with increasing Z, whereas for X-ray levels it increases with increasing Z. This is shown in Figures 52 and 53, representing the observed[2] values of σ_1 for the optical state $3d^9$, corresponding to the X-ray level $M_{\text{IV}}M_{\text{V}}$, and the optical state 4d^9, corresponding to $N_{\text{IV}}N_{\text{V}}$. The increase in σ_1 for X-ray levels we attributed to external screening, which is not operative for optical levels. Moreover, there is no reason to expect σ_0 (which equals σ_1 in this case) to be constant here. When the effective nuclear charge in the outer region becomes very small (Z small) the electron will tend to remain in this outer region, and the value of σ_0 will increase; this provides a qualitative explanation of the observed curves. It is of interest that the curves could easily be extended in such a way as to approach the values 23.8 and 40.0 found for σ_0 by correcting the X-ray values of σ_1 for external screening.

Recent developments in the analysis of isoelectronic spectra have shown that the screening doublet law holds even in much more complicated cases, where one electron configuration gives rise to many different multiplet levels. It is found that the wave-numbers of homologous lines arising from transitions between the same two levels of the multiplet scheme for different atoms are approximately in linear relationship to Z in an isoelectronic sequence. The increase from element to element is different for the different transitions, though they all arise from the same electron configuration.

[1] O. Laporte, "Sommerfeld Festschrift," p. 128, S. Hirzel, Leipzig, 1928; J. E. Mack, O. Laporte, and R. J. Lang, *Phys. Rev.*, **31**: 748, 1928.

[2] These values of σ_1 represent the energy change accompanying the removal of an electron from a completed $3d$ or $4d$ subgroup of ten electrons.

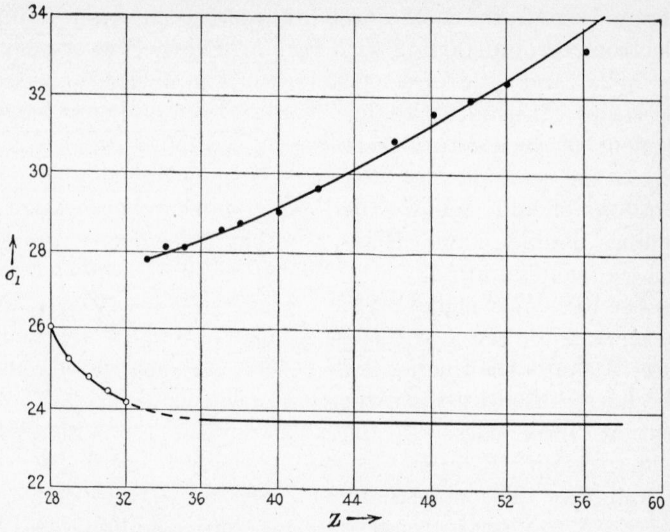

FIG. 52.—Screening constants for the configuration $3d^9$ in optical spectra (shown by open circles). External screening is not operative here; it is seen that these values of σ_1 tend to the σ_0 value found for the X-ray levels (dots represent σ_1 for the X-ray level M_{IV} M_V).

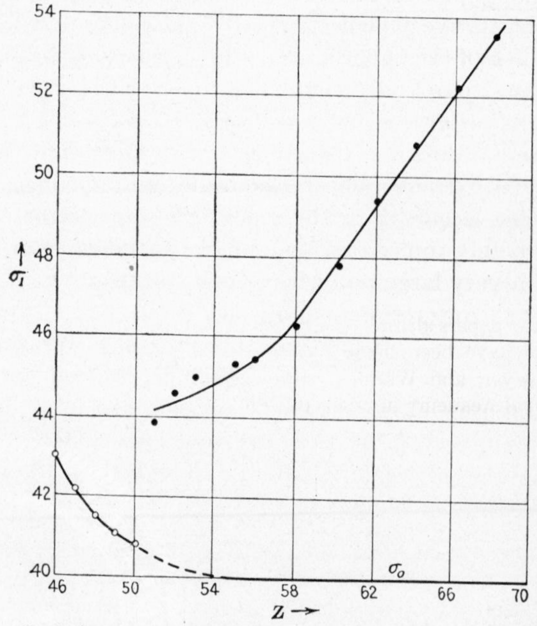

FIG. 53.—Screening constants for the configuration $4d^9$ in optical spectra.

Figure 54 gives the most simple example of this kind. In the isoelectronic group starting with carbon, C_{I}, the two configurations $2s^22p^2$ and $2s2p^3$ are considered. The difference between these states consists in the displacement of an electron from the $2s$ to the $2p$ orbit, and their separation should follow the screening doublet law. However, the configuration $2s^22p^2$ gives rise to a ^3P level and $2s2p^3$ gives a ^3D, a ^3P, and a ^3S state. Figure 54 shows the frequencies of the lines caused by the three transitions from $2s2p^3$ ^3P, ^3D, and ^3S to $2s^22p^2$ ^3P, in C_{I}, N_{II}, O_{III}, and F_{IV}. The transitions give rise to approximately straight lines, but these lines have different slopes.

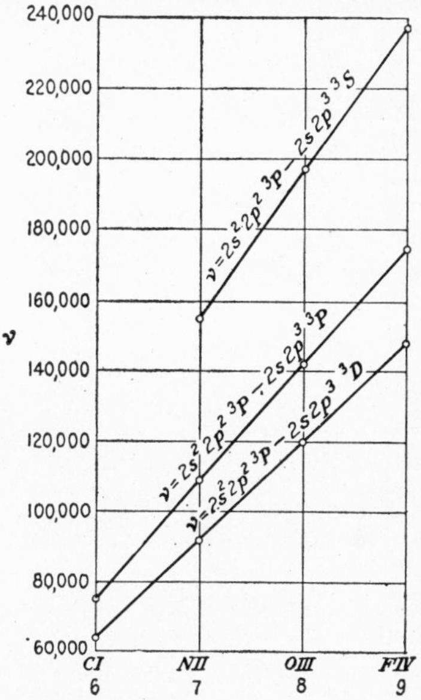

Fig. 54.—Frequencies of corresponding lines of carbon-like atoms as functions of Z.

The foregoing discussions show that we have at present no satisfactory quantitative explanation of the validity of the application of X-ray laws to optical spectra (aside from the laws governing multiplet separations). Nevertheless, it is clear that the use of these laws is of extreme importance in the analysis of complicated spectra. The accuracy with which one can predict lines in spectra of highly ionized atoms has led in recent times to the analysis of a very large number of such spectra.[1]

[1] Besides the papers already mentioned in this section, the most important contributions have been made by Bowen, Gibbs, Lang, Laporte, Mack, Millikan, Sawyer, and White in various papers in the *Phys. Rev.* and the *Proc.*, National Academy of Sciences.

CHAPTER XI

HYPERFINE STRUCTURE AND NUCLEAR MOMENT

49. HYPERFINE STRUCTURE AND ITS INTERPRETATION

It has been observed that many spectral lines, especially those of the heavier atoms, show a narrow fine structure with separations of the order of one wave-number unit. These separations are very much smaller than those of the ordinary multiplet structure of heavy atoms, and for this reason these spectra are said to show *hyperfine structure.* The observed detail cannot be accounted for by means of the electronic configurations provided by the ordinary theory of spectra alone; it seems necessary either to postulate some further property of the electron besides its mass, charge, and spin, or to ascribe the phenomenon to some action of the other constituent of the atom, the nucleus. Of these the latter alternative is the more acceptible.

The interaction of the nucleus of an atom and its surrounding electrons giving rise to hyperfine structure can take place in various ways. At the present time it is difficult to decide which interaction is occurring in a given spectrum; it seems highly probable that for different cases different interactions must be involved, and that for some cases at least two or more are simultaneously operative.

One possible explanation is that the hyperfine structure is due to the existence of isotopes; that the lines due to each isotope are single, but are displaced slightly from those due to the other isotopes of the element. Not the difference in mass (which would lead to very much smaller separations) but the difference in structure of the nuclei is held to be responsible. For example, the complicated nucleus might have a permanent electric dipole moment of different magnitude in the various isotopes; or the nucleus might be polarizable in the electric field of an electron, with the polarizability varying from isotope to isotope. In either case the effective field of the nucleus would not be exactly Coulombian and the energies of corresponding quantum states would be slightly different for the different isotopes. Since we observe only spectral lines, which measure the differences between energy levels, and since there could be no intercombinations between the levels of any two isotopes, it would be difficult to deduce from spectral data the relative positions of the energy levels of the different isotopes arising from such an interaction with the nucleus.

It is also important to note that the presence of a permanent or induced electric dipole in the nucleus would not affect the magnetic properties of the quantum states, and hence the Zeeman effect for all the hyperfine structure components would be the same and would agree with the ordinary theory of the Zeeman effect. The Zeeman patterns of the different components would show no influence on each other, since they have their origin in different atoms. The experimental observation of complicated and unexpected hyperfine Zeeman effects for spectra such as that of bismuth (Sec. 52) eliminates such an explanation of hyperfine structure in these cases. The Zeeman effect for the p^5s levels of neon as observed by Hansen[1] is, however, just that to be expected if the hyperfine structure arises from the isotope effect (neon has three isotopes[2] of mass number 20, 21, and 22). Very probably some of the many hyperfine components of the mercury lines are also to be accounted for in this way.

Pauli[3] pointed out that the existence of hyperfine structure also could be accounted for if the nucleus had an "ausgezeichnete Achse." This axis could be associated with a magnetic moment, whose interaction with the extranuclear electrons would give rise to the energy terms causing hyperfine splitting of the levels. Just as in the case of the spinning electron, such a magnetic moment would be associated with a mechanical moment, whose magnitude may be represented by $ih/2\pi$, in which i is a new quantum number, the *nuclear spin quantum number*.

Recent developments in the theory of the band spectra[4] and heat capacity[5] of molecular hydrogen have shown that the hydro-

[1] H. Hansen, *Naturwiss.*, **15**: 163, 1927.

[2] T. R. Hogness and H. M. Kvalnes, *Nature*, **122**: 441, 1928.

[3] W. Pauli, *Naturwiss.*, **12**: 741, 1924; see also G. Joos, *Phys. Z.*, **26**: 357, 1925.

[4] W. Heisenberg, *Z. f. Phys.*, **41**: 239, 1927; F. Hund, *ibid*, **42**: 93, 1927.

[5] D. M. Dennison, *Proc.*, Roy. Soc., A **115**: 483, 1927.

gen nucleus, like the electron, possesses a spin moment corresponding to $i = 1/2$. Its magnetic moment is probably e/Mc times the mechanical moment, in which M denotes the mass of the proton, and is thus only $1/1838$th of that of the electron. The influence of such a magnetic moment on the spectrum of atomic hydrogen would be so small as to escape experimental observation. For heavy atoms, in which the electrons approach the nucleus much more closely than in hydrogen, even such a small nuclear magnetic moment would give rise to observable hyperfine structure separations. On the other hand, we know that atomic nuclei contain electrons which may contribute to the moment of the nucleus, with the production of a magnetic moment of the order of one Bohr magneton. This would give rise to observable hyperfine structure separations even for the very light elements.

The hyperfine structure of energy levels and spectral lines arising from a magnetic nucleus can be easily described with the help of the vector model, as it is only necessary to add the nuclear moment vector to the model used in the previous chapters. The model also permits the discussion of Zeeman effect phenomena, which, as was pointed out by Pauli, are of extreme importance in the study and interpretation of hyperfine structure.

50. THE INTERACTION OF A MAGNETIC NUCLEUS AND EXTRANUCLEAR ELECTRONS

If we denote the mechanical moment vector of the nucleus by **i** and the total mechanical moment vector of the extranuclear electrons by **j**, as usual, then the resultant of **i** and **j** may assume different values, which correspond to the different hyperfine structure levels. We shall call this resultant **f**. The *hyperfine quantum number* f was first used by Ruark[1] in his attempts to derive level schemes for different hyperfine structures. The number of hyperfine structure levels is given by either $2j + 1$ or $2i + 1$, according to whether j or i is the smaller of the two. The possible resultants for various values of i and j are shown in Figure 55, in which the quantum vectors have been given the magnitudes $\sqrt{2i + 1}$, $\sqrt{2j + 1}$, and $\sqrt{2f + 1}$.

[1] A. E. Ruark and R. L. Chenault, *Phil. Mag.*, **50**: 937, 1925; A. E. Ruark, *ibid.*, **1**: 977, 1926; See also W. McNair, *ibid.*, **2**: 613, 1926; A. Schrammen, *Ann. d. Phys.*, **83**: 1161, 1926; E. H. Collins, *Phys. Rev.*, **32**: 753, 1928.

The quantum vectors **i** and **j** will precess uniformly about their resultant **f**, since their interaction is magnetic, and similar to that of **s** and **l**. Considerations similar to those given in Section 33 for **s**, **l**, and **j** could be repeated here; they would lead to the same exclusion rule for f as for j:

$$\Delta f = +1,\ 0,\ -1, \text{ with } f = 0 \rightarrow 0 \text{ forbidden.}$$

The intensity and interval rules given for ordinary multiplets are also expected to be valid here as a first approximation. The quantum numbers l, s, and j of the formulas of Section 34 are to be replaced by j, i, and f, respectively. The validity of these rules, however, requires that the interaction energy

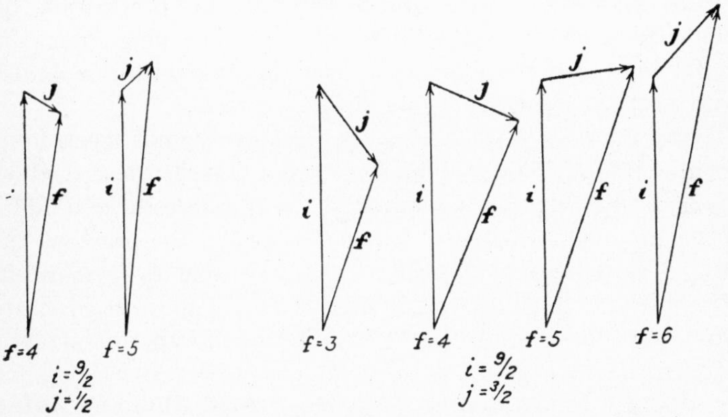

FIG. 55.—Composition of vectors **i** and **j** to form the resultant **f**.

between the magnetic nucleus and the extranuclear electrons be proportional to the cosine of the angle between **i** and **j**. This requires verification.[1]

The interaction energy under consideration consists of two parts: first, the interaction of the nuclear moment and the orbital motion of the electrons, and second, that of the nuclear moment and the electron spin moments. The first can be calculated in a way similar to that used for the interaction between electron spin and orbital motion (Sec. 15). It is first necessary to find the strength of the magnetic field produced by the orbital motion of the electron at the nucleus. The magnetic energy of the nucleus in this field is then given by the expression

$$W^1_{il} = \frac{e}{m_0c}\frac{lh}{2\pi}\overline{\left(\frac{1}{r^3}\right)}ig(i)\frac{eh}{4\pi m_0c}\overline{\cos(\mathbf{il})}. \qquad (1)$$

[1] See E. L. HILL, *Proc.*, Nat. Acad. Sci., **15**: 779, 1929.

In this expression $ig(i)$ is the magnetic moment of the nucleus expressed in Bohr magnetons, $eh/4\pi m_0 c$; $g(i)$ is the Landé g-factor for the nucleus, and may be very small. The factor to the left of $ig(i)$ gives the magnitude of the magnetic field produced by the orbital motion of the electron at the nucleus. The average value of $1/r^3$ is given in Section 7. When the precession of **l** about **j** is uniform the average value of cos (**il**) is given by

$$\overline{\cos (\mathbf{il})} = \cos (\mathbf{ij})\, \overline{\cos (\mathbf{jl})},$$

so that this interaction energy is indeed proportional to the cosine of the angle between **i** and **j**.

The interaction energy between the nuclear spin and the spin of an electron is given by[1]

$$W^1_{is} = -ig(i)\frac{eh}{4\pi m_0 c}\cdot sg(s)\frac{eh}{4\pi m_0 c}\overline{\left(\frac{1}{r^3}\right)}\left\{\overline{\cos (\mathbf{is})} - 3\,\overline{\cos (\mathbf{ir}) \cos (\mathbf{sr})}\right\} \tag{2}$$

in which **r** represents a vector drawn from the nucleus to the electron. This expression must first be averaged over the fast precessional motion of the penetrating orbit in its own plane (Chap. III), which gives[2]

$$\overline{\cos (\mathbf{is})} - 3\,\overline{\cos (\mathbf{ir}) \cos (\mathbf{rs})} = -\tfrac{1}{2}\,\overline{\cos (\mathbf{is})} + \tfrac{3}{2}\,\overline{\cos (\mathbf{il}) \cos (\mathbf{sl})}.$$

This expression can be further changed by taking into consideration the uniform precession of **l** and **s** about **j** and of **j** and **i** about **f**:

$$-\tfrac{1}{2}\,\overline{\cos (\mathbf{is})} + \tfrac{3}{2}\,\overline{\cos (\mathbf{il}) \cos (\mathbf{sl})} = -\tfrac{1}{2} \cos (\mathbf{ij})\left\{\overline{\cos (\mathbf{js})} - 3\,\overline{\cos (\mathbf{jl}) \cos (\mathbf{sl})}\right\}$$

[1] The mutual energy of two magnetic dipoles of moments M_1 and M_2 is equal to

$$\frac{M_1 M_2}{r^3}\left\{\cos (\mathbf{M}_1\mathbf{M}_2) - 3 \cos (\mathbf{M}_1\mathbf{r}) \cos (\mathbf{M}_2\mathbf{r})\right\}$$

[2] Let **r** lie in the xy-plane, so that **l** is parallel to the z-axis. Then cos (**ir**) cos (**sr**) $= (\alpha_i\alpha_r + \beta_i\beta_r + \gamma_i\gamma_r)(\alpha_s\alpha_r + \beta_s\beta_r + \gamma_s\gamma_r)$ in which α, β, γ denote direction cosines. If **r** precesses uniformly in the xy-plane we have

$$\overline{\alpha_r^2} = \tfrac{1}{2},\ \overline{\beta_r^2} = \tfrac{1}{2},$$

all other averages $= 0$, so that the expression becomes simply

$$\tfrac{1}{2}(\alpha_i\alpha_s + \beta_i\beta_s) = \tfrac{1}{2}(\alpha_i\alpha_s + \beta_i\beta_s + \gamma_i\gamma_s) - \tfrac{1}{2}\gamma_i\gamma_s$$
$$= \tfrac{1}{2} \cos (\mathbf{is}) - \tfrac{1}{2} \cos (\mathbf{il}) \cos (\mathbf{sl})$$

The result of this averaging will be changed if the quantum mechanics is used. The change will be of importance for small values of l especially. The formula given above leads to an infinite interaction energy between the nuclear spin and the spin of an extranuclear electron in an s-state ($l = 0$).

In this expression, too, there occurs the factor cos (ij). The total interaction energy of an electron and the magnetic nucleus can accordingly be written

$$W^1_{ij} = aij \cos(\mathbf{ij}) = a\frac{f(f+1) - i(i+1) - j(j+1)}{2}, \quad (3)$$

which shows that these hyperfine structure levels follow the ordinary interval rules. The proportionality factor a is given by

$$a = \frac{e^2h^2}{8m_0{}^2\pi^2c^2}\overline{\left(\frac{1}{r^3}\right)}g(i)\left\{\frac{l}{j}\cos(\mathbf{lj}) + \frac{s}{2j}\cos(\mathbf{sj}) - \frac{3s}{2j}\overline{\cos(\mathbf{jl})\cos(\mathbf{sl})}\right\},$$

which becomes on substituting for $\overline{\left(\frac{1}{r^3}\right)}$ its value given in Section 15a

$$a = \frac{Rhc\alpha^2Zz^2}{n^{*3}l(l+\frac{1}{2})(l+1)}g(i)\left\{\frac{l}{j}\cos(\mathbf{lj}) + \frac{s}{2j}\cos(\mathbf{sj}) - \frac{3s}{2j}\overline{\cos(\mathbf{jl})\cos(\mathbf{sl})}\right\}. \quad (4)$$

For many-electron atoms the expression in curly brackets must be summed over all the extranuclear electrons, except those forming closed groups. For numerical application one must know the values of the cosines of the angles between the quantum vectors.

The order of magnitude of the hyperfine structure corresponding to Equations 3 and 4 can be estimated by comparing these equations with those giving the separations of ordinary multiplets (Secs. 15 and 29). Except for the form of the cosine expressions, it is seen that the equation for the hyperfine structure separations differs from that for multiplets only by the factor $g(i)/Z$. If the nuclear magnetism is due to spinning protons, $g(i)$ will be equal to 2/1838. For penetrating orbits of mercury, thallium, bismuth, etc., the effective nuclear charge in the inner part of the orbit is about 80, so that the magnetic hyperfine structure separations will be about 80,000 times smaller than the multiplet separations. In bismuth the multiplet separations correspond to values of a of about 15,000 cm.$^{-1}$, and the three low terms whose hyperfine structure has been studied have a equal to -0.04, 0.08, and 0.37, in good agreement with these considerations.

50a. Separation Formulas for Hyperfine Structure.—A quantum mechanics treatment of the interaction energy between nuclear spin and the extranuclear electrons will certainly lead to formulas which differ considerably from those given above, especially in their dependence on quantum numbers. The part of the interaction energy which contains the interaction between the electron spin and the nucleus will very probably be most changed. It is, therefore, of little use to apply the formulas of the previous section to the available data as we can not expect to find agreement except in order of magnitude. The main result, that the total interaction energy will be proportional to ij cos (**ij**), leading to the interval rule, will probably still be valid in the quantum mechanics treatment.

Recently Hargreaves[1] attacked the problem of the interaction of the nuclear magnetic moment with the electron orbit with the aid of the quantum mechanics and more recently Casimir[2] also included the electron spin. Their results show that we actually must expect large deviations from the classical formulas in many cases. The quantum mechanics picture of an electron in an s state is a spherically symmetrical charge distribution (Section 6*b*) around the nucleus. The spin may be represented as a rather complicated rotational stream in this charge distribution, the stream direction being that of the spin in the old picture. This motion of the charge will produce a magnetic field at the nucleus, its direction being that of a left-handed screw rotating in the same direction as the spin of the negative electron. Remembering that the nucleus is a spinning positive particle, we see that its most stable state will be the one in which the nuclear spin is opposite to the direction of the electron spin. Suppose the nuclear spin quantum number to be i; the s state will then be split up into two energy levels, the lower one with $f = i - \frac{1}{2}$, the upper one with $f = i + \frac{1}{2}$. It is of importance to note that this result is just opposite to that which would be obtained with the orbital picture for the s state. The results of Casimir further make it very probable that the interaction energy between nuclear spin and an electron in the s state will be of the form

[1] J. Hargreaves, *Proc.*, Roy. Soc., A **124**: 568, 1929.

[2] We are very much obliged to Dr. H. B. G. Casimir, of Leiden, for placing his as yet unpublished results at our disposal.

$$W_i = ais \cos (\mathbf{is}). \tag{5}$$

The considerations given above show thus that a must be positive, if the nuclear magnetism is due to positive particles. The exact expression for a is not yet known with certainty.[1] The formulas for electrons in other than s states have also not yet been derived completely.

If we may assume that for a given electron configuration involving one or more s electrons the observed hyperfine structure is mainly due to these s electrons alone, Equation 5 may be used to derive relations among the hyperfine structures of the different energy levels in that configuration. Now happily s electrons are just the ones which penetrate nearest to the nucleus in the orbital picture and the quantum mechanical treatment also leads to the expectation that they will have comparatively large interaction with the nuclear spin. As a matter of fact, most of the hyperfine structures which have so far been observed are for configurations containing a deeply penetrating s electron.

Considering a configuration of an s electron and another electron in an arbitrary state, the hyperfine structure can easily be expressed in terms of the quantum vectors[2] with the assumption that only the s electron contributes appreciably to the interaction energy. A procedure quite similar to that of Section 22, with the use of Equation 1 and the assumption of Russell-Saunders coupling, gives for the interaction energy the expression

$$W_i = ais_1 \cos (\mathbf{is}_1) = ais_1 \cos (\mathbf{ij}) \cos (\mathbf{js}) \cos (\mathbf{ss}_1) = Aij \cos (\mathbf{ij}).$$

Here $\mathbf{s}_1$ denotes the spin vector of the s electron and $\mathbf{s}$ and $\mathbf{j}$ the resultant spin and the resultant extranuclear moment, as usual. The quantum vectors of the second electron will be denoted by an index 2. The factor A is again the proportionality constant of the interval rule and governs the magnitude of the separations:

$$A = a\frac{s}{j} \cos (\mathbf{js}) \frac{s_1}{s} \cos (\mathbf{ss}_1) = a\frac{j(j+1) + s(s+1) - l(l+1)}{2j(j+1)} \cdot \frac{s(s+1) + s_1(s_1+1) - s_2(s_2+1)}{2s(s+1)} \tag{6a}$$

A can be expressed in terms of the Landé g-factor for the state under consideration. Comparing Equation 6a with Equation

[1] Very probably $a = 8R\alpha^2 Z_i z^2 g(i)/3n^{*2}$ for penetrating orbits.

[2] S. Goudsmit and R. F. Bacher, *Phys. Rev.*, **34**: 1499, 1501, 1929. See also H. E. White, *Phys. Rev.*, **34**: 1288, 1929; **35**, 1, 8, 1930.

6 of Section 27, and remembering that $s_1 = s_2 = \frac{1}{2}$, we obtain

$$A = \tfrac{1}{2}a(g - 1). \tag{6b}$$

As a is positive, the hyperfine structure of the level may be expected to be inverted when g is smaller than 1.

For the extreme (jj) coupling a similar treatment gives

$$\left.\begin{aligned} W_i &= ais_1 \cos(\mathbf{ij}) \cos(\mathbf{js}_1) = Aij \cos(\mathbf{ij}), \\ \text{with} \\ A &= a\frac{s_1}{j}\cos(\mathbf{js}_1) = \\ &a\frac{j(j+1) + s_1(s_1+1) - j_2(j_2+1)}{2j(j+1)} = a\frac{g - g_2}{2 - g_2}. \end{aligned}\right\} \tag{7}$$

It is of importance to mention that there exist between the values for A in the different couplings sum relations similar to those known for the g- and Γ-values.

The special case of two s electrons can be treated without neglecting the influence of either, giving the relation

$$A = \tfrac{1}{2}a_1 + \tfrac{1}{2}a_2.$$

The hyperfine structures in the spectrum of ionized thallium found by McLennan, McLay and Crawford[1] are in good agreement with Equations 6 and 7. The $^3D_1$ terms have an inverted

TABLE I.—HYPERFINE STRUCTURE OF THALLIUM II

Configuration	$\Delta\nu$	Interval rule	A	a_1
$6s7s\ ^3S_1$	5.0 cm.$^{-1}$	$3A/2$	$a_1/2 + a_2/2$†	5.2 cm.$^{-1}$
$6s6p\ ^3P_2$	3.5	$5A/2$	$a_1/4$	5.6
$^1P_1$	0	$3A/2$	0	
$6s7p\ ^3P_2$	3.4*	$5A/2$	$a_1/4$	5.4
$^3P_1$	3.9*	$3A/2$	$a_1/2$	5.2
$[^1P_1]$	−0.6*	$3A/2$	$-a_1/4$	
$6s6d\ ^3D_2$	1.6	$5A/2$	$a_1/12$	7.7
$^3D_1$	−2.0	$3A/2$	$a_1/4$	5.3
$^1D_2$	2.4	$5A/2$	0	
$6s7d\ ^3D_3$	3.6	$7A/2$	$a_1/6$	6.2
$^3D_2$	0.6	$5A/2$	$a_1/12$	2.9
$^3D_1$	−2.3	$3A/2$	$-a_1/4$	6.1
$^1D_2$	0.3	$5A/2$	0	

* (jj) coupling.
† The value $a_2 = 1.6$ is derived from TlI.

[1] J. C. McLENNAN, A. B. McLAY, and M. F. CRAWFORD, *Proc.*, Roy. Soc., A **125**: 570, 1929.

hyperfine structure, corresponding to the value $g = \frac{1}{2}$. The configurations all involve a 6s electron. Only for a few of the levels is the separation known with enough accuracy to show quantitative agreement. The fact that each level is split into two leads to the value $i = \frac{1}{2}$, giving the thallium nucleus the spin moment $\frac{1}{2} \cdot h/2\pi$.

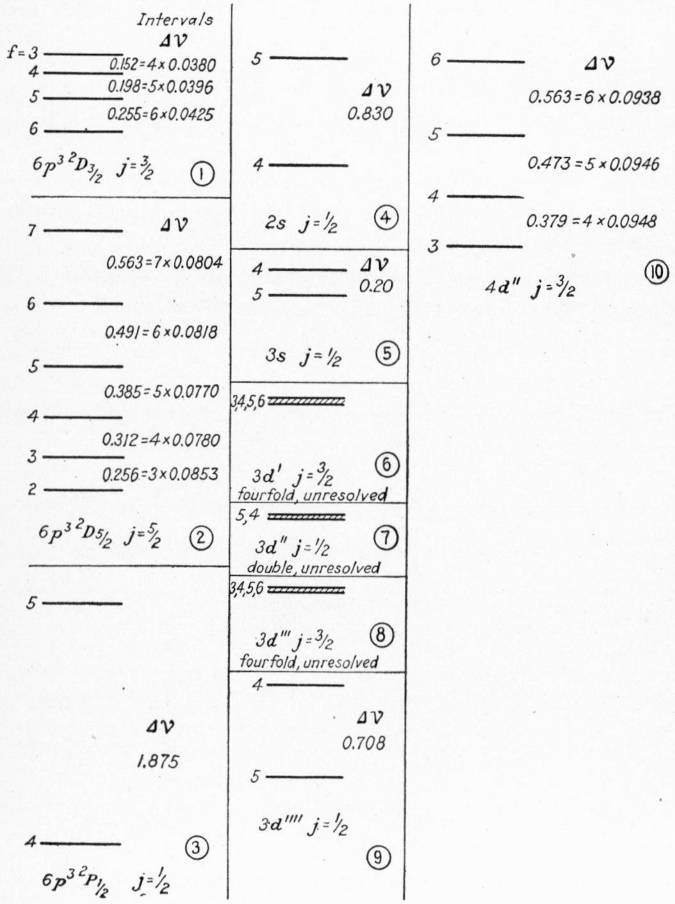

FIG. 56.—The hyperfine structure of a number of terms in the bismuth spectrum.

51. THE HYPERFINE STRUCTURE OF THE BISMUTH SPECTRUM

Of the many spectra in which hyperfine structure is found that of bismuth was the first to be given a satisfactory theoretical interpretation.[1] Many interesting attempts have been made to construct energy level schemes from the observed hyperfine structure in other spectra,[2] but, partly because the energy levels are not always known with sufficient certainty, it has been possible to explain theoretically the derived hyperfine struc-

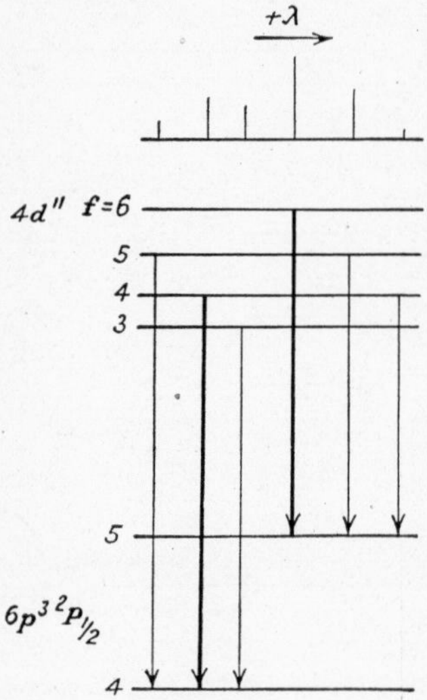

FIG. 57.

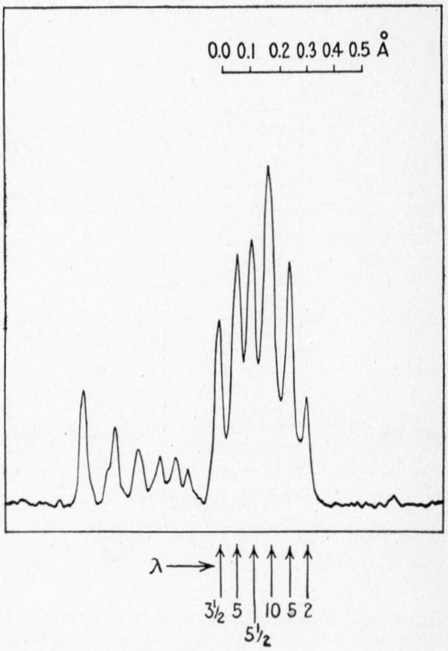

FIG. 58.

FIG. 57.—The hyperfine structure of the line λ3596 of bismuth (above) and the corresponding level diagram.

FIG. 58.—Photometer curve of λ3596 (in the third order) and λ2696 (fourth order) of bismuth. The theoretical values of the relative intensities of the components of λ3596 are given below the curve.

ture of the quantum states in only a few cases. Bismuth (atomic number 83, atomic weight 209.0) has, according to Aston, only one isotope. Back has made extremely interesting and beautiful measurements of the hyperfine structure and of its complicated Zeeman effects, which can be fully explained by the assumption that the nucleus possesses a mechanical moment and a magnetic moment.

[1] S. GOUDSMIT and E. BACK, *Z. f. Phys.*, **43**: 321, 1927; E. BACK and S. GOUDSMIT, *ibid.*, **47**: 174, 1928.

[2] See, for example, G. JOOS, *Phys. Z.*, **26**: 357, 1925, and G. HANSEN'S article in the "Handbuch der physikalischen Optik," II, p. 218.

The hyperfine structure of a number of levels in bismuth[1] is shown in Figure 56. Thorsen[2] classified the spectrum before its hyperfine structure had been investigated, and assigned j-values to the various terms on the basis of the observed combinations in such a way that the selection rule $\Delta j = \pm 1$ or 0 was satis-

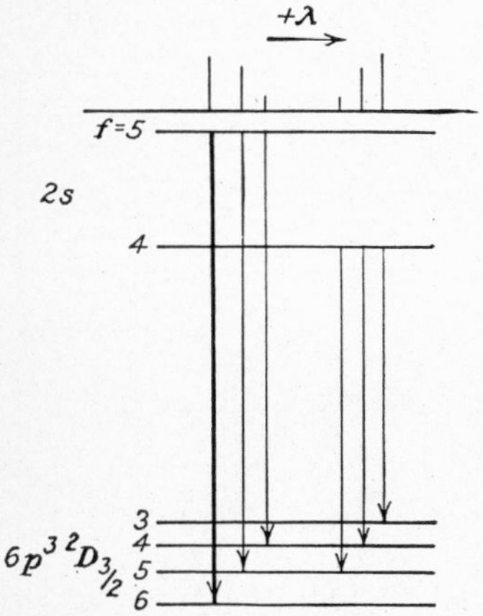

FIG. 59.

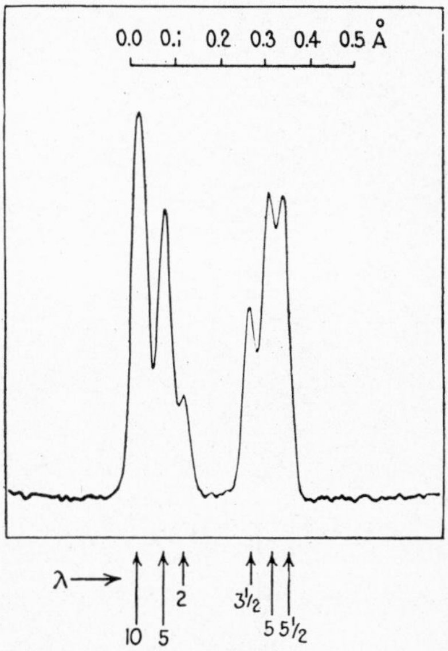

FIG. 60.

FIG. 59.—The hyperfine structure of λ4722 of bismuth.
FIG. 60.—Photometer curve of λ4722 of bismuth (in the fourth order), showing agreement with the theoretical values of the relative intensities of the components.

fied. The number of observed hyperfine sublevels in every case where there is resolution of the hyperfine structure is seen to be $2j + 1$, in agreement with theory. That this is true also for $j = 5/2$ shows that i must be equal to or larger than $5/2$. From the

[1] S. GOUDSMIT and E. BACK, *Z. f. Phys.*, **43**: 321, 1927.
[2] V. THORSEN, *ibid.*, **40**: 642, 1926. Except for the five lowest levels, which arise from the configuration $6p^3$, the electron configurations for the bismuth levels are not known with certainty. In order to facilitate reference to the literature, we have used the symbols originally introduced by Thorsen, which from the present point of view are, however, completely meaningless. Thorsen's symbols for the five lowest levels are

	p_1	p_2	p_3	p_4	p_6
for $6p^3$	${}^4S_{3/2}$	${}^2D_{3/2}$	${}^2D_{5/2}$	${}^2P_{1/2}$	${}^2P_{3/2}$

Thorsen's "2s" is probably the lowest state of the configuration $6p^2 \cdot 7s$.

interval ratios f and i can be determined approximately in accordance with Equation 3. It is found that i must be equal to about 4 or 5, and the analysis of the Zeeman effect (discussed in the following section) leads unambiguously to the value $i = 9/2$.

It will be seen from the intervals given in Figure 56 that the interval rules are not exactly obeyed; the deviations are as large as ± 5 per cent for $^2D_{5/2}$, for example. These are not to be entirely accounted for as due to experimental error. In this case, as well as for many ordinary multiplets, the interactions of the quantum vectors are more complicated than was assumed in the theoretical treatment of the idealized model.

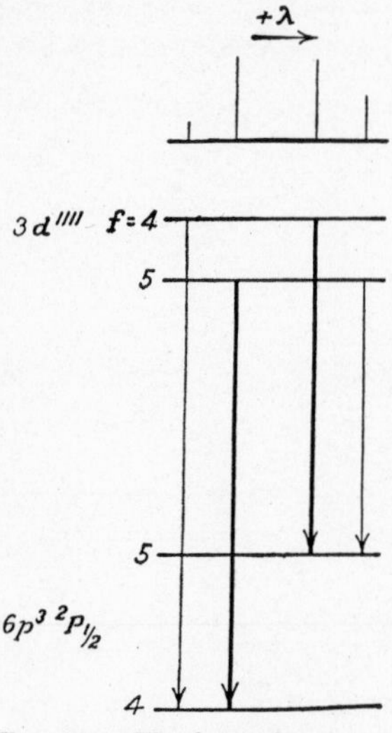

FIG. 61.—The hyperfine structure of λ4122 of bismuth.

The hyperfine structure of the spectral lines $^2P_{1/2} - 4d''$, λ3596, $^2D_{3/2} - 2s$, λ4722, and $^2P_{1/2} - 3d''''$, λ4122, are represented diagrammatically in Figures 57, 59, and 61. Wave-lengths and wave-numbers of the individual components and the corresponding term schemes are given in Table II. Figures 58 and 60 are photometer curves for λ3596 and λ4722 made by Professor P. Zeeman with the Zeiss microphotometer from plates of Professor E. Back. The line λ2696 also shown in Figure 58 is a combination between a wide sixfold level not represented in Figure 56 and the fourfold level $6p^3\ ^2D_{3/2}$.

It is of some interest to note the good agreement between the calculated intensities of Table II and the photometer curves. For values of f smaller than j the intensity formulas[1] of Section 34 give the qualitative rule that the strongest lines are those for which f and j change in the same direction. In this case, however, f is considerably larger than j, and the hyperfine structure intensities become more like intensities in the Zeeman effect. As f increases in magnitude the separation of successive hyperfine

[1] As was mentioned above, s, l, and j must be replaced by i, j, and f, respectively, in order to make the formulas applicable to the hyperfine structure.

TABLE II.—HYPERFINE STRUCTURE OF BISMUTH LINES

$^2P_{1/2} - 4d''$, λ3596

λ	Intensity	ν
3596.2560 Å	2	27,798.794 cm.$^{-1}$
6.1950	5	9.266
6.1220	10	9.829
6.0625	5.5	800.290
6.0135	5	0.669
5.9520	3.5	1.144

4d''	$^2P_{1/2}$ $f = 4$		$f = 5$
$f=6$			27,799.829
			0.563
5	27,801.144	*1.878*	27,799.266
	0.475		*0.472*
4	27,800.609	*1.875*	27,798.794
	0.379		
3	27,800.290		

$^2P_{1/2} - 3d''''$, λ4122

λ	Intensity	ν
4122.021 Å	6.5	24,253.138 cm.$^{-1}$
1.898	10	3.849
1.700	10	5.015
1.581	3.5	5.721

3d''''	$^2P_{1/2}$ $f = 4$		$f = 5$
$f = 4$	24,255.721	*1.872*	24,253.849
	0.706		*0.711*
5	24,255.015	*1.877*	24,253.138

$^2D_{3/2} - 2s$, λ4722

λ	Intensity	ν
4722.6520 Å	5.5	21,168.640 cm.$^{-1}$
2.6180	5	68.792
2.5740	3.5	68.989
2.4330	2	69.621
2.3890	5	69.819
2.3325	10	70.074

2s	$^2D_{3/2}$ $f = 6$		5		4		3
$f = 5$	21,170.074	*0.255*	21,169.819	*0.198*	21,169.621		
			0.830		*0.829*		
4			21,168.989	*0.197*	21,168.792	*0.152*	21,168.640

levels tends to become constant, as can be seen from the interval rule, and at the same time the intensities change in such a way as to make the line pattern appear more symmetrical.

52. THE ZEEMAN EFFECT OF HYPERFINE STRUCTURES

The Zeeman effect of spectra showing hyperfine structure as the result of a magnetic nucleus is most easily described for the case that the external magnetic field is strong; that is, that the interaction of the quantum vectors (here **j** and **i**) with the field is much larger than their mutual interaction. The description of the Zeeman effect is then completely analogous to that of the Paschen-Back effect for ordinary multiplets. The coupling between the nuclear moment **i** and the extranuclear moment **j** will be broken and each will have its own quantized projection on **H**, the external field (Fig. 62). We shall denote the component of **i** along **H** by $\mathbf{m}_i$, that of **j** by $\mathbf{m}_j$. We anticipate that these vectors, in common with the magnetic quantum vectors previously introduced, will require to be given the integral or half-integral magnitudes m_i and m_j in order that equations derived with them will reflect the quantum mechanics and reality.

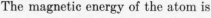

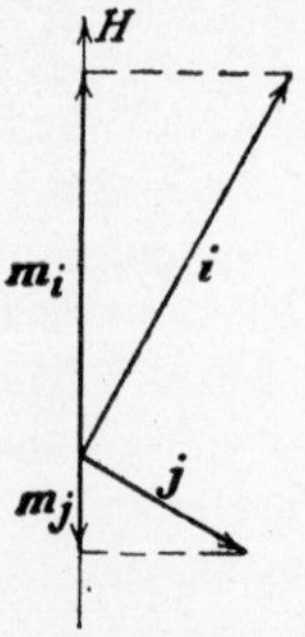

FIG. 62.—The orientation of the vectors i and j in a strong magnetic field.

The magnetic energy of the atom is

$$W_H = o\{m_i g(i) + m_j g\},$$

in which o is the Lorentz unit, $\frac{eh}{4\pi m_0 c}H$, customarily used in the discussion of the Zeeman effect. g is the ordinary Landé g-factor for the extranuclear electrons. Since $g(i)$ is very small we may neglect the term $m_i g(i)$ as being experimentally undetectable. Furthermore, since the coupling between the magnetic nucleus and the orbital motion of the extranuclear electrons is very weak, the correspondence principle leads to the expectation that m_i will not change during a transition, and that the ordinary selection and polarization rules will hold for m_j.

If this were the whole story, the Zeeman effect would be exactly the same with a nuclear moment as without, for the nucleus would affect neither the Zeeman energy levels nor the possible transitions. But we have neglected the interaction energy of the magnetic nucleus and the extranuclear electrons, as given in Section 50*a*. The total interaction energy becomes

$$W = o\{m_i g(i) + m_j g\} + Aij\,\overline{\cos(\mathbf{ij})} \qquad (8)$$

We are considering the case of a strong field, for which the second term is smaller than the first. To a first approximation, then, the Zeeman effect is the same with a nuclear moment as without. It is possible, however, to detect the influence of the second term with the best modern spectroscopic apparatus.

The cosine of the angle between **i** and **j** is not constant, since **j** precesses about **H** a thousand times more rapidly than does **i**. Its average value is found in the usual way to be such that

$$ij\,\overline{\cos(\mathbf{ij})} = ij\cos(\mathbf{iH})\cos(\mathbf{jH}) = m_i m_j,$$

so that the expression for the energy becomes

$$E = om_j g + Am_j m_i. \qquad (9)$$

m_i can assume any of the $2i + 1$ integral or half-integral values from $-i$ to $+i$. Hence, every Zeeman level, which would be single in the absence of a nuclear moment, will now be split into $2i + 1$ equidistantly spaced hyperfine levels, with a separation Am_j. Since m_i does not change during a transition, each of the $2i + 1$ hyperfine levels of the initial Zeeman state can combine with only one of the $2i + 1$ levels of the final state, the one having the same value of m_i. This leads to a very simple complete Zeeman pattern for the spectral lines themselves; each Zeeman component is itself split into $2i + 1$ equidistant hyperfine components, whose separation is given by the difference of the product Am_j for the initial and the final states. The values of A for the various states can be obtained from the hyperfine structure in the absence of an external magnetic field, assuming the interval rule to be approximately correct, so

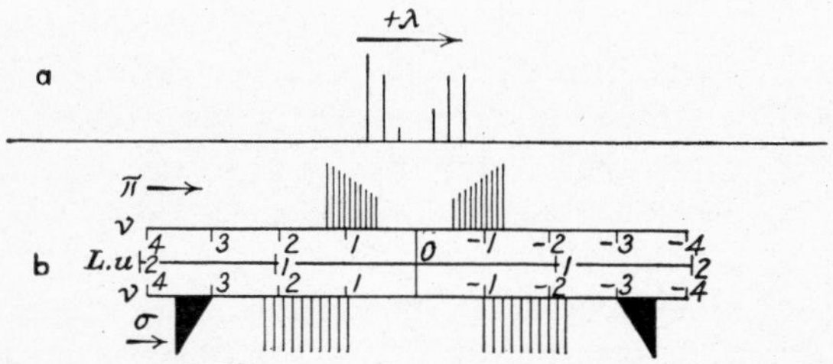

FIG. 63.—The Zeeman effect of the line λ4722 of bismuth in a strong magnetic field. (*a*) The line in the absence of an external field. (*b*) The line in a field of strength 43,340 gauss. The figures are to scale. Between the representation of the π-components and that of the σ-components are scales in wave-numbers ν and in Lorentz units (L. U.); the scale also applies to the line without field.

that it is possible to predict quantitatively the hyperfine structure of the Zeeman components of a spectral line from its observed hyperfine structure.

There is shown in Figure 63 as an example the Zeeman resolution of $^2D_{3/2} - 2s$ of bismuth, λ4722. Here Back succeeded in resolving the hyperfine structure of four Zeeman components. Each was split into ten lines. From this it follows that for the bismuth nucleus $2i + 1 = 10$ or $i = 9/2$. The ordinary hyperfine structure of this line gives $j = 1/2$, $A = 0.166$ for the initial state and $j = 3/2$, $A' = -0.040$ for the final state. The parallel polarized components occur when $m_j = +1/2$ or $-1/2$ for both states. The separation of the hyperfine Zeeman components should then be

$$Am_j - A'm'_j = 0.166 \cdot 1/2 - (-0.040) \cdot 1/2 = 0.103 \text{ cm.}^{-1}.$$

The observed value is 0.098 cm.$^{-1}$. The inner perpendicularly polarized components arise from the transition in m_j from $1/2$ to

$3/2$ or $-1/2$ to $-3/2$. The predicted spacing of the hyperfine components is

$$0.166 \cdot 1/2 - (-0.040) \cdot 3/2 = 0.143 \text{ cm.}^{-1},$$

while that observed is 0.141 cm.$^{-1}$. For the outer perpendicularly polarized components only the total breadth could be measured. The predicted value for it is

$$9\{0.166 \cdot 1/2 - (-0.040) \cdot (-1/2)\} = 0.567 \text{ cm.}^{-1};$$

that observed is 0.520 cm.$^{-1}$. The agreement is sufficient to provide considerable support for the theory.

The deviations from the calculated separations shown by the parallel and the outer perpendicular components are larger than can be accounted for as due to error in measurement. These deviations probably are connected with observed anomalies in the intensities of the hyperfine components. The same reasoning which showed that m_i should not change during a transition leads to the conclusion that m_i should not affect the intensities of the lines. We could accordingly expect each original Zeeman line to be split into ten hyperfine components of equal intensity. This is observed only for the inner perpendicular components, for which there is also complete agreement between predicted and observed separations; the other components show a dependency of intensity on m_i, shown in the figure.

The probable explanation of this anomaly is that an applied field of 43,000 gauss is not strong enough to produce a complete Paschen-Back effect; that is, to orient the vectors **i** and **j** completely. This would lead one to expect to observe "forbidden" transitions and components not obeying the polarization rules. For, on account of the interaction between **i** and **j**, m_j might sometimes change by ± 2, provided that m_i simultaneously changes by ∓ 1 to give a change of ± 1 in the total m. This would give rise to weak perpendicularly polarized components with twice the displacement of the strong perpendicular components. These "forbidden" components have actually been observed.[1] It may also happen that m_i will change by ± 1 during a transition in which m_j does not change, giving a weak component with perpendicular polarization coinciding with a strong parallel component. These infractions of the polarization rules have also been observed for bismuth.

[1] Unpublished results obtained by E. Back and S. Goudsmit.

The hyperfine Zeeman effect in weak fields is very difficult to observe, since "weak" fields are those in which the Zeeman separations are smaller than the already very small hyperfine structure separations. In predicting this effect it is necessary to calculate the $g(f)$ value for each hyperfine level. $g(f)$ can be calculated in terms of $g(i)$, the Landé g-factor for the nucleus, and g, that for the extranuclear electrons, in a way analogous to that described in Section 27. This leads to the equation

$$g(f) = g(i)\overline{\overset{i}{f}}\cos(\mathbf{if}) + g\overline{\overset{j}{f}}\cos(\mathbf{jf}),$$

which becomes, on neglecting the term in $g(i)$ and introducing the quantum mechanics values for cos (**jf**),

$$g(f) = g\frac{f(f+1) + j(j+1) - i(i+1)}{2f(f+1)}. \tag{10}$$

Preliminary observations on bismuth in very weak magnetic fields (7000 gauss) made by Professor Back seem to be in agreement with this equation. The experimental difficulties are such, however, that it is not possible to deduce the g-values with accuracy from the observations. It can only be said with certainty that $g(i)$ is smaller than 0.01, in agreement with theoretical considerations and with the order of magnitude required by the hyperfine separations in the absence of a magnetic field.

For intermediate field strengths it is possible to make use of the formulas derived by Heisenberg and Jordan and by Darwin (Sec. 28a), after replacing m_s by $g(i) \cdot m_i$ and m_l by $g \cdot m_j$. The key equation of Darwin as given in Section 28a when adapted to the hyperfine structure problem[1] becomes

$$-X_{m_j-1,m_i+1} \cdot \frac{A}{2}(j - m_j + 1)(i + m_i + 1) + X_{m_j,m_i}(W - Am_jm_i - gm_j\omega - g(i)m_i\omega) - X_{m_j+1,m_i-1} \cdot \frac{A}{2}(j + m_j + 1)(i - m_i + 1) = 0.$$

For a given value of the total projection

$$m = m_i + m_j,$$

this leads to a chain of equations, the number of which is restricted by the possible values of m_i and m_j. The roots of the determinant of this chain of equations give the energy values

[1] S. Goudsmit and R. F. Bacher, *Phys. Rev.*, **34**: 1499, 1929.

W associated with the given value of m.[1] To obtain the intensities there must first be calculated the values of the X's for each of the roots W from the chain of homogeneous equations together with the following so-called normalizing relation:

$$\sum_{m=\text{constant}} (X^{if}{}_{m_j,m_i})^2(i + m_i)!(i - m_i)!(j + m_j)!(j - m_j)! = 1.$$

These values of the X's for the initial and final level introduced in the following expressions give the intensities for a transition from a level with j to one with $j' = j \pm 1$:

For $m \rightarrow m \pm 1$; perpendicular components:

$$I(j, f, m \rightarrow j', f', m \pm 1) = [\sum_{m=\text{constant}} X^{if}{}_{m_j,m_i}\, X^{j'f'}{}_{m_j+1,m_i}(i + m_i)!$$
$$(i - m_i)!(j + m_j)!(j - m_j)!]^2,$$

For $m \rightarrow m$; parallel components:

$$I(j, f, m \rightarrow j', f', m) = 4[\sum_{m=\text{constant}} X^{if}{}_{m_j,m_i}\, X^{j'f'}{}_{m_j,m_i}(i + m_i)!$$
$$(i - m_i)!(j + m_j)!(j - m_j)!]^2.$$

The primes refer to the final state. For the case that $j' = j$, the formulas are the same except that the factor 4 in front of the intensities of the parallel components must be omitted.

An interesting example is the line $6p\,^2P_{1/2} - 7s\,^2S_{1/2}$, λ3776, of thallium. In this atom $i = 1/2$, and $j = 1/2$ for both initial and final state. For the initial state, $7s$, $\Delta\nu = A = 0.40$ cm^{-1}; $g = 2$ and for the final state $\Delta\nu = A = 0.70$ cm.$^{-1}$, $g = 2/3$. In a field of 43,350 gauss the initial level shows a practically complete Paschen-Back effect, whereas the splitting of the final level is still rather distorted. Table III gives the calculated intensities and the calculated and observed positions of the components of this line in cm.$^{-1}$, referred to the center of gravity.

Notice the slight asymmetry in the pattern, due to the incompleteness of the Paschen-Back effect, and also the occurrence of weak "forbidden" components from transitions for which m_i changes. These weak components were estimated to be about one-tenth as strong as the regular ones. We are very much indebted to Professor E. Back[2] and Dr. J. Wulff at Tübingen for providing us with the preliminary results of their investiga-

[1] Each root W can be ascribed to one of the hyperfine structure levels designated by the quantum numbers j and f. That is why the X's appear in the following formulas with these quantum numbers as indices. W could just as well have been chosen as an index for them.

[2] A photograph of this line, showing the strong components only, can be found in a paper by E. Back, *Ann. der Phys.*, **70**: 338, 1923.

TABLE III.—ZEEMAN EFFECT FOR λ3776 OF THALLIUM

Parallel components			Perpendicular components		
I	Position		I	Position	
	Calculated	Observed		Calculated	Observed
0.8	−2.74	−2.75	10	−3.00	−3.02
10	−1.43	−1.42	9.4	−2.52	−2.54
9.2	−1.20	−1.22	0.02	−1.65	
			0.6	−0.99	−0.98
10	+1.28	+1.35[1]	0.02	+1.09	
9.2	+1.36		0.6	+1.55	+1.53
			10	+2.45	+2.43
0.8	+2.89	+2.90	9.4	+3.08	+3.10

[1] Too narrow for resolution, double intensity.

tion. The agreement is so excellent that it is perhaps more suitable to consider it as proof of the accuracy of the work of these investigators rather than as proof of the theory.

Without nuclear moment the Zeeman effect of this line in the same field would have been:

parallel:	−1.38	+1.38
perpendicular:	−2.76	+2.76,

similar to the weaker one of the yellow sodium lines.

It is very probable that in the near future the investigation of the Zeeman effect of hyperfine structures will provide us with ample material to test the theory in any case. For ordinary multiplets the separations are nearly always too large to give Paschen-Back effects and the few narrower multiplets occur mainly in lighter elements where the lines are often too diffuse for a detailed investigation. Comparison with experiments for ordinary multiplets has been made for the *sd* − *sp* triplet transitions in magnesium.[1] Here the *sd* ^3D separations are extremely small so as to cause complete Paschen-Back effect in the applied field, whereas the ^3P state shows no Paschen-Back effect at all.

53. NUCLEAR MOMENTS

Although the investigation of the hyperfine structure of spectra is only in its inception, results have already been obtained showing that the laws governing the structure of the nucleus

[1] L. MENSING, *Z. f. Phys.*, **39**: 24, 1926.

are not identical with those for extranuclear electron configurations. As both the proton and the electron have spins of $\frac{1}{2} \cdot h/2\pi$, we would expect the total nuclear moment to be an integral multiple of the quantum unit for a nucleus composed of an even number of particles, and a half-integral multiple for an odd number. But the expectation is not fulfilled.

The hyperfine structure of the cadmium spectrum has been examined by Schüler and Brück,[1] who discovered the important fact that the observed pattern must be caused by two or more isotopes with different nuclear moments. Omitting the strongest line of each hyperfine structure pattern, the remaining components can be explained as arising from a nuclear moment of $\frac{1}{2} \cdot h/2\pi$. The strongest line is attributed to a different nucleus, with no nuclear moment or with such a small magnetic moment as to give an unresolved hyperfine separation. It has further been shown[2] that this single line is just at the center of gravity of the pattern arising from the isotope with $i = \frac{1}{2}$. This is to be expected in case the shift of the energy levels due to different mass or different constitution of the isotopic nuclei (except the magnetic moment) is negligibly small, so that it provides further corroboration of Schüler and Brück's interpretation.

Cadmium has many isotopes and it is not possible at present to ascribe the observed nuclear moments to definite ones. But since the atomic number is even ($Z = 48$), *all* of the isotopes contain an even number of particles in the nucleus, so that the observed half-integral nuclear moment is very surprising.[3]

[1] H. Schüler and H. Brück, *Z. f. Phys.*, **56**: 291, 1929.

[2] S. Goudsmit, *Naturwiss.*, **17**: 805, 1929. It is to be regretted that the paper by Schüler and Brück contains several errors, which, though small, prevent their arguments from being completely convincing. We have accordingly rechecked their results and have tested them with the intensity formulas and separation formulas, and have also investigated several alternative possible explanations of the origin of this hyperfine structure. This study led to a complete confirmation of the interpretation suggested by Schüler and Brück; there is no doubt that the nuclear moment of at least one of the isotopes of cadmium is $\frac{1}{2} \cdot h/2\pi$.

[3] The first case of this kind to which attention was directed is that of nitrogen. The nitrogen nucleus contains 14 protons and 7 electrons, an odd number of particles. R. de L. Kronig (*Naturwiss.*, **16**: 335, 1928) remarked that the alternating intensities in the band spectrum of N_2 indicate a nuclear moment of $h/2\pi$, rather than the expected half-integral value. But the more easily interpretable Raman spectrum of nitrogen obtained by F. Rasetti (*Proc.*, Nat. Acad. Sci., **15**: 515, 1929; *Nature,* **123**: 757; **124**, 792,

Another interesting result is that the hyperfine structures of this cadmium isotope are inverted, which means that a is negative. This indicates that the nuclear moment is due to negatively charged particles instead of to protons. But the magnetic moment of the nucleus is not of the order of magnitude of a Bohr magneton, as might be expected in case that it were produced by either the spin or the orbital motion of nuclear electrons; the hyperfine separations indicate a moment roughly one-thousandth as great. It is barely possible that the electrons form a configuration with $g = 0$, and the protons one such that their magnetic moment is opposed in direction to the mechanical moment. A similar thing occurs in certain electron configurations (with large l and small j and with $s < l$), which have negative g-values. The apparent non-existence of any heavy nuclei with large magnetic moments makes a more generally valid explanation preferable. It is probable that the large energy changes accompanying the union of electrons and protons to form nuclei have the effect of decreasing very greatly the g-factor for electrons.[1] (For example, the relativistic increase in mass of an electron moving with high velocity would lead to a g-factor less than 1 for its orbital motion.)

Besides the elements mentioned above, bismuth, thallium, and cadmium, the hyperfine structures of only a few spectra have so far been successfully interpreted.

In the praseodymium spectrum, all lines were found to be sixfold and to look about like the bismuth line λ2696. Gibbs, White, and Ruedy[2] interpreted this by assuming that the nucleus of Pr has a moment $5/2 \cdot h/2\pi$, which splits each level into six hyperfine levels, and that for some reason only the six strongest combinations between two such splitted levels could be observed. It can easily be proved that their interpretation is completely correct. In fact, the lowest states in Pr will all have very large

---

1929) points definitely to a moment of $\frac{1}{2}h/2\pi$, in agreement with expectation. The anomalous intensities discussed by Kronig have yet to be explained. A further difficulty pointed out by Heitler and Herzberg (*Naturwiss.*, **17**: 673, 1929) is that the symmetry character of the nitrogen nucleus seems not to be that of its constituent protons and electrons.

[1] G. Breit, *Nature*, **122**: 649, 1928.

[2] R. C. Gibbs, H. E. White, and J. E. Ruedy, *Proc.*, Nat. Acad. Sci., **15**: 642, 1929.

values of j, as can be seen from Table II of Chap. IX; namely, about 6. Now if i is considerably smaller than j the intensity formulas give the result that the strongest lines will be those for which f and j make the same changes. For this special case, with $i = 5/2$ and j about 6, all other transitions will be only about one-tenth as strong. This explains why only the six strongest transitions in each hyperfine multiplet are observed. Moreover, if the interval rule holds for both the initial and the final state it will also hold roughly for the separations between these six strongest lines, in agreement with observation.

An interesting fine structure has been found in the spectrum of ionized lithium by Schüler.[1] It has not yet been explained, but it is of the same order of magnitude as the ordinary multiplet separations in this spectrum. If it is produced by a nuclear magnetic moment, its magnitude must be large, of the order of a Bohr magneton.[2] Indeed, lithium has one isotope with an odd number of electrons (atomic weight 6); but as yet nothing about its magnetic moment can be said with certainty.[3]

Schüler[4] also discovered that each one of the yellow sodium lines is double, and showed that the lowest s state of sodium possesses a hyperfine structure with $\Delta\nu = 0.060$ cm.$^{-1}$. This $^2S_{1/2}$ state is split up into two because $j = 1/2$, and as the splitting of the other levels is not known we can not say what the nuclear moment of sodium is, other than that it is at least $1/2 \cdot h/2\pi$. Perhaps a more detailed investigation of the intensity ratio of the hyperfine structure components can be carried out, leading to the determination of this moment. The band spectrum of Na_2 shows that i is probably greater than 2.

Similar hyperfine structures have been found in cesium[5] and in rubidium.[6] For cesium, the splitting of the ^2S state is $\Delta\nu =$ 0.30 cm.$^{-1}$, for rubidium 0.11 cm.$^{-1}$.

[1] H. Schüler, *Z. f. Phys.*, **42**: 587, 1928.

[2] W. Heisenberg, *Z. f. Phys.*, **39**: 516, 1926.

[3] See the discussion of the Stern-Gerlach experiment for lithium in Section 54.

[4] H. Schüler, *Naturwiss.*, **16**: 512, 1928.

[5] D. A. Jackson, *Proc., Roy. Soc.*, A **121**: 432, 1928. The speculations of Jackson about the nuclear moment of cesium are very uncertain. He also erroneously assumes that the hyperfine structure of the levels will be inverted.

[6] A. Filippov and E. Gross, *Naturwiss.*, **17**: 121, 1929.

For several other elements[1] attempts have been made to interpret their hyperfine structure and it is certain that the material will increase rapidly in the near future. It is of particular interest that only the rare earth elements of odd atomic number (which form a much smaller fraction of the earth's crust than those of even atomic number) show an observed hyperfine structure. King[2] has found hyperfine structure for europium (Z = 63), terbium (65), and holmium (67), in addition to the previously mentioned lanthanum (57) and praseodymium (59). He states that the structure of the lines often resembles that of praseodymium discussed above.

The quantum mechanics calculations of Casimir give for the bracketed part of Equation 4 simply $l(l + 1)/j(j + 1)$. If we multiply the last two terms in the brackets with $l(l + 1)/(l - \frac{1}{2})(l + \frac{3}{2})$ and use quantum mechanics cosines Equation 4 will give the same result as obtained by Casimir. This multiplying factor replaces the classical averaging used in the derivation of Equation 4 by its quantum mechanical equivalent (footnote 2, page 206). For large l the quantum mechanics expression becomes identical with the classical one.

This way of interpreting Casimir's result has the advantage that it distinguishes between the part due to the spin and that due to the orbital motion of the electron. This is necessary for future applications to many-electron configurations. (See, for instance, S. Goudsmit, *Phys. Rev.*, **35:** 446, 440, 1930.)

The discussion of the nuclear magnetic moment of Li given on pages 224 and 229 is incorrect. The error lies in the fact that the hyperfine structure caused by the deeply penetrating 1s electron was there compared with the multiplet separation caused by the non-penetrating 2p electron. Applications of the results of Casimir and of Fermi (*Nature*, **125:** 16, 1930) to this case show that the magnetic moment need not be large to explain the order of magnitude of the observed hyperfine structure. (See forthcoming note in *Nature* by S. Goudsmit and L. Young.)

Schüler and Brück (*Z. f. Phys.*, **58:** 735, 1929) have given a preliminary interpretation of the Li^+ hyperfine structure. If it is correct the nuclear moment of the main isotope is ½, but a is negative as in cadmium.

[1] A most promising case seems to be the lanthanum spectrum, according to a preliminary note by W. F. Meggers and K. Burns, *J. Opt. Soc. Am.*, **14:** 449, 1927.

[2] A. S. King, *Phys. Rev.*, **34:** 540, 1929.

CHAPTER XII

MAGNETIC PHENOMENA OTHER THAN THE ZEEMAN EFFECT

There is a close connection between the spectroscopic evidence of interaction between atoms and an applied magnetic field, as shown by the Zeeman effect, and certain other magnetic phenomena; namely, those which can be interpreted as having their origin in the permanent magnetic moment of the atom. The Stern and Gerlach experiment is of prime importance in verifying our representation of the atom as having a magnetic moment which can assume only specified orientations relative to a magnetic field. The pattern of lines shown by a given atom in this experiment can be predicted entirely from a knowledge of the value of its moment j and Landé g-factor. Similarly, spectroscopic data permit the calculation of the paramagnetic susceptibility of a monatomic substance. These topics as well as the magneto-mechanical effect and resonance polarization are discussed in the following sections.

The diamagnetic susceptibility of atoms is, of course, determined by the nature of their electron orbits, or, rather, by the eigenfunctions representing them; and the quantum mechanics provides the mechanism for its calculation.[1] Ferromagnetism has its origin without doubt in the characteristic resonance phenomenon of the quantum mechanics, although as yet the details of the theory have not been satisfactorily worked out.[2] These subjects bear no close connection to spectral phenomena, and an extended discussion of them is not needed here.

54. THE STERN AND GERLACH EXPERIMENT

In 1921 Stern[3] suggested an experiment designed to test the predicted[4] spatial quantization of electron orbits, according

[1] W. Pauli, *Z. f. Phys.*, **2**: 201, 1920; J. H. Van Vleck, *Proc.*, Nat. Acad., **12**: 662, 1926; *Phys. Rev.*, **31**: 587, 1928; Linus Pauling, *Proc.*, Roy. Soc., A **114**: 181, 1927.

[2] W. Heisenberg, *Z. f. Phys.*, **49**: 619, 1928; "Sommerfeld Festschrift," p. 114, 1928.

[3] O. Stern, *Z. f. Phys.*, **7**: 249, 1921.

[4] A. Sommerfeld, *Phys. Z.*, **17**: 491, 1916; P. Debye, *ibid.*, **17**: 507, 1916, *Göttinger Nachr.*, June, 1916.

to which only a discrete number of orientations of the mechanical moment vector of an atom relative to an external magnetic field are possible. (Although spatial quantization leads directly to the Zeeman splitting of spectral lines, this cannot be said to be a very direct test of the theory, for only differences in term values come into consideration, and, moreover, the normal Zeeman effect could be explained with the classical theory entirely without recourse to such a new and artificial mechanism.) The experiment was the following one. If an atom of finite magnetic moment is subjected to the action of an external magnetic field it will orient itself in such a way that its field energy is

$$-mg\frac{eh}{4\pi m_0c}H, \tag{1}$$

as was seen in Sections 17*b* and 27; the component of its magnetic moment along the field direction, **H**, is, then, equal to $mg\frac{eh}{4\pi m_0c}$; that is, to mg Bohr magnetons. The magnetic quantum number m can assume the $2j + 1$ values $0, \pm 1, \cdots \pm j$ or $\pm 1/2, \pm 3/2, \cdots \pm j$. If a stream of such atoms is sent through a uniform field the atoms will be oriented but not deflected by the field. If, however, the field is non-homogeneous, there will be exerted on the magnetic dipole a force of magnitude

$$mg\frac{eh}{4\pi m_0c}\frac{\partial H}{\partial s} \tag{2}$$

in which $\partial H/\partial s$ represents the inhomogeneity in the field. This force would lead to the separation of the stream of atoms into $2j + 1$ individual streams, whose deviation from the original direction would be given by the factor mg.

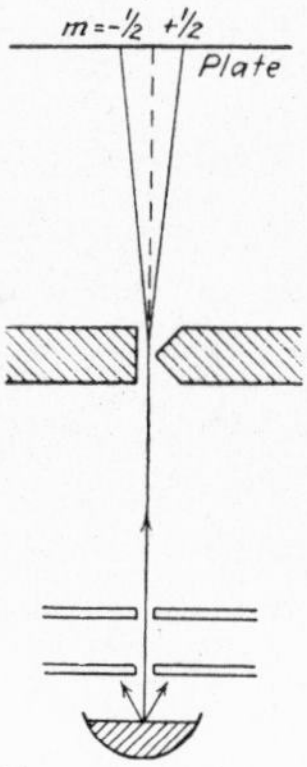

FIG. 64.—Diagram representing the Stern and Gerlach experiment.

This experiment was carried out by Gerlach and Stern,[1] whose apparatus is pictured diagrammatically in Figure 64. Silver is boiled from the vessel at the bottom into a high vacuum. A narrow stream of atoms, segregated by a slit, is passed

[1] W. GERLACH and O. STERN, *Z. f. Phys.*, **8**: 110, 1921; **9**: 349, 1922; **9**: 353, 1922; *Ann. d. Phys.*, **74**: 673, 1924.

through a highly inhomogeneous field produced by the shaped pole pieces of a magnet. The deflected streams impinge on a plate, and their traces are afterwards brought out for measurement by a process of development. It was found that the original stream of silver atoms was split into two, one of which was deflected to the right and the other to the left by the same amount. The deflections corresponded to $mg = +1$ and -1, so that the experiment showed that silver atoms orient themselves in such a way that their component of magnetic moment along the field is ± 1 Bohr magneton.

This result is to be expected. The normal state of the silver atom is a $^2S_{1/2}$ state, so that m can assume only the values $+1/2$ and $-1/2$; and moreover the Landé g-factor is for this state 2, leading to the possibilities of $+1$ and -1 for mg.

The Stern-Gerlach deflections to be expected for various spectral states are given by the following table, which can be easily extended with the use of the g-values in Table V, Chap. VII.

TABLE I.—STERN-GERLACH DEFLECTIONS

Normal state	g	mg					Stern-Gerlach pattern
$^1S_0$..........	$0/0$			0			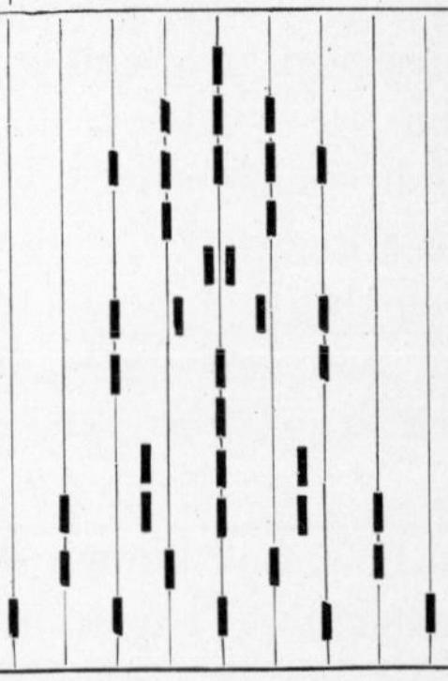
$^1P_1$..........	1		-1	0	$+1$		
$^1D_2$..........	1	-2	-1	0	$+1$	$+2$	
$^2S_{1/2}$..........	2		-1		$+1$		
$^2P_{1/2}$..........	$2/3$		$-1/3$		$+1/3$		
$^2P_{3/2}$..........	$4/3$	$-6/3$	$-2/3$		$+2/3$	$+6/3$	
$^3S_1$..........	2		-2	0	$+2$		
$^3P_0$..........	$0/0$			0			
$^3P_1$..........	$3/2$		$-3/2$	0	$+3/2$		
$^3P_2$..........	$3/2$	$-6/2$	$-3/2$	0	$+3/2$	$+6/2$	
$^4S_{3/2}$..........	2	-3	-1		$+1$	$+3$	
$^5S_2$..........	2	-4	-2	0	$+2$	$+4$	

It has been similarly found, in part with the use of apparatus of increased accuracy,[1] that hydrogen,[2] copper,[3] gold,[4] sodium,[5]

[1] O. STERN, *Z. f. Phys.*, **39**: 751, 1926; **41**: 563, 1927; F. KNAUER and O. STERN, *ibid.*, **39**: 764, 1926.

[2] T. E. PHIPPS and J. B. TAYLOR, *Phys. Rev.*, **29**: 309, 1927; E. WREDE, *Z. f. Phys.*, **41**: 569, 1927.

[3] W. GERLACH, *Ann. d. Phys.*, **76**: 163, 1925.

[4] W. GERLACH and A. C. CILLIERS, *Z. f. Phys.*, **26**: 106, 1924.

[5] J. B. TAYLOR, *Phys. Rev.*, **28**: 576, 1926.

and potassium[1] show the same Stern-Gerlach pattern as silver, in agreement with the assignment of the same ground state $^2S_{1/2}$ to them (as given in Table II, Chap. IX). Thallium[1,2] is found to show two streams, with mg equal to $+1/3$ and $-1/3$; this corresponds to the ground state $^2P_{1/2}$. Lead, tin,[2,3] zinc,[1] and cadmium,[1] with $j = 0$ in the ground state, show no deflection. Nickel[3] shows a complicated pattern, not completely resolved, indicating a moment of two or more magnetons. Preliminary experiments on iron[3] showed no deflection.

The normal state of the bismuth atom is known to have $j = 3/2$.[4] Its coupling is probably not Russell-Saunders, however; so that the value $g = 2$ for the predicted normal state $^4S_{3/2}$ is probably not correct. Thus the state $p^3\ ^2D_{3/2}$ was found by Back and Goudsmit[5] to have $g = 1.224$, whereas if the coupling were strictly Russell-Saunders g would be equal to 0.800. The Stern-Gerlach pattern found by Leu[6] was resolved into only two broad lines, instead of the four predicted. Their intensity distribution is, however, compatible with the values $j = 3/2$ and $g = 1.45$, and this g-value is within the possible range for abnormal coupling.

The investigation of lithium was of considerable interest because of Heisenberg's[7] suggestion that the hyperfine structure observed by Schüler in the lithium spark spectrum might be due to a nuclear moment of the order of magnitude of one Bohr magneton. Taylor[8] obtained a Stern-Gerlach pattern showing that the nuclei do not possess a moment larger than one-third of a magneton. (This is on the assumption that all the nuclei have the same moment. A larger moment possessed by the rarer isotope would not have been detected.)

55. PARAMAGNETISM

The well-known theory of Langevin,[9] based on classical mechanics, led to an explanation of the large paramagnetic

[1] A. Leu, *Z. f. Phys.*, **41**: 551, 1927.

[2] W. Gerlach and A. C. Cilliers, *Z. f. Phys.*, **26**: 106, 1924.

[3] W. Gerlach, *Ann. d. Phys.*, **76**: 163, 1925.

[4] V. Thorsen *Z. f. Phys.*, **40**: 642, 1926; S. Goudsmit and E. Back, *ibid.* **43**: 321, 1927.

[5] E. Back and S. Goudsmit, *Z. f. Phys.*, **47**: 174, 1928.

[6] A. Leu, *Z. f. Phys.*, **49**: 498, 1928.

[7] W. Heisenberg, *Z. f. Phys.*, **39**: 516, 1926.

[8] J. B. Taylor, *Z. f. Phys.*, **52**: 846, 1929.

[9] P. Langevin, *Jour. de Phys.*, **4**: 678, 1905; *Ann. de Chim. et de Phys.*, **5**: 70, 1905.

susceptibilities shown by a number of substances by attributing to their constituent atoms or molecules a permanent magnetic moment μ, which is oriented in the magnetic field in such a way as to lead to an average component along the field direction of

$$\bar{\mu} = \frac{1}{3}\frac{\mu^2}{kT}H, \tag{3}$$

in which k is Boltzmann's constant and T is the absolute temperature. The corresponding value of the molal susceptibility is

$$\chi = \frac{N\bar{\mu}}{H} = \frac{C}{T}, \tag{4}$$

in which the Curie constant C is given by

$$C = \frac{N\mu^2}{3kT} \tag{5}$$

with N Avogadro's number. This equation (which is valid for H not too large) accounts quantitatively for the observed temperature dependence of the susceptibility. From measurements of the molal susceptibility it is possible to evaluate μ.

In the derivation of his equations Langevin assumed that all orientations of the magnetic moment of the atom or molecule relative to the field direction have the same a priori probability. In the quantum mechanics this assumption is no longer justified. The value of $\bar{\mu}$, the average moment along the field direction, can instead be obtained by the consideration of the Zeeman levels shown by the atom, ion, or molecule. For an atom with given values of j and g the possible orientations in a magnetic field correspond to the field energy values

$$W_m = \mu_m H = mg\frac{eh}{4\pi m_0 c}H. \tag{6}$$

The states with low field energy will, in accordance with the Boltzmann distribution law, be favored over those with high energy to such an extent that the average field energy will be given by

$$\overline{W} = \frac{\sum_{m=-j}^{+j} W_m e^{-\frac{W_m}{kT}}}{\sum_{m=-j}^{+j} e^{-\frac{W_m}{kT}}}, \tag{7}$$

or, expanding the exponential expressions and neglecting all but the first two terms,

$$\overline{W} = \frac{\sum_m W_m\left(1 - \frac{W_m}{kT} + \cdots\right)}{\sum_m (1 - \quad \cdots)} = -\frac{\sum_m W_m^2}{(2j+1)kT}$$

$$= -\left(\frac{eh}{4\pi m_0 c}\right)^2 H^2 \frac{g^2 \sum_m m^2}{(2j+1)kT}. \quad (8)$$

Now the value of $\sum_m m^2$ is $\frac{1}{3}\, j(j+1)(2j+1)$, for j either integral or half integral, so that $\overline{W}$ reduces to

$$\overline{W} = -\left(\frac{eh}{4\pi m_0 c}\right)^2 H^2 g^2 \frac{j(j+1)}{3kT}, \quad (9)$$

or, writing $\overline{W} = \overline{\mu}_j H$,

$$\mu_j = \frac{H}{3kT} j(j+1) g^2 \left(\frac{eh}{4\pi m_0 c}\right)^2. \quad (10)$$

Comparison of this equation with Equation 3 shows that the molal susceptibility is then

$$\chi = \frac{C}{T}, \text{ with } C = \frac{N}{3kT} j(j+1) g^2 \left(\frac{eh}{4\pi m_0 c}\right)^2. \quad (11)$$

The similarity of Equations 11 and 5 is striking, and suggests the immediate interpretation of $\sqrt{j(j+1)}\; g\frac{eh}{4\pi m_0 c}$ as the permanent magnetic moment of the atom with given j and g. This is in accord with the model we have used throughout this book, in which the mechanical moment vector **j** has been given the magnitude $\sqrt{j(j+1)}$. The corresponding magnetic moment, in Bohr magnetons, is then obtained simply by multiplying by the Landé g-factor. With this interpretation the original equations of Langevin are still valid in the quantum mechanics.[1]

[1] The general validity in the quantum mechanics of the classical expressions of this type when moment vectors are assigned magnitudes $\sqrt{j(j+1)}$, etc., has been shown by J. H. Van Vleck, (*Phys. Rev.*, **29**: 727, 1927; **31**: 587, 1928). It is evident that the vector **j** could be given the magnitude j, and that the correct Equation 11 would not thereby be changed; instead, it would be interpreted as showing that the classical factor $\frac{1}{3}$ should be replaced by a quantum factor $(j+1)/3j$. This procedure was necessary in the old quantum theory (W. Pauli, *Phys. Z.*, **21**: 615, 1920; A. Sommerfeld,

The measurements of the paramagnetic susceptibilities of monatomic gases can accordingly be made the basis of an experimental determination of the magnetic moment $\sqrt{j(j+1)}g$ (in Bohr magnetons) of the atoms; and, conversely, a knowledge of the spectral state permits the prediction of the susceptibility. Introducing numerical values in Equation 11, we obtain

$$\mu_j = g\sqrt{j(j+1)} = 2.83\sqrt{C}. \qquad (12)$$

For the alkali metals, silver, monatomic hydrogen, and, in general, all atoms with a ^2S ground state, $g\sqrt{j(j+1)}$ is equal to $\sqrt{3}$; so that the magnetic moment as calculated from the paramagnetic susceptibility should be $\sqrt{3}$ Bohr magnetons. Measurements made by Gerlach[1] on potassium vapor actually lead to just this value.[2]

The diamagnetism of most ionic compounds is to be attributed to the fact that most stable ions have the spectral state ^1S, for which the magnetic moment is zero. The principal exceptions are discussed in the following sections.

55a. Magnetic Moments of Ions of the Rare Earth Elements.— The number of paramagnetic monatomic substances whose

"Atombau," 4th ed., p. 637, etc.). The simplicity introduced through the use of the classical expression is one of the strongest arguments for the adoption of the alternative interpretation. With the old quantum theory, the correct expression for paramagnetic susceptibility was obtained *only* with the assumption of strong spatial quantization. The value of $\overline{\cos^2\theta}$ then became $(j+1)/3j$, with μ^2 equal to j^2g^2. The difficulty introduced by this treatment was that the experiments were carried out under conditions such that there was no spatial quantization. The number of collisions in unit time of an atom or ion with others in the case of Gerlach's experiments with sodium, as well as in the rare earth solutions and crystals, is very much larger than the frequency of Larmor precession in the applied fields. Under such circumstances there is no spatial quantization and the classical value, $\frac{1}{3}$, is valid for $\overline{\cos^2\theta}$. This would lead to a formula in direct contradiction with the observations.

The new quantum mechanics avoids this difficulty, by giving the value $\frac{1}{3}$ to the averaged value of $\overline{\cos^2\theta}$ both with and without spatial quantization, and placing $\mu^2 = j(j+1)g^2$.

[1] W. Gerlach, *Proc.*, Como Congress, Vol. I, p. 77, 1927.

[2] In the solid state these metals no longer retain their spectral state; instead, each is composed of positive ions, with ground state ^1S (and hence diamagnetic), and metallic electrons. The explanation of the observed small temperature-independent paramagnetic suscept bility of the alkali metals as resulting from orientation of the spin moments of the metallic electrons was given by W. Pauli, *Z. f. Phys.*, **41**: 81, 1927.

susceptibility can be measured in the vapor phase is not large. It is possible, however, to interpret the paramagnetism shown by many salts, in particular those of the rare earth elements and the elements of the iron group, as arising from the orientation of the permanent magnetic moments of the cations in the magnetic field, and to apply Equation 12 to them. This procedure seems justified especially in the case of aqueous solutions, in which the ions presumably can orient themselves freely. It might be expected that in solid salts surrounding atoms would

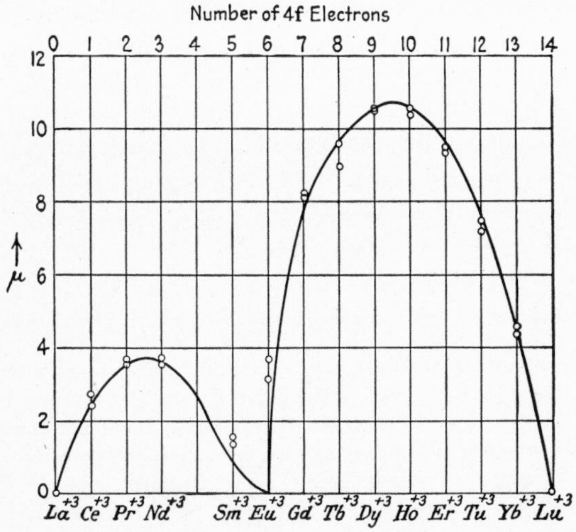

FIG. 65.—The spectroscopic magneton numbers for rare earth ions (points on the curve) and the values calculated from the observed paramagnetic susceptibilities (open circles).

interfere with the orienting process; it is found experimentally, however, that the molal susceptibility of solid salts is usually close to that shown by the same salts in solution.

Hund[1] was strikingly successful in applying these considerations to the series of rare earth elements. All of these elements, from lanthanum, $Z = 57$, to lutecium, $Z = 71$, form trivalent ions; and their salts are usually strongly paramagnetic. The spectra of the rare earths have not been analyzed. Hund assumed the usual structural rules: (1) that all of the outer

[1] F. HUND, *Z. f. Phys.*, **33**: 345, 1925.

electrons in the ions are $4f$ electrons[1] (as in Table II, Chap. IX), (2) that the stable term (with Russell-Saunders coupling) is in each case that with the largest s and the largest l, and (3) that the terms are regular for the first half (small j stable) and inverted for the second half (large j stable) of the series; and in this way predicted the j and g values given in Table II. These values are in good general agreement with the experimental ones, as is seen from Figure 65 also. The discrepancy shown by europium, $Z = 63$, is unexplained; it is possible that it arises from impurities in the sample used.[2]

These considerations indicate strongly that the normal states of these ions are the ones predicted.

55b. The Paramagnetic Susceptibility of Ions of the Iron-group Elements.—Hund pointed out that calculations similar to those which he made for the rare-earth ions do not lead to results in good agreement with experiment in the case of compounds of elements in the iron group. The expected normal states of ions from Sc^{3+} and Ca^{++}, with no $3d$ electrons, to Cu^+ and Zn^{++}, with ten $3d$ electrons, are given in Table III. The

[1] R. C. Gibbs and H. E. White (*Phys. Rev.*, **33**: 157, 1929) have recently presented evidence that the normal state of Ce^{+3} as a gas is $5d\,^2D_{3/2}$, instead of $4f\,^2F_{5/2}$ as assumed by Hund; it is possible, however, that $4f\,^2F_{5/2}$ is stable for Ce^{+3} in solution and in crystals.

[2] The discrepancy shown by trivalent samarium has been explained by Dr. S. Freed, to whom we are indebted for the personal communication of the following results. Magnetic measurements on $Sm_2(SO_4)_3 \cdot 8H_2O$ of great purity (purified by the late Prof. C. James of the University of New Hampshire) showed that several states of the samarium ion exist at ordinary temperatures. The magneton number calculated from the low temperature susceptibility approaches Hund's predicted value. At higher temperatures the magneton number is larger, for an appreciable fraction of the ions are in an upper state with larger moment. Spectroscopic proof of these states has been reported by Freed and Spedding, *Nature*, **123**: 525, 1929.

The magneton number of divalent samarium in $SmCl_2$ was found by Freed to be about the same as that given by St. Meyer for trivalent europium, indicated in Figure 65. Freed pointed out that this agrees well with the predicted moment if it is assumed that the configuration is $4f^4 5d 6s$; but this configuration is improbable. Very recently J. H. Van Vleck and A. Frank, *Phys. Rev.*, **34**: 1495, 1625, 1929, have applied Van Vleck's formula for paramagnetic susceptibility taking into account second-order terms to the rare-earth ions, obtaining theoretical magneton numbers in better agreement with experiment than those given by the simple theory. The values which differ by more than 0.1 from those in Table II are Il^{+3}, 2.83; Sm^{+3}, 1.66; Eu^{+3}, 3.53. This work makes the agreement between theory and experiment complete. (See footnote on p. 237.)

TABLE II.—MAGNETIC MOMENTS OF RARE EARTH IONS

Ion	Number of 4*f* electrons	Ground state	*j*	*g*	$g\sqrt{j(j+1}$	Experimental values of $2.83\sqrt{C}$	
						Cabrera	St. Meyer
La^{+3}	0	^1S	0	0/0	0.00	diamagnetic	
Ce^{+3}, Pr^{+4}	1	^2F	5/2	6/7	2.54	2.39	2.77
Pr^{+3}	2	^3H	4	4/5	3.58	3.60	3.47
Nd^{+3}	3	^4J	9/2	8/11	3.62	3.62	3.51
Il^{+3}	4	^5J	4	3/5	2.68		
Sm^{+3}	5	^6H	5/2	2/7	0.84	1.54	1.32
Eu^{+3}	6	^7F	0	0/0	0.00	3.61	3.12
Gd^{+3}	7	^8S	7/2	2	7.9	8.2	8.1
Tb^{+3}	8	^7F	6	3/2	9.7	9.6	9.0
Dy^{+3}	9	^6H	15/2	4/3	10.6	10.5	10.6
Ho^{+3}	10	^5J	8	5/4	10.6	10.5	10.4
Er^{+3}	11	^4J	15/2	6/5	9.6	9.5	9.4
Tu^{+3}	12	^3H	6	7/6	7.5	7.2	7.5
Yb^{+3}	13	^2F	7/2	8/7	4.5	4.4	4.6
Lu^{+3}	14	^1S	0	0/0	0.00	diamagnetic	

TABLE III.—MAGNETIC MOMENTS OF IRON-GROUP IONS IN LOWEST STATE

Ion	Number of 3*d* electrons	Term	*j*	*g*	$g\sqrt{j(j+1)}$	Experimental values of $2.83\sqrt{C}$[1]
K^+, Ca^{++}, Sc^{+3}, Ti^{+4}	0	^1S	0	0/0	0.00	diamagnetic
V^{+4}	1	^2D	3/2	4/5	1.55	1.7
V^{+3}	2	^3F	2	2/3	1.63	2.4
Cr^{+3}, Mn^{+4}, V^{++}	3	^4F	3/2	2/5	0.78	3.8, 4.0
Cr^{++}, Mn^{+3}	4	^5D	0	0/0	0.00	4.8
Mn^{++}, Fe^{+3}	5	^6S	5/2	2	5.96	5.8–5.9
Fe^{++}	6	^5D	4	3/2	6.76	5.2–5.3
Co^{++}	7	^4F	9/2	4/3	6.68	4.8–5.0
Ni^{++}	8	^3F	4	5/4	5.64	3.2–3.4
Cu^{++}	9	^2D	5/2	6/5	3.56	1.8–2.0
Cu^+, Zn^{++}	10	^1S	0	0/0	0.00	diamagnetic

[1] The experimental values are for solutions and solid salts as collected by B. CABRERA, *Jour. de Phys. et le Radium*, **6**: 241, 273, 1925, and E. C. STONER, "Magnetism and Atomic Structure," London, 1926, except for the various ions of vanadium, values for which were reported by S. FREED, *J. Am. Chem. Soc.*, **49**: 2456, 1927.

corresponding values of $g\sqrt{j(j+1)}$, giving the expected number of Bohr magnetons for compounds containing these ions, are plotted in Figure 66, together with the experimental values of μ for these compounds. It is seen that the agreement is poor except at three points; namely, Ca^{++} and Sc^{+3}, with $^1S_0$; Mn^{++} and Fe^{+3}, with $^6S_{5/2}$; and Cu^{+} and Zn^{++}, with $^1S_0$ as ground state.

Laporte and Sommerfeld[1] were led by this observation to develop an explanation for the discrepancy. The S states are all single; there is for them only one possible value of j. Each

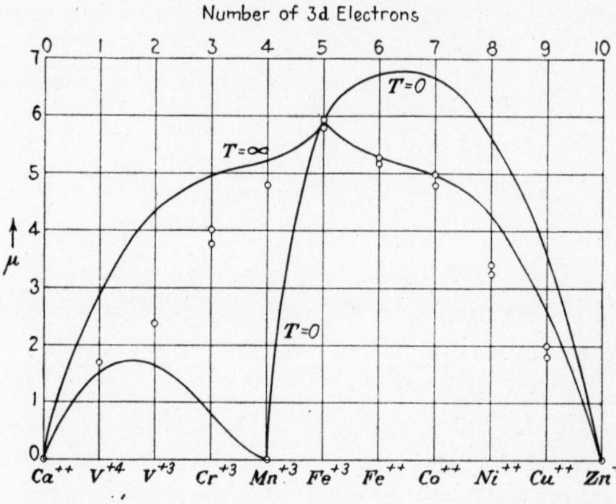

FIG. 66.—Theoretical magneton numbers for the iron group ions (points on the curves) and values from the paramagnetic susceptibilities of solid salts and solutions (open circles).

of the D and F states, on the other hand, leads to a number of multiplet levels. For each of the rare-earth ions only one of these levels need be considered; namely, the one with the smallest or largest j, according to whether the state is regular or inverted; for the multiplet separation is so large that for thermodynamic equilibrium at ordinary temperatures all but a negligibly small fraction of the ions are in the lowest state. The multiplet separations for the iron-group ions are expected to be small, however, so that there may be present appreciable numbers of ions in levels other than the lowest.

The number of ions occupying one of the levels of the multiplet, characterized by the value of j and by the energy difference

[1] O. LAPORTE and A. SOMMERFELD, *Z. f. Phys.*, **40**: 333, 1926.

ΔW_j between the level under consideration and the lowest level, is given by the statistical equation

$$N_j = N\frac{(2j+1)e^{-\Delta W_j/kT}}{\sum_j (2j+1)e^{-\Delta W_j/kT}}, \tag{13}$$

in which $2j + 1$ is the quantum weight of the jth level. The moment of each ion is $g\sqrt{j(j+1)}$; and the susceptibility of the substance is determined by the averaged square of the moments of all the ions present. It is further assumed that the applied external field is not strong enough to produce the Paschen-Back effect for the multiplet under consideration. This leads to the equation

$$\mu = 2.83\sqrt{C} = \left\{\frac{\sum_j g^2(j)j(j+1)(2j+1)e^{-\Delta W_j/kT}}{\sum_j (2j+1)e^{-\Delta W_j/kT}}\right\}^{\frac{1}{2}} \tag{14}$$

The values of $\bar{\mu}$ resulting in two limiting cases are easily computed. In case ΔW_j is large compared with kT only the lowest level is occupied by an appreciable number of ions and the magneton numbers reduce to those of Table III. If ΔW_j is small compared with kT the exponential terms can be replaced by unity and the sums evaluated. On doing this there result the values of $\bar{\mu}$ given in Table IV. These values are symmetrical about the point with five $3d$ electrons, for under these conditions the distinction between regular and inverted terms vanishes.[1]

[1] An expression differing from Equation 14 has been derived by Van Vleck (*Phys. Rev.*, **31**: 587, 1928) for the case of ΔW_j small compared with kT; namely,

$$\bar{\mu} = \{4s(s+1) + l(l+1)\}^{\frac{1}{2}}.$$

This includes certain large second-order Zeeman-effect terms not included in the treatment of Laporte and Sommerfeld. The values of $\bar{\mu}$ given by the expressions usually differ by no more than 2 or 3 per cent, however, so that Equation 14 can be used in most cases. The formula given by Van Vleck is identical with the one obtainable by the method of Sommerfeld and Laporte if the applied field is assumed to be strong enough to produce the Paschen-Back effect for the multiplet under consideration. Van Vleck's result thus shows that a large kT has the same effect on the susceptibility as a strong external field.

At first sight, one might expect the presence of a nuclear magnetic moment, as treated in the previous chapter, to have some influence on the susceptibility. The hyperfine splitting is so small, however, that kT is very much larger than ΔW. This leads to the same result as in a strong field, where

TABLE IV.—MAGNETIC MOMENTS CALCULATED FOR IRON-GROUP IONS WITH ΔW SMALL

Number of 3d electrons	Term	j	g	μ
0 10	^1S	0	0/0	0.00
1 9	^2D	3/2 5/2	4/5 6/5	2.92
2 8	^3F	2 3 4	2/3 13/12 5/4	4.34
3 7	^4F	3/2 5/2 7/2 9/2	2/5 36/35 26/21 4/3	4.97
4 6	^5D	0 1 2 3 4	0/0 3/2 3/2 3/2 3/2	5.23
5	^6S	5/2	2	5.95

It is seen from Figure 66 that the new curve agrees well with the experimental values for Fe^{++} and Co^{++}, as well as for the ions with single ground states, for which the curves coincide. The experimental values for Cr^{++} and Mn^{+3} as well as for Cr^{+3} and Mn^{+4} lie between the two limiting curves, but near the one corresponding to small multiplet separation. All of these results are gratifying. It is, however, not possible at the present time to account for the location of the experimental points for Ni^{++} and Cu^{++}, which lie outside of the region included by the two limiting curves.[1]

56. THE MAGNETO-MECHANICAL EFFECTS

The Barnett[2] effect and its inverse,[3] the Einstein-de Haas effect, are of some interest in connection with spectral states. In the Barnett experiments a cylindrical bar of a ferromagnetic substance is set into rapid rotation, and the ratio of the magnetic moment to the angular momentum set up is measured.

the coupling between the nuclear moment and the extranuclear electrons is broken. It may be easily verified that the nucleus will have no influence on the susceptibility under these circumstances. It must be mentioned that for this case only the treatment given by Van Vleck is correct; the method of Sommerfeld and Laporte would have given quite different results.

[1] O. LAPORTE, *Z. f. Phys.*, **47**: 761, 1928, has calculated ΔW for these elements with the spin-doublet formula, and introduced these values in Equation 14, without getting better agreement with experiment.

[2] S. J. BARNETT, *Phys. Rev.*, **6**: 239, 1915; **10**: 7, 1917; see also O. W. RICHARDSON, *Phys. Rev.*, **26**: 248, 1908.

[3] A. EINSTEIN and W. J. DE HAAS, *Verh. d. deutsch. phys. Ges.*, **17**: 152, 1915; A. EINSTEIN, *ibid.*, **18**: 173, 1916; W. J. DE HAAS, *ibid.*, **18**: 423, 1916; *Proc.*, Amsterdam Acad., **18**: 1281, 1916; J. Q. STEWART, *Phys. Rev.*, **11**: 100, 1918; E. BECK, *Ann. d. Phys.*, **60**: 109, 1919.

This experiment, as well as its inverse, leads to values for the ratio of magnetic to mechanical moment (in the usual quantum units) of about 2 for all substances, which corresponds to the Landé g-factor for the electron spin moments. The recent accurate experiments of Barnett,[1] however, give 1.87 – 1.89 for this ratio, the same value resulting from measurements of the Barnett effect and the Einstein-de Haas effect. The ratio to be expected for the spin moments of the conduction electrons in the metals is the g-factor for electron spins, which is 2. It seems probable that the observed deviation from 2 arises from the contribution of the metal ions. In iron, for example, with which most of the experiments were made, there are probably both trivalent and divalent ions present. For Fe^{+3}, as is seen from Tables III and IV, the g-factor is equal to 2 at all temperatures, and for Fe^{++} it is equal to $3/2$. It is possible that these ions might be present in such numbers as to lead, together with the metallic electrons (with $g = 2$), to an average g equal to that observed.

57. POLARIZATION OF RESONANCE RADIATION IN A MAGNETIC FIELD

A phenomenon which also is closely connected with the Zeeman effect is the polarization of resonance radiation in an external magnetic field. Wood and Ellett[2] discovered that if resonance radiation (Sec. 12c) is produced by means of an incident beam of polarized light, the polarization of the resonance radiation will be influenced by the presence of an external magnetic field. Even the earth's field is sufficient to cause partial depolarization. We shall demonstrate the explanation[3] of this effect with the help of a simple example, the yellow sodium lines. Figure 21 of Section 17d represents the level scheme of these lines in a magnetic field. In the unexcited vapor all atoms will be in either one of the two magnetic levels of the ^2S state. If a beam

[1] S. J. Barnett and L. J. H. Barnett, *Proc.*, Amer. Acad., **60**: 127, 1925; S. J. Barnett, *Phys. Rev.*, **31**: 1116, 1928.

References to other recent articles are given in the *Proc.*, Amer. Acad. paper.

[2] R. W. Wood and A. Ellett, *Proc.*, Roy. Soc., A **103**: 396, 1923.

[3] A. E. Ruark, P. Foote and F. L. Mohler, *Jour. Opt. Soc. Amer.*, **7**: 415, 1923; W. Hanle, *Naturwiss.*, **11**: 690, 1923; G. Breit, *Phil. Mag.*, **47**: 832, 1924; P. Pringsheim, *Z. f. Phys.*, **23**: 324, 1924; G. Joos, *Phys. Z.*, **25**: 130, 1924.

of unpolarized light of the correct range of wave-lengths is sent in, absorption will bring the atoms into all the magnetic levels of the ^2P state. In falling back to the normal state the resonance line will show the ordinary Zeeman effect. In the experiments on resonance radiation, however, the intensity is too small to use spectographs of sufficient resolving power to show this, and all Zeeman components of both the sodium lines are seen as one line. As the intensity of all parallel components is equal to the intensity of all perpendicular components this one line will generally appear to be unpolarized.[1]

Suppose now that the incident beam is directed at right angles to the lines of force of the magnetic field, and that the light is polarized with the electric vector parallel to these lines of force. In this case only the parallel components of the Zeeman pattern can be absorbed by the vapor. The atoms will be raised only to those magnetic levels of the ^2P state which have $m = +\frac{1}{2}$ or $-\frac{1}{2}$, the two levels with $m = +\frac{3}{2}$ and $-\frac{3}{2}$ remaining empty. When the atoms then fall back into the normal state the Zeeman pattern of the resonance line will be incomplete, with two of the perpendicular components missing. This means that the unresolved observed line will contain an excess of parallel polarized light and so be partially parallel polarized. This excess divided by the total intensity of both parallel and perpendicular light is called the degree of polarization and can be easily obtained by means of the intensity formulas of Section 35. For this special example it is found that the expected degree of polarization is 60 per cent. Similar considerations can be used if the incident beam is perpendicularly polarized.

In a general case it is necessary to be rather careful in the computation of the degree of polarization. The intensity formulas of Section 35 hold only in case the initial states are normally filled; that is, the population must be the same for all values of m. The special type of excitation, however, may cause this condition to be not fulfilled. In accordance with the sum rules of Section 35, the normal population of each level is proportional to the intensity of the parallel plus twice the intensity of the perpendicular components arising from that level. In the case that the incident beam is parallel polarized, the population of the upper states due to the absorption will then only be proportional to the intensity of the parallel components of which they are the

[1] See however footnote 2 on the next page.

final state in absorption. Let us denote the magnetic levels of the upper state by a subscript[1] α. The sum of the parallel components having the level α as final level in the case of absorption we will call π_α, the sum of all the perpendicular components σ_α. Omitting the proportionality factor, the population of this level under normal conditions of excitation will be

$$A = \pi_\alpha + 2\sigma_\alpha,$$

and this will be the same for all levels of this state. But if we take the incident beam to be parallel polarized this population will be only π_α. The emitted Zeeman components of the resonance light will thus have only π_α/A times their normal intensity. The total intensity of all the emitted parallel light will be proportional to

$$\sum \frac{\pi_\alpha}{A} \cdot \pi_\alpha,$$

in which the sum is to be taken over all the magnetic levels of the upper state. There is similarly found for the total intensity of all perpendicular components

$$\sum \frac{\pi_\alpha}{A} \cdot \sigma_\alpha = \sum \frac{\pi_\alpha(A - \pi_\alpha)}{2A},$$

and finally for the degree of polarization

$$\frac{\Sigma\pi_\alpha(3\pi_\alpha - A)}{\Sigma\pi_\alpha(\pi_\alpha + A)}.$$

In certain simple cases we may introduce for π_α its expression in terms of quantum numbers, but in general this does not give a simple formula. It is not difficult to derive the expressions for the case that the incident beam is perpendicularly polarized.[2]

The actual experiments are not in complete agreement with the calculations. No satisfactory explanation for some of the discrepancies has been given up to the present time. Recently Dr. A. Ellett suggested to us that the presence of a nuclear moment might be the cause of the deviations. Indeed one sees that in weak magnetic fields, not strong enough to produce a

[1] We cannot use the quantum number m for this purpose, as we are thinking of the general case where both the upper and the lower state are multiplets, so that a certain value of m can occur several times.

[2] Our method also shows that when an unpolarized incident beam is used perpendicular to the field the populations will not be normal, but only $\pi_\alpha + \sigma_\alpha$, giving partial polarization. We have assumed above that the incident beam is of uniform intensity over the whole line pattern; complications are introduced if this is not fulfilled in the experiment.

Paschen-Back effect upon the hyperfine structure, the considerations given above for the yellow sodium lines will be altered considerably. It is very probable that the idea put forward by Dr. Ellett will prove to be of great value in determining nuclear moments in cases where the hyperfine structure can not be investigated successfully.[1]

In the complete absence of an external magnetic field the resonance polarization will be the same as in the presence of a weak field parallel to the electric vector of the incident beam. There will, of course, not be a sudden discontinuity between "no field" and a very weak field. According to Bohr the external field can only be considered as being "present" if the atoms have time to make at least one complete Larmor precession around the field before they are disturbed by collisions or other causes. Fermi and Rasetti[2] have investigated the resonance polarization of mercury in rapidly alternating magnetic fields. They found that if the frequency of the field is larger than the Larmor frequency of the state under consideration the polarization of the line is the same as in the absence of a field.

[1] W. MacNair, *Phys. Rev.*, **31**: 986, 1928, has shown that discrepancies in the resonance polarization of the mercury line λ2537 are due to some of its fine structure components, which have a different Zeeman effect from the main line.

[2] E. Fermi and F. Rasetti, *Nature*, **115**: 764, 1925; *Z. f. Phys.*, **33**: 246, 1925.

APPENDIX I

VALUES OF PHYSICAL CONSTANTS[1]

Velocity of light	$c = (2.99796 \pm 0.00004) \times 10^{10}$ cm. sec.$^{-1}$
Electronic charge	$e = (4.770 \pm 0.005) \times 10^{-10}$ abs.-*e.s.u.*
	$e/c = (1.5911 \pm 0.0016) \times 10^{-20}$ abs.-*e.m.u.*
Specific electronic charge (spectroscopic)*	$e/m = (1.761 \pm 0.001) \times 10^{7}$ abs. *e.m.u.* g.$^{-1}$
	$(e/m)c = (5.279 \pm 0.003) \times 10^{17}$ abs. *e.s.u.* g.$^{-1}$
Specific electronic charge (deflection)	$e/m = (1.769 \pm 0.002) \times 10^{7}$ abs. *e.m.u.* g.$^{-1}$
	$(e/m)c = (5.303 \pm 0.006) \times 10^{17}$ abs.-*e.s.u.* g.$^{-1}$
Planck's constant	$h = (6.547 \pm 0.008) \times 10^{-27}$ erg sec.
Rydberg constant for hydrogen	$R_H = 109677.759 \pm 0.05$ cm.$^{-1}$
Rydberg constant for ionized helium	$R_{He} = 109722.403 \pm 0.05$ cm.$^{-1}$
Rydberg constant for infinite mass	$R_\infty = 109737.42 \pm 0.06$ cm.$^{-1}$
	$R_\infty c = (3.28988 \pm 0.00004) \times 10^{15}$ sec.$^{-1}$
Avogadro's number	$N = (0.6064 \pm 0.0006) \times 10^{24}$ mole^{-1}
Boltzmann constant	$k = (1.3709 \pm 0.0014) \times 10^{-16}$ erg deg.$^{-1}$
Mass of electron (spectroscopic)	$m_0 = \dfrac{e}{c(e/m)_{sp}} = (9.035 \pm 0.010) \times 10^{-28}$ g.
Mass of proton	$M_P = (1.6609 \pm 0.0017) \times 10^{-24}$ g.
Ratio mass proton to mass electron (spectroscopic)	$= 1838 \pm 1$
Ratio mass proton to mass electron (deflection)	$= 1847 \pm 2$

[1] From the compilation of R. T. Birge, *Phys. Rev. Sup.*, **1**: 1, 1929.

* The probable values of e/m as determined spectroscopically and from deflection experiments are in disagreement. For use in spectroscopy the spectroscopic values are preferred.

Wave-number associated with 1 abs-volt	$= 8106 \pm 3$ cm^{-1} abs.-volt^{-1}
Wave-length associated with 1 abs.-volt	$= \frac{hc^2}{e} = (12336 \pm 5) \times 10^{-8}$ cm. abs.-volt.
Energy of 1 abs.-volt-electron	$= (1.5911 \pm 0.0016) \times 10^{-12}$ erg
Fine-structure constant	$\alpha = \frac{2\pi e^2}{hc} = (7.284 \pm 0.006) \times 10^{-3}$
Reciprocal of fine-structure constant	$\frac{1}{\alpha} = 137.29 \pm 0.11$
Square of fine-structure constant	$\alpha^2 = (5.305 \pm 0.008) \times 10^{-5}$
Bohr unit of angular momentum	$\frac{h}{2\pi} = (1.0420 \pm 0.0013) \times 10^{-27}$ erg sec.
Magnetic moment of 1 Bohr magneton (spectroscopic)	$\mu_0 = (0.9175 \pm 0.0013) \times 10^{-20}$ erg gauss^{-1}
Magnetic moment of 1 Bohr magneton (deflection)	$\mu_0 = (0.9216 \pm 0.0016) \times 10^{-20}$ erg gauss^{-1}
Magnetic moment per mole for 1 Bohr magneton per molecule (spectroscopic)	$\mu_0 N = 5564 \pm 10$ erg gauss^{-1} mole^{-1}
Same (deflection)	$\mu_0 N = 5589 \pm 11$ erg gauss^{-1} mole^{-1}
Zeeman displacement per gauss	$= (4.674 \pm 0.003) \times 10^{-5}$ cm.$^{-1}$ gauss^{-1}
Radius of Bohr orbit in normal H	$a_0 = (0.5285 \pm 0.004) \times 10^{-8}$ cm.
General spectroscopic doublet constant	$R_\infty \alpha^2 = 5.822 \pm 0.009$ cm.$^{-1}$
Hydrogen doublet constant	$\frac{R_H \alpha^2}{16} = 0.3637 \pm 0.0006$ cm.$^{-1}$
Energy per mole for 1-abs.-volt-electron per molecule	$= 23055 \pm 4$ cal.$_{15}$ mol^{-1}
Multiplier of (Curie constant)$^{1/2}$ to give magnetic moment per molecule	$\left(\frac{3k}{N}\right)^{1/2} = (2.604 \pm 0.003) \times 10^{-20}$ erg$^{-1/2}$ deg.$^{-1/2}$ mole$^{1/2}$
Same to give Bohr magnetons per molecule	$\frac{(3k/N)^{1/2}}{\mu_0} = 2.8384 \pm 0.0019$ erg$^{-1/2}$ gauss deg.$^{-1/2}$ mole$^{1/2}$

APPENDIX II

RELATIONS AMONG ENERGY QUANTITIES

The first line of the table has the following significance: the energy of a quantum of light of wave-number 1 cm.$^{-1}$ is 1.963×10^{-16} erg, and is also 1.234×10^{-4} times the energy of an electron which has fallen through a potential drop of 1 volt; and a mole of such quanta has a total energy of 2.844 cal.

1 cm.$^{-1}$ = 1.963×10^{-16} erg = 1.234×10^{-4} v.e. = 2.844 cal/mole
1 v.e. = 23055 cal/mole = 8106 cm.$^{-1}$ = 1.591×10^{-12} erg.
1 cal/mole = 0.3516 cm.$^{-1}$ = 0.6901×10^{-16} erg = 4.338×10^{-5} v.e.
1 erg = 0.6285×10^{12} v.e. = 1.440×10^{16} cal/mole = 0.5095×10^{16} cm.$^{-1}$

The wave-length λ, in Ångstroms, of light a quantum of which has the same energy as an electron which has fallen through the potential drop V, in volts, is given by the relation

$$\lambda V = 12{,}336$$

APPENDIX III

THE DETAILED DISCUSSION OF REPRESENTATIVE SPECTRA

THE SPECTRUM OF IRON

In Figure 67 there are shown the term values for the lowest known levels in the spectrum of neutral iron. The nuclear charge of iron is 26, so that the atom contains eight more extra-

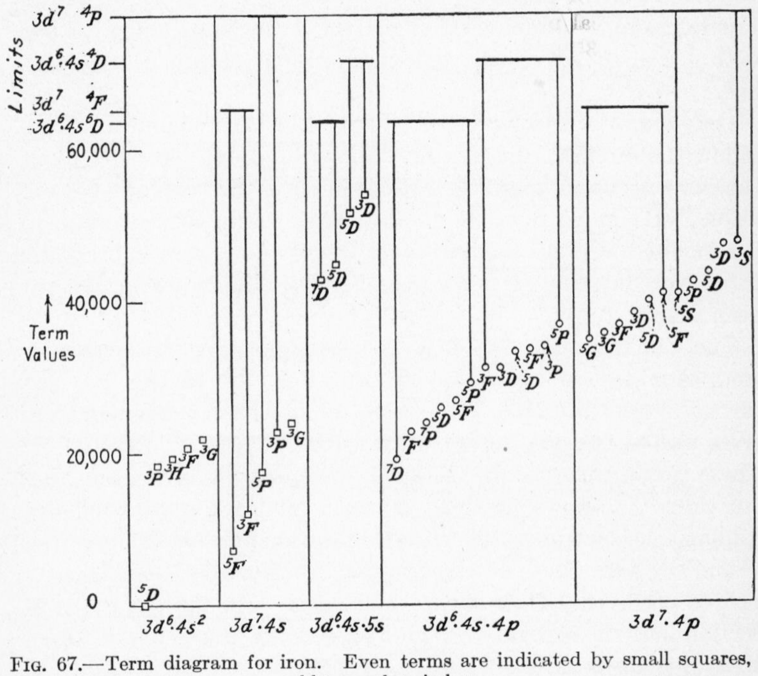

FIG. 67.—Term diagram for iron. Even terms are indicated by small squares, odd terms by circles.

nuclear electrons than the rare gas argon. These eight electrons are divided between the $3d$ and the $4s$ shell. As can be seen from the diagram, the very lowest level arises from the configuration $3d^6 \cdot 4s^2$; it is the low ^5D term of this configuration. The diagram further shows that this configuration is not very much more stable than the configuration $3d^7 \cdot 4s$. The multiplet levels of the two configurations are spread out over a large range, the known ones extending as far as 22,000 cm.$^{-1}$ above the lowest state; there are certainly many more even higher than this, but unknown at present.

The Configuration $3d^6 \cdot 4s^2$.—This configuration gives rise to the following possible multiplet levels:

$$^5D,\ ^3H,\ ^3G,\ ^3F,\ ^3F,\ ^3D,\ ^3P,\ ^3P.$$

The ^5D term follows the interval rule fairly well, as can be seen from the following table:

$^5D: j =$ 4	3	2	1	0	
$\Delta\nu =$ 415.930	288.069	184.130	89.938		cm.$^{-1}$
$A =$ 103.982	96.023	92.065	89.938		cm.$^{-1}$

Furthermore, it is an inverted level, the lowest state being the one with $j = 4$, in agreement with the formulas obtained in Section 39*b*.

Only four of the expected seven triplet levels are known. They follow the interval rule to a first approximation, and with about the same accuracy their separations agree with the expressions of Table XIII in Section 39*b*. All of these terms are inverted, in agreement with the theoretical expressions. These expressions further predict that ^3D is regular; this level has, however, not yet been found.

The Configuration $3d^7 \cdot 4s$.—This configuration can be considered as obtained from the configuration $3d^7$ of the ion Fe^+ through the addition of a $4s$ electron. The $3d^7$ configuration gives rise to two low terms, an inverted ^4F and an inverted ^4P. These terms are actually known in the spectrum of ionized iron, but only ^4F follows the interval rule, ^4P being quite irregular. Adding a $4s$ electron to the ^4F state of the ion produces an inverted ^5F and a ^3F term, both of which follow the interval rule sufficiently well to prove that their separations agree with the equations of Section 39*c*, the separation factor of ^5F being indeed about three-fifths of that for ^3F:

$3d^7(^4F)4s\ ^5F: j =$ 5	4	3	2	1
$\Delta\nu =$ 488.488	351.294	257.726	168.931	
$A =$ 97.698	87.823	85.909	84.466	

	$j =$ 4	3	2
$3d^7(^4F)4s\ ^3F$:	$\Delta V =$ 584.688	407.615	
	$A =$ 146.172	135.872	

Adding a $4s$ electron to ^4P of the ion leads to a ^5P and a ^3P level. The distance between ^4F and ^4P of the ion is about 11,000 cm.$^{-1}$, which is of the same order of magnitude as the distance between the P terms and the F terms of the configuration $3d^7 \cdot 4s$. If we knew higher series members, with $5s$, $6s$, $7s$, etc., it would be found that the P terms converge to a limit which lies 11,000 cm.$^{-1}$ higher than the limit to which the F terms converge; these two limits are just the ^4P and ^4F levels of the ion, respectively. Each of these limits is itself composed of several levels. Indeed, it would be found that before reaching the limit the Russell-Saunders coupling changes into (**jj**) coupling and that the levels converge to different ones of the limiting quartet levels.

The ^5P and ^3P levels do not follow the interval rule, the deviation being of the same kind as that observed for ^4P of the ion, from which they have been built up:

$Fe^+\ 3d^7\ ^4P: j =$	5/2	3/2	1/2	
$\Delta\nu =$	198.68	231.70		
$A =$	77.47	154.47		
$Fe\ 3d^7(^4P)4s\ ^5P: j =$	3	2	1	
$\Delta\nu =$	176.814	200.392		
$A =$	58.938	100.196		
$3d^7(^4P)4s\,^3P: j =$		2	1	0
$\Delta\nu =$			108.47	104.90
$A =$			54.23	104.90

Besides the above four terms there is known a ^3G term which very probably also belongs to this configuration, being built upon ^2G of the $3d^7$ configuration of Fe^+. It is difficult to decide which of the two known low ^3G terms belongs to the configuration $3d^6 \cdot 4s^2$ and which one to $3d^7 \cdot 4s$. Their interval separations cannot help to decide as they deviate too much from the interval rule and, moreover, the application of the equations of Section 39c shows that their separations are expected to be about the same. It is also not possible to decide from their combinations with other terms, and as they are both about equally high the only way to classify them is by remarking that the one assigned to the $3d^6 \cdot 4s^2$ configuration follows the interval rule better than the other one.

Of the next series member, $3d^7 \cdot 5s$, the ^5F and ^3F levels are known. They lie much higher in the level scheme, at about

48,000 cm.$^{-1}$ above the lowest state. The two multiplets are very near together, and, in fact, overlap, but nevertheless the interval rule holds well. The separations are close to those for the same terms in the configuration $3d^7 \cdot 4s$, again in agreement with expectation.

The Configuration $3d^6 \cdot 4s \cdot 5s$.—This configuration gives rise to a number of high terms, all over 42,000 cm.$^{-1}$ above the normal state. In some respects this configuration could be considered as a higher series member of the configuration $3d^6 \cdot 4s^2$, but as the two s electrons are no longer equivalent, the configuration involving a $5s$ electron gives rise to a different set of multiplets. This same problem occurs also in the simple singlet-triplet spectra of the second column in the periodic table, such as magnesium. Here we may ask whether the $s^2\ {}^1S_0$ term is to be considered as the first series member of the singlets arising from $s \cdot s$ configurations with the second s electron excited. Series formulas show that it is possible to consider the lowest state in this way. It is accordingly very probable that similar considerations will also hold in more complicated cases. For the iron spectrum this would mean that the multiplets of the $3d^6 \cdot 4s^2$ configurations may indeed be taken as the first series members of the corresponding multiplets of the $3d^6 \cdot 4s \cdot ns$ configurations, which, however, give rise to further multiplets which do not occur in the lowest state.

For our purpose, we consider the $3d^6 \cdot 4s \cdot 5s$ configuration to be built upon the configuration $3d^6 \cdot 4s$ of the ion. The lowest states for this configuration of the ion are a ${}^6D$ and a ${}^4D$ level, both inverted. They are both known, the first one being the normal state of the ion, and they follow the interval rule well. Adding a $5s$ electron produces a ${}^7D$ and a ${}^5D$ term and somewhat higher a ${}^5D$ and a ${}^3D$ term. The first two also follow the interval rule fairly well, the other two not so well. The ${}^4D$ level of the ion lies about 8000 cm.$^{-1}$ above the ${}^6D$ level; this separation is the same as that of the two groups of terms built upon them.

For both this configuration and the foregoing one the states of the ions on which they are built, which are at the same time the convergence limits for higher series members, are also indicated in the diagram. As no actual series are known for iron, the distance of these limits from the lowest level cannot be given with great accuracy. According to Russell and Moore, the $3d^6 \cdot 4s\ {}^6D$ limit lies about 63,400 cm.$^{-1}$ above the normal state.

Considering the relative position of the levels in the configurations considered above, we see that Hund's rule that the terms with the highest multiplicity lie lowest is fulfilled. But it is to be noticed that in the case of the triplets of the $3d^6 \cdot 4s^2$ configuration the one with largest l is not the lowest.

The Odd Configurations.—The above configurations, containing only d and s electrons, are all even, so that no combinations among them occur. They combine with the configurations containing a p electron; namely, $3d^6 \cdot 4s \cdot 4p$ and $3d^7 \cdot 4p$. The first configuration gives the lower terms. All those which are built upon $3d^6 \cdot 4s$ ^6D and ^4D of the ion have been found; namely,

$$\text{on } {}^6D\text{: } {}^7(F, D, P)\ {}^5(F, D, P);$$
$$\text{on } {}^4D\text{: } {}^5(F, D, P)\ {}^3(F, D, P).$$

They all follow the interval rule fairly well. As the level diagram shows, the septets are lower than the quintets built upon ^6D, but the D terms lie lowest, rather than the F's. The levels built upon ^4D are quite irregularly arranged.

Of the terms arising from the configuration $3d^7 \cdot 4p$, all those based on $3d^7$ ^4F and ^4P of the ion have been found. Most of these terms do not follow the interval rule very closely and they also are not ordered in accordance with the rules given by Hund. All that can be said is that those based on ^4P lie somewhat higher than those from ^4F, as is to be expected.

Besides the terms described above there are known a number of multiplets for which the configurations cannot be given with certainty. The lowest of these unassigned multiplets is a $^5G^\circ$ level 43,000 cm.$^{-1}$ above the lowest level. Its combinations show that it belongs to an odd configuration. The lowest unassigned even level is a ^3D at about 52,000 cm.$^{-1}$. In such cases it is often even difficult to give the correct term symbol; the ^3D term, for instance, might just as well be a ^5P, both terms having the same set of values for j. For simple spectra, it is possible to distinguish between such possibilities by means of intensities, observing that lines corresponding to transitions between levels of the same multiplicity are usually stronger than intercombination lines between terms of different multiplicity. In the complicated case of the iron spectrum, however, this method cannot be used, for very many such intercombinations occur with appreciable intensity.

Quite a number of levels which cannot be arranged into multiplets have also been found. They obviously arise from higher series members which deviate considerably from Russell-Saunders coupling. It has not yet been possible to assign electron configurations to them.

The classification and interpretation of the iron spectrum are among the greatest triumphs of the theory of spectra. The first multiplets in this complicated spectrum were discovered by Walters.[1] Following Walters many attempts were made to extend and to interpret his results. Laporte[2] was by far the most successful in this, and his detailed discussion led at the same time to the discovery of the Laporte rule (Sec. 21*d*). Moore and Russell[3] have recently added a large number of terms, and now practically all lines but the very weak ones have been classified. An interesting study of the structure and series limits in the iron spectrum has been made by Laporte.[4] Meggers[5] gave an important discussion of the connection between the classification and the wave-length accuracy of the standard lines in the iron spectrum. In fact, the relative term values are extremely accurately known, as a result of the accuracy with which many of the standard lines have been measured, so that a number of term values can be given to three decimal places.

It is of especial interest to investigate more closely as to why only the lowest nembers of the various series are known in this spectrum. Assuming an equilibrium distribution of the atoms over the different quantum states, for instance in the case of temperature excitation, the number of atoms in each state will be proportional to

$$p \cdot e^{-W/kT},$$

in which p denotes the quantum weight of the state and W the difference of its energy from that of the very lowest level. We may first consider the effect of the very large quantum weights of the low levels. Each level in our diagram is a multiplet, consisting itself of many levels, each of which has the weight $2j + 1$. Thus the total weight of a ^5F level, considered as one state, is 35. But it is obvious that this does not lead to an explanation of the non-observance of higher terms, for they also are complicated multiplets with large quantum weights, and in

[1] F. M. Walters, *Jour. Wash. Acad. Sci.*, **13**: 243, 1923.
[2] O. Laporte, *Z. f. Phys.*, **23**: 135, and **26**: 1, 1924.
[3] C. E. Moore and H. N. Russell, *Astrophys Jour.*, **68**: 151, 1928.
[4] O. Laporte, *Proc.* Nat. Acad. Sci., **12**: 496, 1926.
[5] W. F. Meggers, *Astrophys. Jour.*, **60**: 60, 1924.

considering the relative populations of lower and higher series members the weights do not give rise to a preference for the lower levels.

The actual cause of the filling up of the low levels only must thus be sought in the exponential factor. Thus not the large quantum weight of the low levels but their small values of W causes them to have a much larger population than the higher series members. If we compare the level scheme of iron with that of sodium, for example, we see at once a great difference. In sodium the normal state is far below the excited states, far compared to the distances between the excited states themselves. If in sodium the excitation is high enough to lift the atom from the normal level to the $4s$ state, it will also suffice to excite all higher states too, as the exponential factors for all the states have values of the same order. A slight exception in the case of sodium is the $3p$ state, which lies about half way between the normal state and the higher excited states. This means that it will be possible to have an equilibrium excitation which produces mainly the yellow resonance line, but as soon as the excitation is able to bring out one more series member appreciably, it will excite the complete series spectrum.

It must be mentioned especially that the above considerations hold only for methods of excitation which can be considered to a first approximation as giving rise to a stationary equilibrium. It is possible to produce quite different distributions among the levels by special types of excitation, such as the absorption of spectral lines (see Sec. 12).

THE SPECTRUM OF NEON

The lowest state of neon is the configuration $2p^6$, which gives rise to the single state $^1S_0$. This configuration is very stable and a large energy is required to bring the atom into the first possible excited state, $2p^5 \cdot 3s$, which lies 13,000 cm.$^{-1}$ higher. All the excited states lie in the region between 130,000 and 174,000 cm.$^{-1}$ from the normal state, so that they will all be excited at the same time, their Boltzmann factors being nearly equal. This causes the neon spectrum to be a typical series spectrum, in contradistinction to that of iron, and in consequence it has been possible to deduce absolute term values in this spectrum with considerable certainty.

The lowest configuration of the neon ion is $2p^5$, which gives rise to an inverted ^2P state, with a doublet separation of 780 cm.$^{-1}$. The excited states of neutral neon are thus built partially upon the lowest $^2P_{3/2}$ state or upon the 780 cm.$^{-1}$ higher $^2P_{1/2}$ state of the ion.

Nearly all configurations clearly show extreme (jj) coupling. Each is divided into two groups of levels, one group built upon

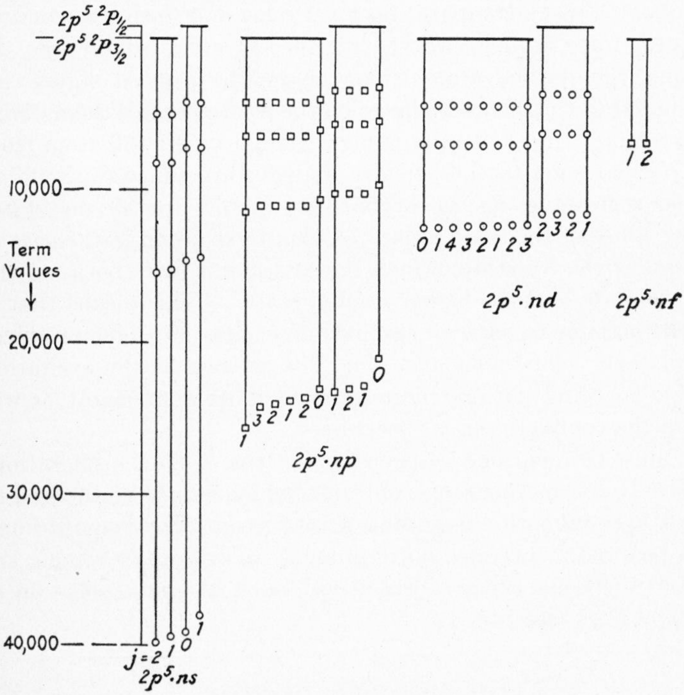

FIG. 68.—Term diagram for neon. The normal state $2p^6\ ^1S_0$ has not been shown on this diagram. It is at 173,930 cm.$^{-1}$. Even terms are indicated by squares, odd terms by circles.

one limit, the other group upon the other (Fig. 68). The separations within each group are, in general, small compared to the distances between these two limits. It would be going too far, however, to say that this is a pure case of (jj) coupling. All that can be said with certainty is that the individual values of j of the ionic states are retained after adding the last electron; it is quite improbable that this is also true for the **j** vector of the added electron itself. This means that we know nothing about the arrangement and further properties (such as the g-values) of the individual levels within each group built upon one ionic state.

The lowest configuration of the $2p^5 \cdot ns$ series, $2p^5 \cdot 3s$, does not deviate very much from Russell-Saunders coupling. The three lowest levels form the inverted ^3P state, the intervals being 418 and 359 cm.$^{-1}$. The ^1P level is 1070 cm.$^{-1}$ above $^3P_0$. The interval rule for the triplet is not fulfilled and the g-values for $^3P_1$ and $^1P_1$ are 1.46 and 1.03, instead of 1.50 and 1.00. For the other coupling the g-values would have been 1.33 and 1.17, so that the observed values indicate approximation to Russell-Saunders coupling. For the higher series members the g-values are unknown, but their position indicates clearly the change in coupling. The distances between the four levels for higher series members are:

	$j = 2$		1		0		1
$2p^5 \cdot 4s$		195		584		154	
$5s$		85		693		50	
$6s$		43		738		21	
$7s$		24		756		11	

The distance between the levels $j = 0$ and $j = 2$ is very nearly constant, from the very first levels on, and equal to the doublet separation of the $2p^5$ configuration of the ion, completely in agreement with the considerations of Section 29a.

Not much can be said about the lowest configuration of the $2p^5 \cdot np$ series. It is even uncertain whether the states with the same value of j have been arranged in the right order so as to form the first series members of the higher levels of this j value. Only in simple cases, such as for the $2p^5 \cdot ns$ configuration, is it possible to tell to which of the limits a certain low level belongs. The rule[1] to be applied is that levels with the same value of j do not "cross over." This means that if for a certain value of n in the $2p^5 \cdot ns$ configuration one of the two levels with $j = 1$ is the higher, the corresponding level in the other $2p^5 \cdot ns$ configurations, with which it forms a series, will also be the higher one. It is probable but not at all certain that a similar rule holds for more complicated configurations.

The g-values for this configuration are also very irregular. They do not agree at all with those calculated from any possible

[1] F. Hund. *Z. f. Phys.*, **52**: 601, 1928.

coupling, showing clearly that the levels under consideration form an intermediate case. The sum rule, however, is obeyed strictly, as can be seen from the following data:[1]

$j = 2$: $g = 1.137$ 1.229 1.301, sum 3.667, calculated 3.667; $j = 1$: $g = 1.984$ 0.669 0.999 1.340, sum 4.992, calculated 5.000.

The relative intensities of the transitions from this configuration to the configuration $2p^5 \cdot 4s$ have been treated in detail in Section 34. The $2p^5 \cdot np$ configurations can not combine with the normal state $2p^6$, but combine exclusively with $2p^5 \cdot ns$. Now a special property of this spectrum is that two of the levels of the $2p^5 \cdot 4s$ state are metastable; they can not combine with the normal state as this has $j = 0$ and the transitions 2 to 0 and 0 to 0 are forbidden. Under certain favorable circumstances, such as low pressure and low temperature (so that few collisions occur), the lifetime of an atom in such a metastable state can be comparatively long. Such states will behave like quasi-normal states, and absorption lines with these states as initial levels can be observed. The main result of this is that a great part of the emitted radiation will arise from transitions among these and higher levels, whereas only a comparatively small part of the radiation will be due to direct transitions to the normal state. This accounts for the unexpectedly large intensity of the neon light in the visible part of the spectrum.[2]

The levels of the $2p^5 \cdot nd$ configurations are distinctly divided into two groups built upon the two ionic states. Not much is known at present about the $2p^5 \cdot nf$ configurations. Their regular combinations with the $2p^5 \cdot 3d$ terms are too far in the infra-red to be studied. By means of a two-electron jump, however, they can combine with the $2p^5 \cdot 3s$ configurations, and that is how some of them are known. In this transition one of the five $2p$ electrons goes into the $3s$ state, while the nf electron jumps to the $2p$ state, so that the first electron has $\Delta l = 1$, and the other $\Delta l = 2$, which gives an allowed transition according to the rule mentioned in Section 21*d*.

The practically complete series analysis of the neon spectrum was one of Paschen's masterpieces, accomplished long before the structure of this spectrum was understood from the theoret-

[1] E. Back, *Ann. d. Phys.*, **76**: 317, 1925.

[2] K. W. Meissner, *Ann. d. Phys.*, **76**: 124, 1925; H. B. Dorgelo, *Physica*, **5**: 90, 1925; *Z. f. Phys.*, **34**: 766, 1925.

ical point of view.[1] It was Meissner[2] who made the important discovery that the series found by Paschen converged to two different limits. Grotrian[3] was the first to understand that these two limits are connected with two possible states of the $2p^5$ configuration and identified their separation with the X-ray L doublet. It is no wonder that this spectrum has had a great influence on the development of our knowledge of the structure of spectra and has been the touchstone for many theories.

[1] F. Paschen, *Ann. d. Phys.*, **60**: 405, 1919; **63**: 201, 1920.

[2] K. W. Meissner, *Ann. d. Phys.*, **58**: 333, 1919.

[3] W. Grotrian, *Z. f. Phys.*, **8**: 116, 1921.

APPENDIX IV

ALLOWED STATES WITH (jj) COUPLING

The following table may be of use in the near future, in the analysis of spectra which deviate from Russell-Saunders coupling. It gives the allowed states for extreme (jj) coupling in the case of equivalent p and d electrons.

Each configuration will give rise to equidistant groups of levels, with the distance between them equal to the doublet separation of a single electron. The lowest group will occur when as many electrons as possible are in the state with the smaller j_i value; the maximum number of these electrons is restricted by the Pauli exclusion principle. The next higher level group will have one electron less in the state with smaller j_i; and therefore one more with the larger j_i value. In the table the number of electrons in each of these Stoner subgroups is shown, the configuration with the minimum energy being given first. However, the order of the levels within each group is unknown at present; in the table they have been arranged according to their values of j.

An actual case will nearly always represent some intermediate step between Russell-Saunders and (jj) coupling, but very little is known at present as to how the transition takes place. It is probable that the very lowest level in Russell-Saunders coupling will also be the very lowest one in extreme (jj) coupling. The table shows, however, that often important changes in the order of the levels must be expected. For instance, in the configuration d^2 a level with $j = 0$ will lie below those with $j = 3$ and 4, whereas with Russell-Saunders coupling the three lowest levels are ^3F with $j = 2$, 3, and 4, the level with $j = 0$ from ^3P coming next.[1]

In the table the configurations have been given only until the group of equivalent electrons is half filled. It is easily verified that for the remaining configurations the results are the same, but upside down, the lowest level group being the one which

[1] A similar example for the case of the p^4 configuration has actually been found in Te; see J. C. McLennan and M. F. Crawford, *Nature*, **124**: 874, (1929).

is given here as the highest. For instance, d^7 will be similar to d^3, but with the lowest level group consisting of three levels with $j = 1\frac{1}{2}, 2\frac{1}{2}$, and $4\frac{1}{2}$.

TABLE I.—ALLOWED STATES FOR EQUIVALENT ELECTRONS WITH (jj) COUPLING

	Sub-groups		*j*-values																
$j_i =$	½	1½																	
p^2	2		0																
	1	1		1	2														
		2	0		2														
p^3	2	1		1½															
	1	2	½	1½	2½														
		3		1½															
$j_i =$	1½	2½																	
d^2	2		0		2														
	1	1		1	2	3	4												
		2	0		2		4												
d^3	3			1½															
	2	1	½	1½		2½	2½	3½		4½									
	1	2	½	1½	1½	2½	2½	3½	3½	4½	5½								
		3		1½		2½				4½									
d^4	4		0																
	3	1			1		2				3			4					
	2	2	0	0	1		2	2	2	2	3	3		4	4	4	5	6	
	1	3	0		1	1	2	2			3	3	3	4	4		5	6	
		4	0				2							4					
d^5	4	1						2½											
	3	2	½		1½	1½		2½	2½			3½	3½		4½			5½	
	2	3	½	½	1½	1½	1½	2½	2½	2½	2½	3½	3½	3½	4½	4½	4½	5½	6½
	1	4	½		1½	1½		2½	2½			3½	3½		4½			5½	
		5						2½											

The above results are obtained by the method outlined in Section 38. There is first constructed a table similar to Table III of that section, but with each electron characterized by its values of j_i and m_{j_i} instead of m_{s_i} and m_{l_i}. From this values of m and then of j can be found.

INDEX

p. 1. Spectrum, analy[illegible]
1. Goudsmit, Samu[illegible], jt. author